Indomitable Spirit

The Life of Ellen Hardin Walworth

By
Patricia Joy Simkovich

To Andy,
Thanks for all your
help!

Ale
5/4/01

The National Society Daughters of the American Revolution (NSDAR) and its members acknowledge and welcome the book, *Indomitable Spirit*, as Patricia Joy Simkovich's account of the life of Ellen Hardin Walworth, one of the founders of the NSDAR. Even so, the NSDAR is unable to guarantee the accurateness of this account. Neither the NSDAR nor its members were participants in the research or writing of this marvelous story about Ellen Hardin Walworth. As a result, this book represents completely the author's version of events in the life of this remarkable woman.

Published by:

The National Society
Daughters of the American Revolution
1776 D Street NW
Washington, DC 20006–5303

Printed March 2001
(0301–1000–OP)

ISBN: 1–89227–04–0

Dedication

This book is lovingly dedicated posthumously
to the author by her family:
her husband, Alex, and their children—
Gregory, Donald, and Chrisia.
Thank you for the undying memories you gave us.

Table of Contents

Table of Contents

Foreword

The awareness of Ellen Hardin Walworth and her incredible life and achievements came to my wife's attention in the early 1980's during a stay in Saratoga and a visit to the Walworth Museum. That discovery led to her decision to research every piece of information pertaining to Ellen's life and to compile it into this present book. Over this period of roughly ten years, Pat took copious notes that are contained in her several notebooks. Only a portion of the sources are referenced in the bibliography as Pat had not indicated the specific sources for many of her remarks. Every effort was made to preserve the final story as an accurate representation of Ellen's unbelievable life.

Alex Simkovich

Acknowledgements

The valuable support of Mrs. Dale Kelly Love, President General, in permitting this book to be published by the National Society Daughters of the American Revolution is very much appreciated and gratefully acknowledged. The assistance of Jan Fitzgerald, Executive Assistant to the President General, in numerous details was key to bringing this project to a successful conclusion. The professional editing by Mrs. Elayne Masters–Eddins of the original manuscript resulted in a truly quality publication. Typing of the initial hand–written manuscript into an easily used format was completed by Mrs. Terrie Walsh. Grateful appreciation is extended to the staff of the President General for lending their talents and their efforts in making this project possible.

Co–operation by the historical societies of Saratoga, NY, Jacksonville, IL, Louisville, KY, and Cooperstown, NY, as well as, the New York City Public Library, the Carnegie Library of Pittsburgh, the Library of Congress, the DAR Library, and the National Archives of Washington, DC, made it possible to conduct and complete the extensive research needed to present the factual story of Ellen Hardin Walworth's life.

Chapter 1

Ellen pressed her forehead against the glass of the railroad car as she strained for her first glimpse of Saratoga Springs. "For heaven's sake, Lemuel, will you please stop pushing!" she said irritably to her ten–year–old brother.

As the train clamored and screeched to a stop on this May afternoon of 1851, Ellen's new stepfather, the Chancellor of New York State, took charge. Reuben Walworth was tall with the bearing of an aristocrat, but with the florid complexion of the New England farmer he had been in his youth. From those humble beginnings, he had pushed himself to become a lawyer. This ambitious young man rose to prominence when he won the highest judicial post in New York. Although at age sixty he was newly retired, the Court of Chancery abolished, he still wore power easily, and his quick gestures, his certainty of command, brought instant respect. "Mansfield," he gestured to his twenty–year–old son, "you take Ellen's valises and help her, and Dolly can help Lemuel. I'll take care of Sarah," the Chancellor said, taking Ellen's mother by the arm.

Sarah gave a backward glance toward Ellen and Lemuel and Dolly struggling to gather their own things, then holding her skirts close to her so as to squeeze past the seats, she moved with the Chancellor toward the front of the car.

A short, thin negro girl stretched to reach Lemuel's valise on the overhead rack, then lost her balance and fell back against Ellen. "Ah'm sorry, Miz Ellen, ah's jist bin sittin' too long."

"That's all right, Dolly," Ellen cautioned her gently, "just don't forget your own valise." At twenty–six, Dolly was frighteningly intimidated by the Chancellor and overawed with her first railroad journey. She had been given to Ellen's mother when Sarah had married her first husband twenty–one years ago. Always close to the eighteen–year–old Ellen, she remained the one constant in the turbulence of Ellen's recent life.

With a swish of taffeta and a bumping of hand–luggage, they descended the train onto a station platform dotted with curious onlookers as hackney drivers strode up and down the platform shouting their services for the various hotels.

Reuben's daughter, also named Sarah, and her husband, John Davison, were there to greet them. John jumped down from the carriage and held his hand out for his new bride to descend. She came forward hur-

1

riedly to embrace Lemuel, then turned to Ellen. Ellen had a strong impression of lavender as Sarah's cheek brushed hers, and then Sarah turned to Ellen's mother. "Hello, Mother," Sarah murmured softly as the two women with the same names and so close in age embraced.

"All right," Reuben boomed, "Mansfield, you and Ellen can ride with Sarah and John. Mother, Lemuel, and I will ride in our carriage."

As they pulled away from the mansard–roofed train station, Mansfield gestured toward the broad verandas of the stately hotels of Saratoga. "That's the U.S. Hotel, and there is Congress Hall, and over there Union Hall." Beyond the hotels, Ellen had a glimpse of graceful elms and manicured lawns stretching up to elaborate houses covered with lacy iron designs and gingerbread fretwork. Suddenly the carriage slowed in front of a thick grove of pine trees bordered by a white picket fence. "Welcome to Pine Grove, Ellen," Mansfield said proudly. Ellen looked beyond the picket fence to a sprawling, story–and–a–half white colonial house nestled among the pines. She had expected a mansion, a stately home with Greek revival columns like her Uncle Abram's in Mississippi. She could not picture President John Quincy Adams coming to this house as the Chancellor said he had, nor the Marquis de Lafayette or Washington Irving.

As they walked up the broad front steps, the door opened and a plain woman about thirty–five years old, her head wreathed in a crown of brown braids, opened the door. "Welcome to Pine Grove," she said merrily, "I'm Mary Elizabeth Jenkins." The Chancellor bounded up to the door and planted a kiss on his daughter's cheek. "Mary, may I present your stepmother, Sarah." The two women embraced. Then Ellen and Lemuel were introduced, and the little group, followed by Dolly, moved into the wide hallway. Mary Elizabeth called to the Walworth servant, Louise, to show Dolly to her new quarters, then turned to Ellen. "Ellen, come with me and I will show you to your room. It used to be mine, so I hope you will like it."

Mary Elizabeth Jenkins was the oldest Walworth child. When she was widowed in 1846, she sold her home in Saratoga and moved back into Pine Grove to care for her ailing mother as well as to gain a measure of comfort from being back in the family circle. Her mother died the following year and Mary remained, acting as surrogate mother to fifteen–year–old Mansfield and as hostess to the rich and famous who continued to be entertained at Pine Grove.

Ellen followed Mary Elizabeth up a half–flight of steps and into a plain, square, old–fashioned room. "Pine Grove boasts the first indoor bathroom in Saratoga, Ellen, so you can have a bath and freshen up before supper. You must be tired after your train ride from Illinois. If you want anything else, just ring the bell. We'll have you feeling at home in no time."

Ellen sat down on the bed and looked at the cream–colored walls enveloping a four–poster bed, a marble–topped table, and a boxed–in washstand. A black walnut writing table with a matching chair stood beneath the window. The room seemed cold to Ellen, curiously empty, as if it had existed amid life yet remained apart from it. She fought the lump that formed in her throat when she thought of her cozy bedroom in Jacksonville, cluttered with the objects that had surrounded her for eighteen years and the bright prairie sunlight that seemed to always flood the room. She touched the gold miniature of her father which she wore at her throat and felt tears of self–pity begin to sting her eyes. Hurriedly, she stood up and unlocked the hand–luggage that contained her dressing gown and slippers. A warm bath would feel good, she thought, and would take the kinks out of her travel–weary body.

Ellen leaned back against the rim of the lead tub. Idly, she rinsed the lavender soap off her body, wondering if she would ever feel at home in this strange place. She scooped up handfuls of water and let them run in rivulets down her skin, postponing the inevitable moment when she would have to step out of the tub and dress for supper. Nothing seemed quite real. Only three months ago, she had been summoned home to Jacksonville from her Uncle Abram's, where she had spent the past year.

Her mother had met Reuben Walworth at a party in Louisville, Kentucky, where he had come on business. After he returned to Saratoga, they had exchanged a few letters, and in his typical hurried fashion he had asked Sarah to marry him. They had been married just two weeks ago in Louisville and now here they were in a new house and a new town. Ellen's thirteen–year–old brother, Martin D., had remained behind to finish out the school year in Jacksonville. With a stab of longing and guilt, she thought of Mary Duncan whom she already missed more than her father. The daughter of Illinois's governor, Mary had been Ellen's closest friend for the past fifteen years. They had gone to school together, galloped on horses across the prairie together, and attended candy pulls. As they reached their teens, they had exchanged confidences, giggled as inexplicably as any teen–aged girls, and whispered the long nights through vowing to keep each other's secrets close to their hearts. They had tearfully promised to write to each other every day of their lives so they could remain dear friends forever.

3

Reluctantly, Ellen stepped out of the tub and, with a thick turkish towel, dried her slender body. "I still can't believe my father is really dead," she thought as she wrapped herself in her dressing gown, "and here I am, part of a new family."

Ellen dressed carefully in her blue cotton gown, which was still a little light for Saratoga's invigorating May air, and leaned across the dressing table to stare at her reflection. So much had changed in her life that she expected another countenance to gaze back, but outwardly she remained unchanged. Ellen was not beautiful but pretty in the way youth is pretty, fresh and innocent with a hopeful, expectant air. In her pleasantly rounded face, her blue eyes had a slight downward turn at the corners. Her lips were full and sensual, and her nose was her father's nose, rather long but broad. After carefully examining her face, she parted her blonde hair in the center and pulled it back across her ears securing it firmly in a chignon at the back of her head.

She walked downstairs just as the supper bell rang. Reuben and Sarah were already in the dining room. Reuben guided Ellen to a chair next to Mansfield and directed Lemuel to sit between John and Sarah Davison.

As she looked about the dining room, Ellen thought how strange it was that a room with exquisite Chippendale pieces, a massive crystal chandelier, and a table around which famous people from every walk of life had gathered, should have such a plain, homey feeling. The black walnut mantel had obviously been selected by the first Mrs. Walworth. Matching boxes, massive and circular with a pineapple motif on top, were used to store the silver and sat commandingly on the sideboard. The rectangular carpet was an olive green with red, beige, and blue flowers strewn around its borders. Two still lifes painted by local artists adorned the walls.

At the head of the table, the Chancellor stood and raised his water goblet. "I know that many happy days and weeks and years are in store for us and all who are connected with us in this new relation. I ask God's blessing on us all."

Chapter 2

The sun was just beginning to wash Saratoga with a pale, milky light when the morning bell rang at seven. Ellen stretched, walked slowly to the marble–topped table, and drowsily poured water from the pitcher into a wash basin. Idly, she wondered what dress would be suitable for a morning walk, then decided to put on the blue cotton dress she had worn at supper the previous evening. The Chancellor had insisted that they walk to Congress Spring before breakfast this morning to drink the water. People came from all over the world to partake of this Saratoga custom, he had explained, and in the height of the season as many as ten thousand people would take a morning stroll to the spring.

In spite of her homesickness, Ellen felt a sense of adventure tinged with anticipation. She dressed carefully, took a pair of white linen gloves and a shawl to ward off the morning chill, and descended the stairs.

Mansfield was waiting for her, along with Lemuel, who looked as misplaced as Ellen felt. "Ready for our walk?" Mansfield inquired gaily. "It's a fine day to show off my new sister at the spring. Despite the reputation of the water, that's really why the fine people of Saratoga and visitors walk to the spring. To show off."

The Chancellor and Sarah joined them, Sarah smiling brightly, her eyes shining with excitement. Sarah was small, almost bird–like, with a face that was both trusting and gracious. Basking in the good fortune of being rescued from widowhood by a prominent husband, she looked much younger than her thirty–eight years.

In early May, Saratoga was enveloped in a warm light, the air soft and perfumed with the scent of lilacs, apple blossoms, and fresh, fertile earth. As they passed the U.S. Hotel, the Chancellor gestured toward the broad front steps. "I make it a practice in the season to stop at all the hotels and check the ledgers before anyone is up and about. If anybody is registered whom I know or ought to know, I extend them an invitation to visit Pine Grove. You can be certain there will be plenty of visitors this summer, as I want everyone to meet my new bride and her family." He smiled at Sarah possessively, and she laughed with delight.

They walked past shops with millinery and fancy goods and past Mr. Stewart's store with its display of paisley shawls in the window. They stopped to look in the window of Rix's New York "Cheap Store," where quality items could be bought for less than anyplace else. They marveled at the stores laden with groceries and liquors, all with displays rivaling each other to catch the fancy and imagination of Saratoga's creative hostesses.

Only a few native Saratogians were walking on the neat gravel path leading to Congress Spring this gentle morning. Congress Spring echoed the charm of Saratoga with its Doric–columned white pavilion decorated with colored glass windows. The dipper boys waited, needy little creatures who, for a few cents, poked into the spring with a tin cup dangling on the end of a stick and brought up a dripping cupful. Ellen took a sip of the ice–cold water and promptly made a face. Mansfield laughed. "Don't you like our water, Ellen?" he asked teasingly. "You must drink it, it will cure all your ailments and magically turn you into a true citizen of Saratoga."

Ellen turned to him, surprised by the anger flaring within her. "I have no intention," she said archly, "of ever becoming a citizen of Saratoga."

"Ellen, my dear," Sarah reprimanded, "you musn't speak so harshly. Mansfield was only trying to be friendly."

Back at the house a substantial breakfast waited, with Dolly passing a platter of ham and eggs and a large bowl of fresh fruit. Ellen was happy to see biscuits and grits appear, obviously a result of Dolly's presence in the kitchen. Their lives had all changed drastically enough, Ellen thought, without having to give up every custom and habit.

"Now, Mansfield," the Chancellor commanded, "after breakfast Mother and I are going to be making some social calls, and I trust you will be able to entertain Lemuel and Ellen." Ellen bridled both at the Chancellor's well–meaning attempt to keep her occupied and at the suggestion that she, like Lemuel, was a child.

"Thank you," she said politely, "but I can take care of myself. I promised Mary Duncan that I would write to her each day. I've never written a letter to anyone before, but she is the most important person to me in the world and I want her to know everything that has happened since I left Jacksonville."

"Let Mary wait for a little while," Mansfield said, "and I shall meet you in the parlor and show you how to write a proper letter."

The parlor was Ellen's favorite room in Pine Grove. It was the only room that felt warm and cozy. She loved the dark walnut furnishings highlighted by a pair of matching apricot love seats. The Walworth coat of arms proclaiming Strike For The Laws was above the mantel. The tiles surrounding the coal–burning fireplace were inscribed with a verse Ralph Waldo Emerson had written celebrating his visit to Pine Grove.

Mansfield disappeared upstairs but quickly reappeared carrying a thick bundle of letters. Ellen sat on the curved walnut sofa while all six feet of Mansfield sprawled at her feet. "I was known as the fastest man at Union College," he said as he opened the bundle, "and I must say the

6

girls did like me. Girls from all over Saratoga wrote to me not knowing anyone else was writing, and sisters of my friends at Union wrote to me as well."

Ellen admired Mansfield's dark hair curled in short, crisp locks and his broad shoulders; she was quite certain that lots of girls must be interested in him.

Animatedly he read the letters, describing the charms as well as the drawbacks of each writer. "Now, dear sister, if I don't know how to write a letter, I certainly couldn't get these answers!"

"Mansfield, you're a rascal," Ellen laughed delightedly.

"And how many beaus did you leave behind in Illinois?" he asked her.

"Quite a few," she said, inclining her head slightly in a flirtatious, teasing gesture. "There were several at Uncle Abrams' plantation in Mississippi, and then there was Charley Blanton. Charley still wants to marry me." Ellen's voice was soft, and she spoke with a slight drawl reminiscent of soft southern nights.

"Now, let's write a letter to Mary," Mansfield said. "What's she like? Is she pretty?"

"As pretty as she needs to be. Mary is the most spirited person I know but gentle and sweet also."

"That's the best thing about me," Mansfield stated confidently. "I'm spirited, and that's why Father can't understand me. I shall tell you a secret, Ellen, and the only person you are allowed to tell is Mary." He lowered his voice to a conspiratorial tone. "I plan on writing novels." He looked at her for a moment, his blue eyes sparkling with the spirit of rebellion. "I'm going to finish my law studies just to please Father, and then I shall earn my living as a novelist. I'll show you some of my stories someday."

"That's wonderful, Mansfield," enthused Ellen. "I didn't know you were so talented. Your father must be very proud of you."

"My father," Mansfield said with a show of exasperation, "has no idea what I intend to do. Of course, I have to finish my law studies first. Law is the only profession he understands. Last year I thought I might join the Army, but when I mentioned that, he shouted in an apoplectic fit, 'You must be more than a common soldier!' "

"I'm surprised he doesn't see the Army as a noble cause," Ellen said defensively. "Your father has become a well–known man by serving the state of New York, and it has enabled him to live a very good life. Nobody knows the soldier riding off into battle, and he certainly isn't going to become wealthy, but he does love his country. That, I think, is real nobility."

"As far as my father is concerned, everything is secondary to the law as a career. That," Mansfield stated flatly, "is the only nobility there is."

"My father was a lawyer and a United States Congressman, and he didn't hesitate to fight for his country," Ellen said.

"Well, the study of law bores me silly," Mansfield complained, "and I can't wait to finish those studies. If it weren't for my brother, Clarence, I suppose I could do what I want. He has been a disappointment to Father because, as the oldest son and a lawyer, he was supposed to carry on the family name, but the Catholic Church certainly dashed those plans. When Clarence joined the priesthood, he ruined my life. I'm going to be watched closely to make certain I do exactly what Father wants."

Ellen felt sorry for Mansfield, wondering how anybody could defy Reuben Walworth's wishes. The Chancellor, she thought, was the most exacting and exhausting man she had ever known.

Reuben Hyde Walworth didn't just converse, he held forth on any and every subject to the exhaustion of his listener. He didn't make requests, he made pronouncements. The Chancellor filled the house with his intelligence and abundant energy. Ellen didn't dislike him, she just wished there wasn't so much of him.

"Do you miss your mother, Mansfield?"

"Of course," he said softly. "She was truly an angel. She was very kind and very religious, as good as a person can be." He pursed his lips in thought for a moment. "I can't even remember what she looked like or what her voice sounded like."

"Don't you have her miniature?" Ellen asked.

"Yes, but there just doesn't seem to be any point in looking at it very often."

"But you should," Ellen admonished. "I look at my father's miniature every day. That way, I feel like I'm linking my soul with his in infinity."

Sadness etched itself upon Mansfield's face for a moment, then he brightened. "Let's get the horses and take a ride this afternoon. We'll take Lemuel and ride out to the lake. But first, dear sister, do feel at ease and call me Manse."

"Oh, Manse, what would I do in this dreary place without you?"

Ellen and Mansfield had been delighted with one another as soon as they met. There was a lonely four–year difference between Ellen and Martin D., and the eight–year span between her and Lemuel made her regard him as only a nuisance. Mansfield, the youngest of the Walworths, had been only fourteen when Clarence, six years his senior, had left for Europe. Now Ellen and Mansfield could forge a companionship within the family circle each had sorely missed, and their loneliness would find an outlet in camaraderie.

"Saratoga's not so dreary, Ellen, you'll see," Mansfield said, taking her hand and pulling her to her feet. "You'll soon be so busy you won't even think about Jacksonville."

Ellen thrilled to the freedom of the ride as their horses trotted down Union Avenue and then broke into a gallop across meadows still barren of flowers, the Green Mountains in the distance forming protective arms about the land which was just beginning to respond to the spring warmth. Lemuel's shrieks of happiness at the sudden abandonment of proprieties added to the merriment and freedom they all felt. The road climbed up to a grassy bluff, and they stopped the horses and looked below them to the placid waters of Lake Saratoga.

"Manse, why can't you come to New York City with us next month? It will be so dreary just being with the old folks and no one to talk to!"

"I'm afraid I must stay home and act like I am diligently pursuing the study of law, so His Honor the Chancellor will smile upon me once again. But I would rather, much rather, be seeing the sights of New York City with my sister, Ellen."

In the following days, if Mansfield was unavailable, Ellen stayed in her own room as much as possible, reading or writing long letters to Mary. With the exception of Mansfield and possibly Dolly, she felt that no one in the family cared whether she was around or not. Always an inquisitive child, Lemuel was busy exploring his new surroundings. And her mother was so caught up in the excitement of being the Chancellor's wife that Ellen felt completely ignored.

Sarah and the Chancellor were moving in an endless whirl of dinners and parties and new friends. Sarah's sweet and loving temperament, plus her indisputably Southern hospitality, consorted admirably to her husband's own disposition. She loved to keep open house and reveled in the life of Pine Grove, alive with laughter and music and incessant visitors. Ellen wondered how Sarah could be so happy, questioning whether it was right or proper when Sarah's real husband, Ellen's father, lay in his grave forever.

Ellen stood before the window of her room looking out at the sperm oil street lamps, their lights flickering dimly through the pines. Slowly, she unfastened the chain around her neck and lovingly looked at the gold miniature of her father.

9

John Hardin had been a handsome man with dark hair and snapping dark eyes, a distinguished Roman nose, and a full, sensuous mouth. He had been as great a force as the Chancellor, and their big brick mansion in Jacksonville had been every bit as alive as Pine Grove. John Hardin had been educated at Transylvania University in Lexington, Kentucky. Unable to resist the lure of politics in this large, growing country, he had won election as a Whig representative to Congress. When he withdrew from the Congressional nomination in 1846, his votes were thrown to his friend Abraham Lincoln, who then won the Congressional seat. Now the name of Abraham Lincoln was heard more and more in political discussions and newspapers, and Ellen often reflected how it could be, and maybe should be, the Hardin name being discussed.

She felt a stab of anger toward the Chancellor. What right did he have to take Sarah from her? She needed her mother and would like to spend some time with her alone, feel her arms about her, and know childhood security once again. But Ellen was eighteen, and her mother was happily swept up into this new life with a new love, the very freshness of it a shining jewel to behold.

If there was one thing in this life she could be thankful for, Ellen thought, it was Mansfield. Fate might have unwittingly handed her a new life, but in doing so it had thoughtfully provided her a glorious companion.

Chapter 3

Ellen lay on her bed listlessly, listening to the music of the Aeolian harps Mansfield had placed in her window. The music of the harps made a thin, tinkling sound as a warm breeze floated through the room. She closed her eyes and thought of the wind blowing under the warm sun over the prairie and tears slid below her eyelids. Just once again, she thought, I should like to go back to our home and wander through those rooms. I would like to spend an afternoon with Mary enjoying that wonderful sense of belonging, feeling free and happy.

A knock at the door interrupted her reverie, and she stood up quickly. Wiping her eyes carefully with the back of her hand, Ellen stood up and smoothed her skirt, then called, "Come in."

Mansfield popped his head around the corner of the door. "Do you want to go to the park? You look like you could stand some sunshine."

"I thought you were busy studying this afternoon," Ellen said with surprise.

"I am. I just thought I would sneak out and find you for a little while and get away from those boring books."

"Manse, your smile rights everything. You are perfect sunshine."

They raced from the front porch, down the steps, and across the street to the park. Out of breath and laughing, they reached an elm tree whose protective limbs swung low to the ground. Mansfield caught a branch and swung himself onto it. With quick, graceful movements he climbed on the branches until he reached the place where two branches grew together making a wide resting spot. Ellen, grateful for the bloomers she had bought in New York, gathered her skirts tightly around her and followed him, settling herself against the tree trunk, her legs swinging down over the high branch. The noise of the horses' hooves pulling the carriages down Broad Street made them feel happily isolated from the world. Music from the band at Congress Spring and from the hotels swept about them in the warm August air. Ellen never knew what to expect from Mansfield, and she loved his capriciousness. When Mansfield was happy, there was no one on earth more joyous or spirited. He often fluctuated from happy to depressed, but when he was happy, his mood was infectious, lifting everyone's spirit. Recently, he had been ill, and for more than a week he was listless. He would hardly talk or leave his room. Today though, his eyes were twinkling, and his small mouth beneath the black mustache was stretched in a smile. Throwing his head back he laughed, sounding sweeter than the perpetual music of a Saratoga summer.

"Let's have a party Saturday night, Ellen." Mansfield's eyes sparkled as they looked into hers. "You've kept me so busy this summer, I've hardly seen any of my friends."

"Manse, you know I feel like an outsider here. Some of the people I've met, even those our own age, I find stupid, and others downright ludicrous. Oh, some are intelligent and interesting, but the society here all in all is just too Yankee."

"And what's wrong with Yankees? It seems to me we've accomplished quite a bit, and we love art and literature and music and parties, and we even laugh now and then. I think we're a pretty good lot."

"I'll never belong, Manse. Northerners are so cold–hearted and so outrageously conceited and selfish that they think it a moral impossibility for anybody from the other side of the Alleghenies to be refined or proper in any respect."

"Well," Mansfield said with mock dignity, "I shall prove to them that my Nelly is as refined and proper as any lady in Saratoga. And you are, you know. Besides, you're much prettier than anybody else I know."

Ellen's heart skipped a beat as she looked at her handsome half–brother. "Manse, I guess it doesn't matter whether I like the people or not, because I have all my happiness here at home. If you weren't here, I should be very lonely and disconsolate. But having you here makes me happy."

"Then let's have the party," Mansfield enthused, "and just be happy. We'll have music and dancing. Of course, you'll have to laugh," he teased, "because that's what parties are for. You go tell Dolly that there will be a party Saturday night! I'm going back and sit at my desk so it looks like I'm studying, and I will draw up a guest list. You, my dear sister Nelly, are going to have a grand time."

Saturday night Ellen dressed carefully in a white organza gown which was caught tight at the waist with a wide blue ribbon and ended in a huge bow at her back. On the hem, the dress was trimmed with small blue bows. It was her most daring dress, baring her shoulders and emphasizing her bosom. It was the dress of a young girl who just announced that she is now a woman. Ellen's blue eyes shone as she admired herself nervously in the dressing mirror. Her blonde hair had been arranged in long ringlets, and she pinched her cheeks for a bit more color before descending the stairway and walking into the parlor.

Pine Grove shone with expectation, and the crystals hanging from the chandeliers blazed with festivity. Ellen could hear the musicians who had been engaged for the evening tuning their instruments. Feeling like a child playing at being grown–up, she welcomed them in her best hostess manner. Turning, she found that Mansfield had entered the room.

"It looks like an enormous ball at the U.S. Hotel," he exclaimed delightedly. He turned to the musicians and explained the number of waltzes and round dances they should play, as well as the newest craze, the Grecian Bend.

It was now eight o'clock and the open carriages began rolling to a stop in front of Pine Grove. The first to arrive was Mary Putnam, the only girl in Saratoga who came close to being a real friend to Ellen. She was dressed in lavender organdy with silk violet flowers and green leaves spilling down the swinging circumference of her skirt. With her was Mansfield's good friend, William Morley. Next came Margaret Batchellor, wearing rose organza and a pair of exquisitely embroidered and quilted slippers her father had brought from Japan, accompanied by her fiance who had recently been admitted to the bar. There was Rhoda Thompson, dressed in white organdy, the skirt trimmed with pearls and deep rose bows. Isabella Stewart arrived, hair piled high on top of her head in imitation of the fashionable New Orleans' girls summering in Saratoga. Most of the young men had been classmates of Mansfield's at Union College, and many of the young women were his favorite letter writers.

The house was filled with laughter and high spirits. Ellen was ill at ease, even though she caught admiring glances from everyone. She tried to imitate her mother's graciousness and ease in welcoming the guests. She clasped their hands with her own clammy ones and tried to remember an interesting question to ask each person and give an appreciative word now and then about the gown or waistcoat.

When the last couple arrived, Mansfield nodded at the musicians, the music started, and he led Ellen to the floor. For a moment they stood still, each feeling strange, yet wonderful. Then she was in his arms whirling about to the strains of Johann Strauss. Her thoughts and feelings raced through her, their impact almost overpowering. She was glad when the waltz stopped and the musicians began a round dance. Ellen moved through the figures self–consciously, envying the grace of the other girls and smiling with relief when the music stopped.

At eleven Dolly opened the doors of the dining room. The table stood in party splendor, a dozen candles in silver candelabra illuminating the damask tablecloth, and on it were silver bowls of fruit, trays of sliced turkey and hickory–cured ham, plates of Saratoga chips, and filmy sugar meringues topped with red raspberries. Dolly's eyes glistened with excitement as she circulated among the group with a tray of frosted glasses filled with cider and Saratoga water.

Ellen busied herself with the food, trying to sort out the thoughts and feelings that raced through her head. She feigned interest in the party going on around her, listening to the girls laughing and gossiping about the famous and infamous visiting Saratoga and about the fashions being worn this season.

"Have you had a nice summer here in Saratoga, Ellen?" Margaret Batchellor asked. "Have you seen any of the theatre productions?"

"Oh, I love stage plays," Ellen replied gratefully, "but we have been so busy visiting people that we really didn't get to take in very many cultural events. I did hear Jenny Lind sing when we were in New York City. I had heard her before in St. Louis, and her voice is an absolute thrill." They carried on their polite conversation, groping for common ground, while the men discussed their prospects for the future. Mansfield seemed to be in the middle of every group, flirting with the girls, briefly serious with the men, as he discussed his days of study.

As the evening ended, Ellen and Mansfield saw the last guest to the door. Exhausted and grateful that the evening was over, she collapsed on one of the apricot love seats that had been pushed against the wall. "Manse, I am just not like those girls who are so at ease at parties. I just don't know what to say to all of them. They're all friends and have known each other all their lives; they're in my home, and yet I'm the stranger!"

"Then the stranger was the prettiest girl at the party tonight." His eyes locked on hers, somber and questioning at the same time. Pulling her to her feet, he put his arms around her and kissed her lightly on the lips. "Ellen, I want to marry you." It was a statement, almost a command, and then their lips met once again in a passionate embrace. Ellen's heart pounded as she imagined a life with Manse. "Let's let this be our secret for a little while, Nelly," he whispered against her ear.

"You have my honor, Manse," Ellen promised, her face reflecting the tenderness of her youth and beauty, "you have my honor and my heart."

Chapter 4

It was just a little past summer when most of the visitors left Saratoga. The town was pulling its shutters against the outside world, its coffers bearing the harvest of a plentiful season. The music was stilled for another year, and September's warm days were punctuated by a clear coolness in the air, a hint of cold weather to come. Martin D. had been enrolled in school at Ballston Spa, so now he would be close to the family circle at Pine Grove.

Within Pine Grove itself, there was an air of barely concealed anxiety covered by nervous preparations of festivity. Clarence was coming home.

"Brother Clarence is the family saint," Mansfield mockingly informed Ellen, "and the reason I had to study law. Clarence was a lawyer, and he was the one who was supposed to carry on the family name. Instead, he became a Roman Catholic, and now the only tradition he will carry on is the Roman one."

Indeed, Clarence was the child certain to carry on Reuben Walworth's dreams. From earliest childhood he had exhibited introspective traits and shown a pious faithfulness to the ideals of religion. He attended Williams College, and it was while he was there that his inclinations for a scholarly life began to show. He was graduated from Union College and admitted to the bar in 1841. The Chancellor was fulfilled. Now he had a son who would carry on the illustrious Walworth name in the profession of law, and he had no doubt that Clarence would carry it on famously. For Clarence was not only a scholar but also possessed a gregarious personality and a riveting speaking voice.

In the end, it was these traits that inspired Clarence to turn to the study of religion. Although he had been a Presbyterian all his life, he decided to study theology at the General Seminary of the Episcopal Church in New York City. When his mother expressed concern at her son's studying in an Episcopal seminary, the Chancellor quieted her fears, replying that the training would enable Clarence to round out his natural talent for public speaking as well as broaden his culture. It was when he unsuccessfully tried to establish a monastic foundation in the Adirondacks that the family became truly alarmed. In 1845, four years after his admittance to the bar, Clarence joined the Roman Catholic Church. His mother was inconsolable, his father embarrassed and stupefied.

"You see, Father," he had explained to the Chancellor, "in every other science, the acceptance of no other external authority would lead to ignorant presumption. May it not be the same in that deepest of all sciences which looks further than sight and sound can reach? Honor and wealth are earthly ambitions," he continued, "but in my heart I have been called to win men to Christ." While Clarence was persuasive, and the Chancellor vowed to accept his son's vocation, he was never able to understand it.

Clarence's mother had always taught her children to include the missionaries in pagan lands in their prayers and to give contributions for that purpose. Clarence had learned his lesson well, and now it was she who could not understand. To her mind, the Church of Rome was given to idolatry, superstition, and wily wickedness. Clarence tried to reason with her, to quiet her fears, but she had been a lifelong and devoted Protestant and could look no further than her own ingrained beliefs.

In 1845, Clarence applied to the Redemptorist Fathers in New York. He was accepted as a novice by the Order of the Most Holy Redeemer and was to study in Belgium at the novitiate of St. Trond.

Full of excitement at the prospect of leaving for Europe and starting a new life, he visited his disappointed parents in Saratoga, trying to help them understand his calling. His mother tearfully accompanied him as far as Albany. When he put her on the train to return to Saratoga, he watched helplessly as she dropped her head in grief.

Three years later, his mother was dead. She had never been able to overcome the sorrow at losing her promising son to the pomp and pagan majesty of the Catholic Church.

"He looks like his father," Ellen thought as she surreptitiously watched Clarence across the dinner table. She had expected an ascetic walking slowly with slightly bowed head as if listening to confessions of the earth. Instead, she found a replica of Reuben Walworth. He was tall like his father with the same ruddy complexion, reminiscent of outdoor New England. His voice possessed the same power and resonance, so that even in simple conversation he commanded the attention of everyone present. His blue eyes sparkled with intelligence, and he moved quickly with a purposeful grace.

Ellen wondered how he felt, coming back to Pine Grove to find the same surroundings but a new family. Lemuel, who had been given Clarence's room, had now moved into what had been a part of the Chancellor's office so Clarence could occupy his boyhood room once again.

Dinner was elaborate—turtle soup, followed by fresh trout, a filet of beef, all the vegetables the summer's bounty could provide, and a pound cake with ice cream. The nervousness the family felt over Clarence's homecoming had abated. From the start, he referred to

Sarah as "Mother," and if there was a pang in his heart when he said it, it didn't show. He won Martin D.'s and Lemuel's admiration from the first evening, delighting them with his stories of Europe and listening to them as his equals in both age and experience. Clarence accepted and charmed them all, especially Dolly, who showed a protective air toward him from the very start.

Clarence hated slavery, as did his father, and was glad to hear that Reuben had granted Dolly her freedom a few months earlier. Although Dolly was free to leave, the prospect of being parted from her family terrified her. It was her choice to stay and care for them. So, with respect for her dignity, she was given a salary and welcomed as part of the family.

"Who would like to accompany me to the park to walk off Dolly's wonderful dinner?" Clarence asked as he rose from the table. "I'd like to go," Ellen responded rather shyly, "wouldn't you, Manse?"

"Me too," Lemuel piped up. Martin D., caught in the age of fourteen, unsure whether he was a child or an adult, quietly followed.

The golden sun was dropping into the hills, and the pines surrounding the house stirred gently in the evening breeze. The sounds of leaves drifting from the elms and maples and oaks made a kind of fall music, punctuated by the staccato sounds of falling acorns. A deep chill permeated the air, and fireplace smoke curled out of chimneys.

Clarence inhaled deeply the fresh, pine scented air. "Some enterprising soul should bottle this air and sell it along with the water," he said gratefully. "There's a peacefulness here that can only be equaled in Church. It's the peacefulness of God's love that lives in the heart and imparts joy to every moment."

Ellen looked at the sky, still a clear bright blue at this time of evening, and wondered what she would have been like had she lived here all her life. They strolled across the street to the park, and Clarence stopped and surveyed the scene. "When I was a little boy, I used to play here. To me, the greatest adventure the world offered was right here. The Indians used to come and camp here and sell their bows and arrows."

Lemuel ran through the leaves, whooping and hollering. Impulsively, Martin D. picked up some acorns and began pelting Lemuel.

"The Lord had a handful of immense beauty and opened it right over Saratoga," Clarence mused. "I would rather have been born and raised right here than in all the European cities I have just seen."

Ellen could stand it no longer. "I don't see what's so wonderful about Saratoga. It's just bad–tasting water and stuffy people who do nothing but try to outdo each other!"

17

Surprised, Clarence looked at Ellen. "I'm sorry, Ellen, I forgot that you too have been subject to a great deal of change this year. It must have been difficult for you." Tears of self–pity welled in her eyes at this unexpected offer of sympathy. "Everything changes," Clarence mused quietly. "It's difficult sometimes, but we're all changing, as is Saratoga. If life always stayed the same, there would be no challenges to create excitement."

"I beg your pardon, Clarence," Mansfield interrupted politely, "maybe I shouldn't ask this, but do you find it difficult coming home with Mother not here?"

Only their footsteps through the dried leaves broke the silence. They had felt comfortable with one another. Now no one could think of anything to say aloud. Clarence closed his eyes briefly and stroked them with his hand.

"It's very difficult, Manse. It's the same house, the same customs, and yet ... " his voice trailed off softly. "I was afraid the family, you in particular, Manse, would blame me bitterly for Mother's death. But I don't feel that, and for that I thank you. I only needed to understand what I could do to bridge the gap between God and man, and I took the road that I could best travel. I hope Mother can understand that now. As for our new family, I'm delighted." Clarence smiled gently at Ellen and patted her shoulder.

"Speaking of change," Clarence said in a lighter tone, "you have certainly changed, Manse. When I left here, you were a lad of fourteen. Now, you're educated and a man. What do you plan to do with your life?" They turned out of the park and started walking in the general direction of Congress Spring.

"Well," Mansfield answered, "I'm studying law, of course, and when I pass the bar, I guess I'll follow in Father's footsteps."

Clarence looked intently at Mansfield. "And is that what you want to do, in the deepest reaches of your heart?"

Mansfield walked silently for a moment without answering. "No, not really. Actually, I had thought I would like to write books, novels."

"Well, Manse, those ambitions are definitely not in conflict with the practice of law. The ability to impart emotions and make people think is certainly needed for the printed page, along with a certain eloquence. Those are the same qualities that also win court cases." Clarence smiled at Mansfield. "Being Father's son could certainly open doors for you once you have passed the bar, and you would make a very nice living. The rest of the time you could spend writing novels and make a name for yourself in two professions. You're quite bright, Manse, and I've no doubt quite talented. If you would work diligently now, I'm certain you will have a very bright future ahead of you. The important thing is to search your heart for what you desire above all else, and then follow it no matter what anyone says."

Later, Ellen and Mansfield sat together on the porch, Ellen huddled in the cold night air with her chin on her knees.

"I feel so wicked, Manse, don't you? Maybe I'm unhappy because God doesn't think I'm worthy of happiness."

"I never think of God, hardly even in Church," Mansfield replied. "Clarence feels a link with Him in his daily life. I would like that too. I do think all our concerns are probably foolish, and if we focused on the Lord, we would be happier and more fulfilled."

"I just don't understand though," Ellen said doubtfully, "if belief is necessary to find God, how do we find belief?" She looked above the trees in the park across the street and at the stars shining brightly in the clear black blue. "I need you, God," she whispered softly, "I need something larger than the silly pastimes in this silly town."

Chapter 5

As Ellen packed her bags, she glanced out the bedroom window from time to time, watching the snow. It came down in great drifts of white, frosting the pines, and making her feel suspended under glass. She caught her breath. This was different from prairie snows, where the high winds helped to blanket the land in an icy glaze. Here the snow was pure, soft beauty, enfolding the world in a serene silence.

Christmas and the New Year had come and gone quickly with the family in a ridiculous uproar amid the pine and ginger smells of festivity. Ellen still could not understand why Mansfield's announcement of his intention to become Catholic should have caused such a crisis. If she, who loved him, could stand strong enough in her love to try to understand his conviction, why couldn't the rest of the family? As she folded a green velvet dress carefully into her luggage, she thought about the Chancellor's reaction. Here was a man who talked about honor, duty, service to one's country, God, and family, who was now vocally pained because another son desired to join the Roman Catholic Church. Perhaps he was afraid that Mansfield, like Clarence, would become a priest. She wondered if Reuben realized that his values were firmly rooted in quicksand.

She looked out at the snow once again. Manse had been trying to please his father by studying law, even though his heart wasn't in it. He was frequently ill, probably out of desperation; still, he had tried hard to please the Chancellor. Manse was not, Ellen thought, entering into Catholicism lightheartedly. He had spent days and weeks reading and studying various books on the Roman Catholic faith. He had heard Clarence speak of his beliefs and after much prayer and reflection, he finally had made up his mind, only to have the Chancellor throw an absolute temperamental fit. Ellen felt Mansfield had exhibited extraordinary strength in withstanding his father's tirades. She loved Mansfield's strength. If he felt the calling "he would make a magnificent priest," she thought tenderly. "He responds to people so well. Because of his own sufferings from his mother's death and living with such a forceful father, he has a gentle feeling toward other's misfortunes."

There was a light knock on the door, and Sarah excitedly entered the room. "How is the packing coming, dear? Do you need help?"

Sarah, five months pregnant, was elated about this trip to Washington. It would give her a chance to enjoy society before her confinement, to meet new acquaintances, and to renew old friendships. She had been terribly distressed at Mansfield's announcement and alarmed by Ellen's own study of Catholicism. Ellen was certain that under normal circumstances her mother would have been understanding. Now, she felt certain, her mother was more easily distressed because of her condition.

"Ellen, for the reception at the White House wear your blue silk gown with the pearl trim. You look so beautiful in that with your fair coloring and your shoulders bared. To be safe, pack all your gowns. I'm certain we will be invited to more balls once we've been received at the White House. Oh, Ellen, you are going to have such a delightful month!" Sarah bubbled. "You've needed society so desperately and now you will be among the best and most important people in the whole country." Sarah paused for a moment. "This will be important for you, Ellen, in more ways than just socially. Don't forget that in Washington City what looks like mere frivolity is really patriotic power at play. And I hope you will realize your inheritance, Ellen. Don't ever forget that your father and both your grandfathers put their duty to country above all else. And the Chancellor is personally acquainted with President Fillmore. Presidents and foreign dignitaries have been entertained here at Pine Grove for years. What I am trying to say, Ellen, is that you are your ancestors continuity in the history of this country. You can go to Washington with more than just social pride, because your family made it possible for you." Sarah stopped, momentarily out of breath and eloquence. She glanced disapprovingly at the books on Catholicism that lay on the bed. "Perhaps you had better put some lighter reading material in your trunk, dear. You are not going to have much time for brooding."

As the cars bumped along the track, Sarah leaned her head against the window. The Chancellor had walked to another car to glance over some papers he needed, and she and Ellen were alone. "It will do the Chancellor so much good to get away from Saratoga for a while. He's been quite undone by Mansfield you know."

"Yes, that's obvious," Ellen replied, thinking of the arguments that had punctuated the Christmas and New Year's celebrations. "I really think the Chancellor has been quite unreasonable. Manse should be able to live the life he chooses, and if he is convicted by God, I think he should follow his calling."

Sarah looked at Ellen levelly for a moment. "I don't believe he cares one whit about God. I think he is doing this to challenge his father and to amuse his friends. "I don't believe that boy knows what he wants," Sarah said. "It seems to me all he wants is simply to upset the family. I wonder what it will be next."

"Mother," Ellen said softly, "I'm certain there was a misunderstanding. Manse would not do this just to hurt his father."

Ellen said nothing more and looked out at the Maryland countryside. They had left the flat, marshy land, and now a succession of hills began rising toward the Potomac. The train plunged into a deep cutting, and in a few minutes they were steaming through the suburbs of Washington. "I thought it would look better than this," Ellen murmured as the train passed by a succession of old fields, over which there were a few dingy frame houses with outhouses scattered here and there. Pools of stagnant water stood everywhere with pigs, geese, and children swarming about. Suddenly, the huge white dome of the Capitol rose beyond the squalor, and then they saw the city itself.

The leaden January sky was streaked with a gold light when they arrived. Eagerly picking their way through a dirty, cheerless corridor, they emerged into the weak sunshine of New Jersey Avenue and were greeted by shouting hackney drivers. "Metropolitan Hotel over here. National's the best. Willard Hotel, suh, the on'y place a gintlemin goes."

"It's just like Saratoga in July," Ellen commented, "except that somehow this is a more businesslike confusion." The Chancellor hired a hack, and it took only a few minutes to be driven over the rough cobblestones to the Willard Hotel.

Sarah and Ellen walked up the wide stone steps from the carriage entrance of the hotel. The Chancellor, anxious to check in, hurried on ahead. Neither woman spoke, but each looked eagerly around them.

Inside the hotel people strolled or swept past them across the ornate lobby, the men wearing spats and carrying top hats, the women with their swinging widths of skirts bedecked with bows and silken flowers.

"Southern women are so fashionable," Sarah murmured, as the Chancellor strode across the lobby toward them, motioning to them to follow the bellboy up the wide stairs.

After they had unpacked, bathed, and had a light lunch in their rooms, the three of them went out to see the sights of the city. They left their calling card at the White House, then drove the length of Pennsylvania Avenue to see the Capitol. The city itself was a grand mess; and yet, from the teeming litter, power seemed to emanate and intoxicate the very air surrounding them.

Ellen was happy. Sarah breathed a sigh of relief as she heard Ellen's girlish laughter ripple through the constant social whirl. There were balls, as many as three each week, dinners, and luncheons.

They attended a reception at the White House. Ellen was entranced as they walked through a long corridor where portraits of the Presidents lined the walls, and tropical plants were placed casually on the floor. President and Mrs. Fillmore stood in the oval Blue Room to greet their guests, he tall and handsome and she with auburn ringlets crowning her head. The room was elegant, its ornate furnishings upholstered in light blue silk and ornamented in gilt.

Ellen met a lawyer at one of the balls, and he escorted her to two other dances. She enjoyed his company shamelessly, but decided it wasn't only his company, it was the gaiety of the entire visit. She was shocked that she thought of Mansfield so seldom. She felt rather guilty at the thought of him pursuing his study of Catholicism while she had hardly read any of the books she had brought.

Once Sarah had come into her room unexpectedly during her afternoon rest and found her reading one of the books Clarence had recommended. "Ellen, we're having such a good time now, must you spoil it by this religious question again? Look about you. This is the heritage your father died for, and I know he would not approve your interest in the Catholic Church." Sarah sat down in a brocaded chair and looked at Ellen with pleading eyes. "Please, Ellen, be open and candid with me. Don't be afraid of my disapprobation, but do not do anything secretly. After all, the approbation of your own conscience and of God is of more importance than any other consideration." She tried to measure the impact of her words upon Ellen. "The Roman customs and ceremonies," she declared, "are heathenish and Jewish. They lose the pure simplicity of the Gospels as our Savior taught us."

"I am only reading, Mother. I do know that what I read excites and stimulates my mind more than anything I have ever studied. Calvinism seems so rigid, and if you would read some of these books and open your mind, you would see. There is more heart to Catholicism; it demands all of you. Even Episcopalianism seems frivolous by comparison."

Sarah left the room in frustration and close to tears at Ellen's persistence in throwing away all the values she had been taught. Full of contempt for Clarence, Sarah retorted, "Clarence doesn't seem to care what influence he has upon people too young to know their own minds."

The month of January fled by in a rustle of silk, a clinking of tea cups, and the whirling strains of Strauss. Ellen loved the excitement of Washington, but the Chancellor had to return to New York for a few days, and it was decided that she should leave with him. Sarah would stay to represent the Chancellor at a reception the following day.

Ellen kissed Sarah good–bye and boarded the train with the Chancellor. She reluctantly watched Washington recede as the train slowly chugged out of the station with its engine pointed north. Once out into the Maryland countryside, Ellen rummaged through her hand–luggage for her book, then settled back into her cushion and thought of Manse waiting for her.

Chapter 6

"Viva in saecula seculorum," Father Walworth intoned as Ellen and Mansfield knelt in the cold church. Against the wall, flickering candles cast a warmth of hope. Ellen breathed in the strange but comforting scent of incense and thought, "He that cometh to me I will in nowise cast out." She felt her soul illumined as she rose and, grasping Mansfield's arm, walked outdoors into the brittle cold February day.

Ellen shielded her eyes from the bright sunshine. "This is the most important day in our lives, Manse. Now that we are Catholics, every day that we live from here on will be a fulfillment of today." Their footsteps crunched on the icy snow as they made their way from the steps of St. Joseph's Church to the rectory. The echoes of horses' hooves and the metallic whoosh of sleigh runners sliding down Albany's streets made a sound of celebration as the jingling of sleigh bells pealed through the winter air. "This is the purest day of the year," Ellen enthused. "I feel like it's the first day of creation."

"I'm sure the first day of creation was much warmer than this," Mansfield replied as they reached the porch of the rectory. Clarence's housekeeper was full of smiles as she took their wraps and led them into the dining room where a comforting fire crackled. The somber, austere room was warmed by rays of early afternoon sunlight streaming through the leaded–glass windows. They stood as close to the hearth as they possibly could, their body warmth gradually beginning to match the fire in their souls. This day was a celebration, this baptism into a new faith, a celebration not only of faith but of their independent spirits as well.

"I know our parents will understand what we had to do," Ellen said confidently. "We mustn't expect them to understand our souls, but they will see what is right when they see our happiness in the Catholic faith."

Clarence walked into the room beaming, rubbing his hands for warmth. "You will help us explain this to our parents, won't you, Clarence?" Mansfield asked.

"Doubt is the brainchild of Satan. What is done in the Lord's name will always work out," Clarence assured them. "I predict Father and Mother will have a feeling of relief now to have all this behind them."

Mrs. Vance announced dinner, and after a brief grace by Clarence, they sat down gratefully. Chicken and oysters, corn and green beans made the special dinner for three seem like a banquet. Ellen ate slowly and said little. She would be content in this moment forever, she

24

thought, clinging to the glow she felt. She had longed for an anchor in life. This morning in church, kneeling during the ancient ritual while Latin intonations sounded in the silence, she had felt the secrets of the universe unlocked within her. The thought of Sarah's reactions or the Chancellor's gave her no qualms. She alone had made this decision, and she felt proud, defiant, and free.

As the last bit of marmalade ice cream was finished, Mansfield fidgeted with his spoon, then cleared his throat. "Clarence," he said softly, "Ellen and I have decided to marry." Clarence took a cigar from the sideboard, bit off the end, and inhaled the fragrance before lighting it. "I had expected this," he said carefully as he sat down at the table again. "Ellen is a fine woman for you, Manse, but how do you propose to support a family? You haven't yet finished your law studies, let alone passed the bar." Mansfield straightened his shoulders and looked Clarence in the eye. "I intend to work diligently toward my goal. After I have become a lawyer, I shall spend some time of each day writing fiction to see what kind of talent and reputation I can develop for myself."

Clarence looked at him for a moment. "I'm not against your marriage, Manse, but God demands that you be head of the family. It is to you that your wife and children must look for guidance in all things, and that is a great responsibility. If you truly work diligently, you can accomplish fine things, but you must like the work. It's all up to you, with God's grace. I'm not trying to discourage you, please don't think that, and I do congratulate you on your choice of a wife."

Ellen sat quietly listening to the conversation as though she were an invisible observer. Light flooded her being, a steady light which dispelled confusion and doubt and fear. She knew that God's grace shone on them, and together they would build a beautiful life. She understood Mansfield as no one else did, and she loved him. "Manse," Ellen said quietly, "we have vowed to build our lives on the love of God. You know, and I know, that if God's grace is with us, nothing will be against us."

Clarence's prediction proved accurate. The consternation Sarah and the Chancellor felt over Ellen's and Mansfield's conversions were offset by visible relief over their decision to marry. Despite her recent rebelliousness, the elder Walworths felt that Ellen could only have a stabilizing effect on what they viewed as Mansfield's capriciousness.

In addition to the sense of relief that pervaded the household, joy flooded Pine Grove when Sarah gave birth in April. Reuben Hyde Walworth, Jr. was, to the Chancellor, the culmination of a victorious life. He had, at the age of sixty–three, been reborn in this child. His happiness knew no bounds.

In her mother's room, Ellen leaned over Reuben's cradle and laughed. "I shall always think of him as a little monkey, even when he is a great lawyer." She kissed Sarah on the forehead. "I am pleased as much as possible, Mother, considering he isn't a girl. Now, tell me, what shall I do with the pincushion I made and embroidered the name Theresa on?

"You will just have to have your own little Theresa," Sarah laughed gently.

"Don't worry about anything in the household, Mother. Now that I am almost a married woman, I shall supervise spring cleaning and the running of the house. Dolly can guide me, so you can just rest and recover your strength."

Under Dolly's tutelage, Ellen undertook the running of the household wholeheartedly. She felt contented, as though she were already married. When spring cleaning was successfully completed, she breathed a sigh of relief. "I can understand the necessity of a clean home," she told Mansfield, "but here housecleaning is as great an event as moving is in the West."

Mansfield, carried along by the current of general euphoria alive in the house, was studying diligently, and it seemed as though he and Ellen had hardly any time alone.

The harsh winter had given way to the softness of May again, and Ellen and Mansfield sat on the porch steps of Pine Grove breathing in the damp earth smells and listening to the morning songs of the tree frogs. "So much has happened in one year, Manse. Last May, I really would have thought I'd die if I didn't get to see Mary soon. It's been an entire year, and I haven't seen her. I do hope she can come to our wedding."

"You should have gone to visit her this month, Nelly, like you planned, and she could have come back with you for the wedding."

"I couldn't leave Mother now, Manse, when she has so much to do. I would only be there with a troubled conscience. Besides, I do feel more at home here now since Reuben's birth. Part of me, I suppose, will always be a child in Jacksonville, but part of me already feels like a very married lady in Saratoga." She laughed delightedly as Manse put his arm around her. "Between the housework and Reuben and planning for a July wedding, I really don't have time for a long trip. Manse, don't you want a small wedding? I dream of something like lace and violins and soft sounds and Mary here to stand up for me. I can't stand the thought that Mary wouldn't be here, but I could ask Mary Putnam. She's a good friend and a good Catholic, it's just that she isn't the right Mary."

"Ellen, you know that Father is set on having a large wedding. After all, he does have a position to be concerned about. If he invites just a few friends, he will make a dozen enemies all over the state who were upset they weren't invited."

The Chancellor, in his expansive mood, did indeed demand that there be a large wedding with an evening reception. "It would be scandalous," he boomed, "for the son and stepdaughter of the Chancellor of New York State to be married in secret. We have nothing to hide." The Chancellor liked nothing better than constant celebrations, and this one he wanted to be grand.

Later that night, Ellen picked up Reuben from her mother's room so he wouldn't disturb Sarah during the night and carried him to her own room. She placed his cradle close to her bed so that if he fussed during the night, she could rock him. Snuggling her face close to his neck, she kissed him on the soft folds of his skin, then wrapped him tightly in the covers so he would stay warm and crawled into her own bed. Contentment flooded through her as she drifted off to sleep.

Chapter 7

Ellen was aware only of her head, which throbbed so violently she was afraid her skull might burst. Her stomach rose to meet the pain in her head, and she was able to get out of bed and to the wash basin just in time to be violently ill. Weakly, she crawled back into bed and lay there trembling, every muscle in her body tensed against pain. She closed her eyes and tried to breathe deeply, hoping the cool morning air would refresh her. Downstairs, the clock in the hallway chimed five times.

She looked at her wardrobe, where her wedding dress hung ready for the eleven o'clock ceremony. The throbbing in her head intensified, and she wondered wildly if she should ring for Dolly. Then again, she thought, Dolly might tell Sarah and the fuss created by everyone would make her feel worse than the headache was making her feel.

Soon the sound of footsteps downstairs and the murmur of low voices told her the household was awakening. There was a soft tap on her door, and before she could answer, Dolly came in, her face wreathed in a smile and her eyes sparkling with excitement. "Good mawnin', Miss Ellen, looks lak it's goin' to be a fine, fair day."

"Dolly," Ellen said weakly, "don't say anything to anyone, but I don't feel well. I've been sick this morning. Please don't let anyone come up here yet." Dolly laid her cool black hand on Ellen's clammy forehead. "All the fuss that's bein' made jist isn't sittin' well with you, chile. Let me put a cool washrag on your head and see if it doesn't help." Dolly poured water from the pitcher onto a washcloth and wrung it out and placed it over Ellen's forehead and eyes. "I'll be leavin' for a while. You jist close your eyes and rest.

At least she wouldn't be expected downstairs today before she was dressed and ready to leave for the church, Ellen thought gratefully. She closed her eyes and hoped Dolly would stay downstairs for a long time.

It was close to nine o'clock before Dolly returned, and by that time the sharp pain had lessened and in it's place was an ache, dull but manageable. "Miss Ellen," Dolly said anxiously, "you goin' to have to git up or we goin' to have to git the doctor."

"I'm all right, Dolly, don't worry. I'll be all right." When she tried to stand, her legs felt weak and shaky and slowly she moved to the window to inhale the fresh morning air. Already carriages were lined up in front of Pine Grove. This will be a circus, Ellen thought, and I will be the center attraction. She longed for Mary. If Mary were here, they would in bed giggling and laughing with excitement, not only at the day ahead, but in sheer joy at being together again. She had counted so much on Mary that she felt a loss in the day already. She sat down at her desk and with a shaky hand began to write:

> "I have but two hours to be called Nelly Hardin, and I must devote a minute of it to you. It can scarce be but a minute for I am so deathly sick that I can scarce hold up my head and am afraid to go to bed and give up, and I am determined not to have a scene in the church. It will require all my energies to gather up sufficient strength for that, so I have no time for sentiment, and you need not be surprised that I say nothing but God bless you, God bless you my dear, dear Mary."

St. Peter's was a large church, but it seemed to overflow with people. All the Chancellor's political friends, and a few of his political enemies as well, were there, among them the novelist Washington Irving and Senator Seward. Sarah adjusted Ellen's veil once more, then quickly kissed Ellen on the cheek before she was escorted down the aisle by an usher. Ellen clutched the Chancellor's arm tightly as the first chords of organ music resounded through the church. Nothing seemed quite real as she watched first Clarence take his place at the alter and then her cousin Thompson Field walk out, followed by Mansfield. Mary Putnam turned to smile at her, then began to move slowly down the aisle, her wide bell skirt swaying slowly in a swirl of pale blue. Ellen was aware of people standing and soft murmurs of approval as she and the Chancellor began to slowly move down the long aisle. Her blonde hair was painstakingly piled high on her head and crowned with a single wreath of seed pearls from which the veil of Brussels lace flowed down her shoulders and mingled with the train of her dress. Her dress itself was a cotton organza with an overlay of Brussels lace, the high neckline trimmed with more lace and seed pearls. Lace and seed pearls spilled down the long sleeves and over her wide bell skirt, so wide the Chancellor could scarcely escort her. She was aware of masses of white lilies and roses banking the alter, their fragrance mingling with the incense. As she reached Mansfield's side, Clarence was smiling at them with great love in his eyes. It seemed only moments before Mansfield took her hand, slipped a wedding ring on her finger, and lightly kissed her.

The reception officially began at five o'clock, but it seemed to Ellen the house had been filled with gaiety since they returned from St.

Peter's. Music filled the rooms of Pine Grove, and Dolly circulated among the guests carrying trays of frosted glasses filled with fruit juice. Every inch of the dining table was covered with elaborately presented foods—whole smoked salmon and trout, a huge filet of beef, poached chickens, cheeses, fruits and candies. In the center of the table stood the wedding cake, an elaborate tiered confection of white roses and green ivy leaves. The air was redolent with cigars and laughter.

Ellen felt proud to belong to Mansfield, who scarcely left her side, now and then putting a protective arm about her waist. It was almost midnight before they went upstairs, and yet, Pine Grove still resounded with guests. The Chancellor was just hitting his stride and was in no way ready for the party to end.

Sarah and Dolly helped Ellen remove her gown. "Oh Ellen, you were beautiful," Sarah enthused. "I was so proud of my daughter. In the morning, Dolly will bring a tray up early for you will have to have an early start for Trenton Falls." In the morning ... Ellen suddenly felt embarrassed and awkward as her mother and Dolly discreetly left the room. She put on her new white pique nightgown and was wondering whether to leave her hair in its fashionable style or brush it out when the door opened.

Mansfield walked in without knocking, wearing a confident air of ownership. "Mrs. Walworth, might your husband kiss you properly?" Then his arms were about her, his lips pressing hard, first upon her lips, then on her neck. His hands found her breasts, and she stiffened. "Nelly, Nelly, I love you," he moaned as he kissed her breasts softly, then roughly with a desire that wouldn't wait. Before long they were on the bed, Ellen vaguely aware of the music and voices downstairs, of Mansfield's mustache brushing her bare shoulders and breasts, and of his body hard and urgent upon hers.

"Glory be to God on high," Ellen sang wildly, flinging her arms wide. Before them was the great horseshoe of thundering water, the mist around it shot with golds and greens and blues. "Manse," Ellen cried out as she gazed at the beauty and power of Niagara Falls, "I feel no larger than the smallest insect that crawls on earth."

Their honeymoon had been glorious. From Trenton Falls they had traveled to Montreal via the St. Lawrence Seaway, Ellen exclaiming at the beauty unfolding along the waterway, beauty sharply outlined by the love in her heart. Montreal had been perfect. They reveled in the joy of being husband wife. One time the young couple never even left the hotel room the entire day. In public, however, they appeared proper and decorous. They sat in outdoor cafes and attended concerts, trying to make sense of the language spoken around them. "I feel I know what all of France must be like," Ellen marveled to Mansfield as they walked along cobblestone streets and past elegant buildings and shops.

But it was Niagara Falls that stirred Ellen's soul in its wild unleashed force and beauty. "The power of it, Manse," Ellen shouted above the roar of water. "This awesome power makes me want to jump right in the rapids and become a part of it!"

"Then let's get to higher ground before you get carried away," Manse yelled. "Come on, I'll race you back up the stairs."

She reached the top out of breath, her shin aching where it had struck a stair tread. Ellen looked at Manse, at his hair curling out from under his wet hat, at his mustache drooping with water and his clothes soaked. Laughter bubbled out of her as she doubled over, pushing her own wet hair away from her forehead. "We look like creatures from the other world," she gasped.

"Oh, Nelly," Manse laughed, pointing at her. "What the fashionable bride of today looks like after only two weeks of marriage." He pulled her to him happily, and she sighed contentedly, her face pressed against his wet clothes. "I didn't know," she whispered softly there in the sunshine, "that so much beauty and happiness could exist together at one time."

Chapter 8

It was the scream that awakened Ellen. As she bolted out of bed and reached for her dressing gown, she realized the heart–rending cry had come from Sarah, and she raced up the stairs barefooted, her heart pounding wildly in her throat. The Chancellor came bounding up the stairs at the same time, and when they opened the bedroom door, they found Sarah standing there, wild–eyed, holding the still form of little Reuben. "Get the doctor, Ellen, get the doctor," the Chancellor commanded, his voice quiet but with a strangled urgency to it. Ellen cried out for Dolly and ran back to her mother. "I said get the doctor, dammit!" the Chancellor yelled as he raced passed Ellen and down the stairs.

"I don't know what happened," Sarah said weakly. "I went to the nursery and picked him up—oh, where is the doctor?" Reuben's form was still, and his color had a faint bluish cast to it. Sarah hugged the unresponsive child to her. "He isn't breathing," she stated with a mixture of awe and fear and disbelief. "He won't breathe."

By the time Dr. Allen arrived, he simply confirmed what everyone already knew. The Chancellor, his face dumb with shock, stood with his arms around Sarah while her sobs echoed throughout Pine Grove.

In the next two days, an unremitting quiet fell upon the house as the family woodenly moved through their tasks to prepare Reuben's body for burial. Locks of his hair were snipped to put into keepsake brooches, and Sarah had a daguerreotype taken of him. "Why didn't we have one taken when he was so full of life, so bright?" she asked over and over.

Ellen held Sarah close to her, as much to receive comfort as to give it. "Our little bird has flown to brighter climes, Mama. Where he is now he will be even happier than he was here with his bright smile and sweet cooing voice."

The morning sun woke Ellen, and she rose on one arm to look at her sleeping husband. She felt a happiness so strong it was like pain. Too much happiness to contain.

"I am so lucky," she thought, "and so happy. One's husband is a whole world to a wife when she loves him." Manse lay there, handsome and virile; she put a finger to his face and traced the outline of his cheek. He awakened, turned to her, and snuggled down in the covers again. Physically, nothing had changed for Ellen, and yet everything had changed. In just a few short months the center of everything in her life had shifted to Mansfield. She put her hand to his hair and mussed it.

"Good morning, dear husband. Time to get a start on the day." He reached for her and she laughed, pulling the pillow out from under his head. "I'd better ring for Dolly and let her know we're ready for coffee."

Ellen felt a sense of importance these last few days, acting as mistress of Pine Grove. The Chancellor and Sarah had gone to New York City for a week, and she and Mansfield were alone in the house for the first time since their marriage.

"I guess I had better get up and get started," Mansfield said with a yawn. Even though his enthusiasm toward his law studies hadn't changed, his attitude toward responsibility had, and he studied from early morning until late afternoon. "I just want to get these studies over with," he had said last night in answer to her complaint about loneliness. "I don't like them one bit, Nelly, but I am destined by name to be a lawyer. I want to be a writer, but I'm not certain I could support a family that way. As soon as I finish these studies, we'll be able to relax a little." In the evenings after supper, Mansfield had been retiring to their rooms to work on a novel. Ellen had no idea what the novel was about, but she knew he would work on it to the best of his ability. And Ellen believed in his abilities very much.

She knew he was right to be working as hard as he was, and yet she felt that although she had acquired a husband, she had lost a companion. Her empty days unfolded one after the other with no substance to fill them.

"Oh, Mary," Ellen confided to Mary Putnam one afternoon over tea, "the calm settled affection of married life is so wonderful." She knew Mary envied her, married to a handsome man like Mansfield, who no doubt would also be very successful, if not actually famous. "Still," Ellen continued, "there is a great emptiness in my life because he is working so hard and has so little time for me."

"Why not give some parties," Mary suggested. "Let people know you want to know them. Saratoga is a lively town, Ellen, and even in the winter people are ready for a good time." Mary was so pretty, Ellen thought, with her heart–shaped face and shiny black hair. Mary's eyes had the sparkle of fun in them, and with Mary, even a cup of afternoon tea felt like a party.

"I have decided to take some dancing lessons," Ellen said, "to surprise Manse. You know how he likes to dance, Mary, and I'm so awkward. I always feel like such a looker–on at parties." She laughed as she poured more tea. "Here I am, twenty years old, a married woman, and I should feel a bit 'oldish'. But I don't. Not in the least. I feel younger and more lighthearted than ever in my life!"

33

"Then let's fill the winter with parties, Ellen. I'll help you!"

After having coffee and toast on a snowy December morning, Ellen knew that the Christmas parties she and Mary had planned would have to be postponed. Even though she told herself it was just a mild stomach upset from something eaten the day before, deep down she knew this wasn't really an illness at all. Now she was certain she would need those little socks Mary Duncan had jokingly offered to knit for her. Instead of the morning sickness abating, it seemed to grow in intensity until her days were filled with fighting nausea. In the midst of all the Christmas gaieties, she was listlessly pale and wan. Not wanting to disappoint Mansfield, she attended a few parties with him, but by the end of December, she gave up all efforts at pretense. Sarah anxiously called Dr. Allen, who recommended complete bed rest.

The January snows fell and quiet seemed to blanket the world around Pine Grove, quiet broken only by the jingle of bells on the horses' harnesses or the swish of sleigh runners on the snow. Ellen read the days away, feeling more productive than she had ever felt. Mary Putnam came in the afternoons, often with their friend Rhoda Thompson, breezing in to gossip and keep Ellen informed of what was going on in the outside world. "You might as well be here in your own cheery room Ellen," Rhoda said one afternoon when they came, their cheeks bright pink, and their eyes sparkling from the cold. "The trouble with living in a summer resort is having to watch the winter doldrums. It is so bad this year. On so many street corners the poor who work here in the summer have had to build fires to keep warm and are reduced to begging. It's so sad just to walk down the street."

Mansfield sat with her in the late afternoons and every evening after supper, reading to her and making her laugh with silly inane remarks. "Manse," she confessed to him one afternoon, "I was so frightened I would never have a little one, and I am so happy. But I didn't know I would feel so miserable." "And I," he replied, "feel so guilty watching you because I feel only ecstasy at the thought of our child."

In mid–February Dr. Allen said she could leave her room, and with great ceremony Mansfield carried her downstairs, bestowing her like a gift within the family circle once more. The servants laughed joyfully, even as they wiped away a few tears, and the Chancellor had a tenderness on his face that she had only seen reserved for Sarah and little Reuben.

As the feeling of life within her grew more insistent, so did her apprehensions. How could she feel such joy when she so often had a presentiment of death? As her body grew heavier, she felt so burdened that she was certain she would not have the strength to bear a child.

With the coming of spring, her spirits began to lift, and by the time of her confinement in June, she felt like her old self again even if her body was swollen and cumbersome. Although she didn't leave the house or yard until after dark, the world began to look bright again.

The summer visitors started to arrive in hordes, and Ellen laughed uproariously at the efforts of the women to follow the latest fashion. "You know, Manse, it's just as well I can't leave the house," Ellen said one afternoon. "These women who puff their hair out over their ears to look fashionable only seem to present the appearance of certain long–eared animals trying to conceal their indications of stupidity."

In the oppressive heat of an August night, Ellen felt a sharp pain. There was another pain, and she felt a momentary panic. Resisting the urge to awaken Mansfield, she lay there trying to imagine the child that would be theirs in a few short hours. By the time the birds began singing and the household started to awaken, her body was opening and closing within her like waves crashing onto a shore.

The hours went by with the summer sounds of music and laughter floating in through the open window. The pains were harder now, and she wished desperately for a cool breeze. Her long hair and her body were drenched in perspiration, and Dolly and Sarah took turns sponging her face with cool water. She had not known what pain really was until now, and she wondered if her father had had to endure pain like this or worse before he died. She wondered if she would die or if the pain would just consume her and never let go. In the late afternoon Dr. Allen arrived, and sometime after dark, as Ellen grasped Sarah's and Dolly's arms tightly, Frances Hardin Walworth was born. Numbly, she glanced at the black thatch of hair topping a waxy, wizened little face, and sighing gratefully that it was all over, fell into a deep sleep.

35

Chapter 9

Ellen's days were perfect sunshine now. Pine Grove seemed to revolve around little Frank's needs and Ellen's wishes. "I have only one grandchild yet to bear my family name," the Chancellor remarked at supper one evening. "Nelly, you must take good care of him as he is to be a great man if he lives and has health." Ellen smiled, for Frank meant as much to the Chancellor as he did to her and Mansfield. "You're putting a burden on him before his first birthday," she laughed, "and no matter what he does, you will think he is a great man." The Chancellor laughed and leaned contentedly back in his chair. "And you, Manse. If you study hard, you should pass the bar by winter. Do you think that's a fair estimate?" Even though it was said in soft words under relaxed circumstances, the question seemed like an admonition. "I can try, Father."

Mansfield had been given a corner of the Chancellor's courtroom for his study. This room, where famed lawyers had listened to cases, was a small structure attached to the side of Pine Grove. When the house had first been purchased, the Chancellor decided it would expedite matters to have his courtroom near, so he covered a large wood box with carpet and placed an armchair and desk upon it. His energy and dignity overcame the rather humble surroundings, and in that room had been argued some of the most important cases in New York State. Here the law had been scrupulously upheld. Mansfield now spent his days in part of that room dutifully studying law, but in the evenings after supper he would go upstairs to the rooms he and Ellen and Frank shared, where he would work on his novel until late at night.

"When the novel is finished, Ellen, we'll see why I'm not thrilled about being a lawyer. It's almost done, and I think it's rather good." Suddenly, he slammed his fist against the wall with a force so sharp that the lamp on the desk shook. "Why can't he leave me alone? I'm working all day as hard as I can on those studies, I'm bored to death by them, and all he can do is push. I feel like a mule that's forced to pull a plow!" Tears welled in his eyes, and he sat down heavily in a chair and put his face in his hands.

"Oh, Manse," Ellen whispered as she put her arms about his neck and kissed the top of his head. "He means well, he just wants to see us happy."

"It's a curse," Mansfield groaned through his hands. "I was cursed from the day Clarence chose religion."

"Please, Manse, don't say that. It isn't true. You will soon be a lawyer, and then you can work regular hours, and we can have our own home. You're just tired, why don't I have Dolly bring up some tea?"

Ellen felt sorry for Mansfield, but it was up to her to love him and to help him. He needed her. Helping him and raising Frank gave her a sense of importance and fulfillment. Her duty in life was to God, to Frank, and to Mansfield, and she vowed to fulfill those duties brilliantly. If any shadows surrounded her happiness, it was due to Mansfield's preoccupations, but she never permitted herself to say so to him. Only twenty-one, she felt housebound and lonely. When she missed her husband's attentions, she reminded herself that Mansfield would soon pass the bar, and they could build a normal life. Pine Grove was alive with important and fascinating people, more than any home in Saratoga, and in the evenings Ellen often joined in the company. But she longed for stimulating, intimate conversations with a few people of her own age and interests.

One rainy evening in November as she sat in her dressing gown before the mirror brushing her long hair, Manse rushed in, pulled her to her feet, and held her close to him so tightly she felt the breath being squeezed out of her. "I just finished it, Ellen. And it is good, I know it is."

"I must be the first to read it," she demanded with mock authority, "before everybody else in Saratoga gobbles it up."

Mission of Death was set in the year 1739, the story of the martyrdom of Father Ury and the penal laws that declared death to the Catholic citizens of New York. Fascinated with the Catholic religion and proud of her husband, Ellen spent every spare minute reading the novel.

"Manse," Ellen cried, "it's wonderful. Protestants proclaimed perfect license for each man to believe anything or everything. Their persecutions of Catholics assumed the more fearful aspect of the hand committing acts which the lips proclaimed to be outrageous! It's a wonderful book."

"There will be more to follow, Ellen. My happiest moments are spent writing, and I'm certain I will be able to make my mark as an author."

Mission of Death was an outstanding success. Not only were Ellen's predictions that the novel would be gobbled up in Saratoga true, but outside Saratoga, even where the author was unknown, it was also a huge success.

They were giddy with triumph and relief. Ellen gave a dinner party for Mansfield, the first one she had planned and executed as Mrs. Walworth. She bought a new gown for the occasion, a deep rose moiré ꞿhich bared her shoulders and was set off by a ruffle running the width of the bodice. She dressed her hair in a wreath of braids with a matching rose ribbon woven through them.

"Well, Mrs. Walworth," Mansfield told her with admiration in his eyes, "I shall be the most prolific writer in America if my wife dresses like this for every book."

"And if every book is this well received," she said, pirouetting coquettishly, "your wife will have to strive to be beautiful. She shall have to work hard to keep up with her husband." Laughing, arm in arm, they descended the staircase proudly to receive their guests.

Ellen watched in awe as Mansfield moved among their friends, accepting their congratulations graciously. He moved so gracefully and his manners were impeccable, she thought. He had a talent for living, like his talent for writing.

The Chancellor moved to the center of the room and raised his arms for quiet. "I would like to make a toast," he announced. "To the success of *Mission of Death* and all who are enjoying it, and to my future law clerk." As the guests drank to the toast, and the conversation and laughter resumed, Ellen watched Mansfield's jaw tighten and his mouth set in a hard line. A rush of pity flooded her for her husband who couldn't fully enjoy his moment of triumph. Why couldn't his father realize, she wondered, that he was crushing Mansfield's ambitions by forcing him into a future that only the Chancellor envisioned?

"He might as well have told me to stop playing in the sand and grow up," Mansfield complained later that night. "Why can't he understand that I want to prove myself by my writing and not by being in some stuffy law office all my life?"

Stung by Mansfield's hurt, Ellen spoke to Sarah about it the next day. "Father could have given a better toast," she said. "He's always pushing Manse and is never happy with anything he does unless it's what the Chancellor expects."

"Nonsense, Ellen," Sarah replied. "He's very happy that Mansfield has published a book. He simply feels that now Mansfield can get on with his studies without any more interruptions. Ellen, you must understand that being a lawyer with the Walworth name will open every door from here to Washington City and to Jacksonville for you and Mansfield. You two will have a brilliant future." Her mother was right, Ellen knew, and she felt herself being swept away by the important future her mother envisioned for them. Mansfield was brilliant and capable, and there was no real reason he couldn't be successful as both a lawyer and an author.

The new year of 1855 found Pine Grove in a flurry of activity. Ellen and Mansfield were to accompany the Chancellor and Sarah, taking Dolly and little Frank with them, to Washington for a two–month stay. As if to underscore the gaiety and excitement, Ellen had received a letter from Mary Duncan at Christmas promising that she would visit them in April.

"You need to be meeting the right people, Mansfield," the Chancellor had stated. "In Washington City I shall introduce you to people you need to know. I realize you've met some of them before, but only as my son. Now they shall be reminded that you are the one in New York State to be reckoned with." The Chancellor had timed this trip to introduce Mansfield to official Washington while he tended to his endless business affairs as well as to escape the deep snows of a Saratoga winter.

As always, the city's pulse beat with a productive energy that was apparent the moment they stepped off the train at Union Station. Even the carriages seemed to move with a compelling purpose. In the lobby of Willard's Hotel, Ellen again marveled at the well–dressed men and women who, underneath their fashionably slow and gracious manners, gave the distinct impression that no trifles were uttered here.

"Either Washington has grown since my last visit," Ellen told Mansfield once they were in their rooms, "or else I've been confined too long in Saratoga and Pine Grove. For once, I know how those summer women feel in Saratoga. I feel like a girl again!" He was exhilarated too, and Ellen thought that maybe the Chancellor was right, perhaps Mansfield should aim for a political career.

They attended countless receptions, balls, luncheons, and dinners. They went to the National Theatre to watch the ballet *Le Diable a Quatre*, and the comic ballet *Frisac, The Duelist*. Ellen was struck with the intensity of Bellini's opera *Norma*. "It seems strange," she said, "that in Europe the opera is very much a necessity, while here it is such a luxury."

The city was abuzz with controversy. "The slavery question must be dispossessed of its present vantage–ground," a senator from Pennsylvania expounded one evening at an unofficial dinner. "It belongs exclusively within the limits of the States." Having made that declaration, he turned to the woman on his left and said with the utmost sincerity, "Your pearl earrings, madam, they way they reflect the light has rendered me speechless all evening." It was this mixture of the social and the official on a daily level that produced the electricity and fascination that was Washington.

One morning in the first week of February, as she was propped up in bed enjoying a morning cup of chocolate, Ellen's stomach started to grow queasy. Like her pregnancy with Frank, the illness continued to intensify daily until she took to her bed and stayed there. While Ellen missed the gay times, only in resting did she seem to find any relief. Dolly took care of little Frank, who was fussy with a new tooth, while Sarah, the Chancellor, and Mansfield continued their lives. Ellen lay in bed alternating between feelings of happiness at having another child and feelings of despair in having to be confined to her bed. Finally, it was decided that she should return home with Dolly and Frank. Mansfield would stay on to continue business with his father.

"Why don't you come home with me, Manse?" Ellen asked one night when Mansfield had returned from a reception. He removed the studs from his shirt carefully. "I can't do that."

"Why not?"

"One of the reasons we're here is to introduce me to as much of official Washington as Father can. After all," he said with a slight grimace, "this is the start of my 'career'."

"But I'm going to have your child. You should be with me."

"You," he said pointedly, "are having the child. I'm having the career."

With that she burst into tears of rage and frustration. "Mansfield, how can you do this to me? I'll be all alone."

He laughed, and his laughter seemed to Ellen to echo in the stuffy hotel room with a ring of freedom.

"You are being a very silly goose, Nelly. You are not desperately ill, you are just having a baby." As her tears continued, releasing the frustration she felt over being sent back to Saratoga, Mansfield came to the bed and took her in his arms. "As my wife, you are supposed to be helping me. Father is often away from home, Ellen, you know that, and when I am a lawyer, I shall have to be away now and then also." He kissed her forehead. "I love you, Ellen." It was a statement, not a declaration, and if she longed for the caressing warmth of his bare hands, she would just have to keep longing.

Saratoga was buried in snow when she returned with Dolly and Frank, and an icy wind banged against the windows in Pine Grove, an insistent demon demanding entry. She came home like a penitent child, unable to feel anything but sorry for herself. She tried to focus on Mary's upcoming visit, but often headaches would stop all her plans and thoughts, headaches so severe she would be ill and could only lie in her darkened bedroom with cool cloths on her head and wait for the pain to subside. At such times terror would grip her, terror that her baby would

40

be deformed or die, terror that she herself would die. At one point, Dolly became so alarmed she summoned Dr. Allen, who bled Ellen.

Ellen awakened as the early light of April dawn filtered into the bedroom. For the first time since she left Washington, her heart beat lightly and a happy energy gripped her. She didn't notice the cold wind outside which swayed the pines and bent the limbs of the elm trees whose branches would soon be sprouting tender buds. All she was conscious of was that Mary was arriving that very day, Mary, affectionately referred to as Molly, whom she hadn't seen for four years and still loved dearly.

She spent the morning arranging and rearranging Mary's room, bathing her eyes in cold milk in an effort to restore a girlish sparkle, and counting the chimes on the clock until Mary's arrival. She changed her dress four times, finally deciding on a pale blue wool, suitable for the house but flattering. Her waistline was growing thick, but the dress still fit, and it was the first time in two months that she had had to dress to fit an occasion.

Finally, at a few minutes after four, she heard the carriage and ran to the doorway in time to see Mansfield help Mary alight, then she ran down the steps toward her friend. They fell into each other's arms with cries of welcome and delight. "Oh, Molly, it's a dream. This can't be real. "I've waited so long to see you!" Her childhood had returned and a peculiar mix of gladness, homesickness, and nostalgia for what would never be again were all wrapped up in the form of Mary. Ellen couldn't take her eyes off her friend. In place of the blonde curls Ellen remembered, Mary had brushed her hair back smoothly and with a black ribbon had tied it into a club. She wore a gray traveling dress and matching shoulder cape edged with narrow black lace. A traveling hat with a curl of mauve ostrich tips gave a sophistication Ellen had never seen in Mary. Her manner was more self-assured, and she moved with grace and elegance. But bits of errant curl still escaped around her face, and her blue eyes danced with impetuosity. Marriage and distance had not diluted Ellen's love for Mary nor her intense longing for her companionship. "Ours has never been just an ordinary friendship, Molly," Ellen declared when they were alone. "I love you more and more every day."

Mary was shy in Mansfield's presence, but alone she and Ellen talked nonstop about Jacksonville, the changes in the town, and who was marrying whom.

One afternoon as they sat in the parlor with the rain streaming down the outside of the windows and a fire in the grate warming the room, Mary fell quiet as Ellen sat in a rocking chair with Frank. "Nelly, I so

41

envy you, married and a mother," she suddenly exclaimed. Then shyly she said, "I will soon be doing this too. Charlie Putnam has asked me to marry him."

"Molly, that's wonderful!" I'd give you a hug right now if I weren't holding this baby. Oh, I am so happy for you."

"Charlie is handsome," she said somberly, as if it was necessary to explain his virtues, "and attentive and ambitious too. I love him very much, Nelly."

For a moment the only sound in the room was a slight squeak of the rocker as Ellen rocked Frank back and forth. To Mary's surprise, Ellen's eyes filled with tears. "I'm happy for you, dear Molly, I really am. I must tell you though, that sometimes the felicity of an engagement is nearly all imaginary. There is always trouble enough to counterbalance it. Molly, I shouldn't say this, but sometimes even when I am happy, I think to myself, 'and this is all'. It seems that in marriage there is still such sorrow and disappointment where there was the least possibility of finding it."

The month rolled on with parties and sightseeing, with Ellen and Mary clinging to each other's presence. Mary's visit had only served to emphasize the friendship as though the years between the times they had not seen each other had changed nothing at all. As the lawns in Saratoga became colorful with tulips and daffodils and the town began extending its welcome for the summer visitors, Mary made her preparations to return to Jacksonville. "How could a month fly by so fast?" Ellen cried. "Oh, Molly, I waited years for this visit, and it only lasted a moment!"

In the rays of a late afternoon sun, Ellen drove with Mansfield and Mary to the train depot, her heart heavy within her. "Molly, I promise," Ellen said tearfully, "that as soon as Manse passes the bar we'll come to Jacksonville to visit you and Charlie. Maybe—maybe we'll even be able to move back." After hugs and more promises, Ellen watched tearfully as the train carrying Mary slowly moved out of the station. "I wish," she sighed quietly, "I wish I were going back home."

42

Chapter 10

Ellen watched from the upstairs window as carriages shiny with varnish and bits of polished brass here and there pulled to a stop in front of Pine Grove. She saw William Marcy, Secretary of State, alight from his carriage, followed by George Monell and his wife who had traveled from Michigan for the occasion. The Chancellor had been pleased and excited they were both coming at the same time to this event, for they had been his first law associates when he had been admitted to the bar at the age of twenty. Now they were back to see an old friend and to celebrate the occasion of Mansfield's passing the bar. "They will all be here," Mansfield told Ellen before he went downstairs, "everyone who has ever been associated with Father in any way. Even his enemies." And they did come, out of respect for the Chancellor and curiosity about his apparent successor. Mansfield's and Ellen's more successful friends were also invited, but this party was only a graduation steppingstone, not a victory celebration.

As the sounds of talking and laughter floated up the stairs, Ellen seated herself in a brocaded chair, a copy of Thomas Carlyle's *Sartor Resartus* in her hands. Her pregnancy was too far along for her to be included in the festivities, and she was almost relieved to have this time to herself. She had vowed to save some moments just for herself and start reading again in order to be a stimulating mother and Mansfield's intellectual equal. Mansfield was beginning his practice as the Chancellor's law clerk. "An opportunity," the Chancellor had assured them, "that I would have climbed a mountain barefooted for when I was first admitted to the bar." As his law clerk, Mansfield would, among other things, hear arguments in complex cases referred to him by the Supreme Court of the United States.

Ellen was quietly jubilant. Now she would have her husband by her side regularly, and maybe soon they could have their own home before long. Leaning her head back against the chair, she closed her eyes and daydreamed about the home they would have. Images of Uncle Abrams' plantation in Mississippi floated through her mind. A house large enough for their family and friends, but not so large that it would require an inordinate amount of care. Sunlight shining on gleaming woodwork, chandeliers, a piano. Laughter and music. A place of comfort and serenity and happiness where Manse could write his novels in peace.

43

Later that night, after the party, Ellen lay with her head in the crook of Mansfield's arm, her hand lightly stroking the dark hair on his chest. "Manse, why can't we make plans to move West now?" She kissed his cheek. "We don't have to live in Jacksonville, but somewhere where we could begin life on our own. You could certainly have a law office anywhere. Is your father's name really that important to you?"

"Give me time, Nelly. I have to sort out some things on my own. Father already has cases for me to work on, and I want to get back to writing. After the baby is born, we can see where we're heading."

"The property at the edge of town, Manse, that Father mentioned. Why don't we take a look at it? It would always be a good investment for our children, and we could take our time about making up our minds where we want to live."

"All right, Nelly," Mansfield said, "we may have to sneak you through the town, but tomorrow afternoon we'll drive out and have a look at it."

The property was on the edge of Saratoga, twenty acres of rolling ground, where on the highest hill a house could stand surrounded by pasture land with a rocky stream winding through it. Stands of elms and maples presided over it, and a grove of pine trees were clustered on the hillside. "Oh, Manse, it's just beautiful. Here we could live in majesty. Just imagine people driving by fifty years from now saying 'and here is where the celebrated lawyer and author, Mansfield Tracy Walworth, wrote his greatest novels'." Throwing her arms about Mansfield's neck and standing as close to him as her bulk would allow, Ellen kissed him. "Just think, Manse, maybe we're home now."

Within two weeks they had signed an indenture of $25,000 for the property. Along with two houses in Saratoga that the Chancellor had given them for a wedding present, and land in Illinois that Ellen had inherited from her father, this property built a fence of security around them. "We're rich landowners, Manse. We're secure," Ellen exclaimed, sitting as close to Mansfield as she could on the carriage ride home. "At least we have security to dream on."

The air was redolent with the musty scent of October as she sat in the backyard, her face tilted to catch the warm autumn sun, when she felt an intense pressure and then a sharp pain. Her hands went instinctively to her abdomen, but she sat there savoring the last lingering warmth of the year, listening to the hollow sound the leaves made as they dropped from the trees onto the roof and into the yard. She hoped the pains wouldn't be as intense this time, nor the labor as long. She prayed a silent prayer to God for the health of this child, and pulling

44

herself awkwardly to her feet, walked to the kitchen door. Dolly was busy patting out a pie crust, and when she saw Ellen's face, she looked at her sharply. "You not feelin' so good, Miz Ellen? Is it time?"

"I just had a couple of pains, Dolly. I'm certain we have a nice long time to wait."

Dolly's face broke into a wide smile, and her eyes lit up with excitement. "You think maybe we'll have a girl this time?" she inquired happily.

Ellen gripped the back of a chair as a sharp pain ran through her lower back. "Well, I certainly wish we were all having it instead of just me. Right now, Dolly, I just don't care whether it's a girl or not."

Ellen didn't think it possible, but this labor was worse than the first one. The pains seemed to crisscross through her entire body, and at one point the muscles in her calves began to cramp. Sarah and Dolly were there helping, but instead of giving comfort to her, their efficient, authoritative presence weakly irritated her. In the middle of the night on October 18, 1855, John J. Walworth was born. Ellen heard a lusty cry, and then Dolly held him up for her to see that he had all his fingers and toes. Mansfield came in softly in his dressing gown, his hair over his forehead and his eyes blurry from lack of sleep. "Thank you, Nelly," he said tenderly and kissed her damp forehead. "Don't we have a fine family?" Exhausted and satisfied, Ellen drifted into a deep sleep. Later the next afternoon, Mansfield brought Frank in to meet his baby brother. He only glanced at the new bundle and then squirmed onto Ellen's lap and put his chubby arms about her neck. "Mama, there pony."

"What?" Ellen asked.

"Believe it or not," Mansfield said with a chuckle, "Father came home this morning with a new horse." Ellen laughed weakly. "It's handsome and sleek," Mansfield said, "and black as coal. When I reminded him that the baby had only just been born, he looked a bit sheepish and said that Martin D. and Lemuel could have a good time with her until Frank and the baby are ready."

As with Frank, the Chancellor was thrilled over his new grandson. John was named after Ellen's father, as well as the Chancellor's brother, who had been a major in the United States Army during the war with England. "I predict he'll be brave and strong," the Chancellor said with pride, "just like his namesakes."

Christmas was more meaningful than ever with two babies in the house. A Christmas tree reigned in one corner of the parlor, splendidly decorated with fruits and gilded nuts, lace cornucopias, fans, and ribbons. Pine boughs graced the mantels and chandeliers, and Dolly outdid herself in the kitchen baking pumpkin and mince pies, ginger cookies, and fig and plum puddings. Christmas week, guests flooded the home from afternoon until late at night, and if the Chancellor could engage enough people in a game of whist, they would be there until the early hours of the morning. Frank was the center of all attention, and the base of the Christmas tree was piled high with presents for him. A rubber ball from Martin D., a whistle from Lemuel, a spinning top, a stick horse, and when Clarence arrived home from Albany on Christmas night, he brought a sled for Frank. Martin D., home from West Point, and Lemuel, from boarding school in Ballston Spa, carried Frank constantly, either on their shoulders or on their backs, each reliving his own recent childhood. "Come on, Frank," Lemuel coaxed one afternoon in the parlor as he got down on his hands and knees, "get on my back and pretend I'm Pet the horse."

Ellen and Mansfield were invited to more parties than they had been to since they were married. "I just wish," Ellen said wistfully as Dolly struggled to help her button a dress, "that I didn't look like such a cow. My frame has spread so much that I am a large woman with the prospect of growing still larger!"

Every other night, at least, had been filled with parties, dinners, and whist games. Ellen couldn't remember ever feeling so happy.

"Ah, Manse," Ellen said gratefully one evening, "it's so nice to have time with you."

"I must warn you," he replied, "that after the New Year I plan to start work on another novel, so my evenings will be filled for awhile."

Ellen puckered her lower lip and frowned in mock dismay. "And how long will it take to write? Don't forget I must know, because I get a new gown."

It didn't matter if his evenings were spent on another novel, Ellen thought. His studies were over, and he was now a lawyer, no longer a disappointment to his father, so Mansfield was happy. There was a lilt to his step again, and beneath his mustache his mouth turned up at the corners with a ready smile.

When Clarence had asked what he planned to write next, Mansfield had replied, "It's a secret because I'm not quite certain."

Clarence laughed. "Manse, I am content to see you occupied with anything which can offer a grateful heart to God. If, however, you desire to be a good writer, you must be a student also, and especially a student of history. And add lots of local color."

"Manse has already published a book, Clarence," Ellen reminded him, "and many people think he is a good writer now."

"That's what you get," Ellen sighed later when they were alone, "for being the youngest child in the family. Even when you are an old man with a white mustache, you will be treated like a child." She kissed him on the cheek. "It doesn't matter. You're my husband, and I trust you completely."

One snowy Sunday afternoon as she held Johnny, Ellen watched out the window as Mansfield pulled Frank on the sled across the street and into the park. Snow was coming down thick and fast, adding to the depth of white already on the ground. As she watched, Mansfield jumped through the snow looking back at Frank now and then and laughing. "Manse makes a perfect idol of Frank," she said turning to Sarah, "thinking that nothing ever was or will be equal to him. And still, he holds Johnny much more than he did Frank at the same age. It's a shame, isn't it," she mused, "that a man can never have the thrill a mother has when she clasps her newborn to her heart. Even if a nun is more holy, I believe maternity is woman's true glory."

"Speaking of nuns," Sarah said putting down the embroidery she was working on, "Dolly spoke to me this morning. She is planning to convert to Catholicism."

"Why that's wonderful," said Ellen surprised. "I knew she had been reading those books Clarence gave her, but I had no idea she was considering becoming a Catholic. I always knew she had a special grace."

Sarah looked at Ellen with a frown of surprise on her face. Sighing she said, "Clarence's presence could convert the whole world. I guess that's what he means to do anyway. At any rate, I told Dolly she could count on all of us, that we would support her decision."

The entire family was present when Dolly was baptized by Clarence in St. Peter's Church. Even though the Chancellor was reluctant to see another member of his household become a Catholic, he said nothing. Dolly, so much a loved part of their family that she didn't seem like a servant at all, was treated as a special celebrant. Ellen had baked a cake for her and decorated it with a cross on the frosting, and there were presents. Everyone had a special gift for Dolly: a Bible from Clarence, a book by John Henry Newman from Ellen and Mansfield, a lace handkerchief from Sarah and the Chancellor, and letters of good wishes from Martin D. and Lemuel. A special grace seemed to flow through the rooms of Pine Grove, a benediction from God upon the inhabitants of this house who, guided by Clarence, were trying to follow His will.

On St. Patrick's Day, Ellen sat in the ballroom of the U.S. Hotel trying to look as dignified and nonchalant as her pounding heart would allow. Now and then, she nodded to an acquaintance or turned to Sarah with a low remark, but for the most part, she sat erect holding tightly to

47

Frank, staring straight ahead at the podium and at Mansfield who sat to the left of it. Mansfield, as the son of the Chancellor, a lawyer, and a celebrated novelist, had been asked to give a speech this day to the citizens of Saratoga acknowledging the growing influx of the Irish immigrants. Ellen watched with pride as Mansfield strode to the podium. "Daddy," Frank squealed and pointed a chubby finger toward his father.

"Shhhh," Ellen whispered, her face against Frank's cheek. "Listen now." Mansfield told two jokes in an Irish brogue, and then suddenly serious, praised the efforts of the Irish in building prosperity into the state of New York. When the speech was over, Ellen listened with pleased astonishment as applause broke out, and people rose from their seats to acknowledge the speaker. "Manse," the Chancellor said proudly, beaming and patting his son on the back, "you raised the Irish right off the ground."

Sitting in the parlor after dinner that evening the Chancellor looked at Mansfield and said, "We've got a giant of a case coming up. This will definitely make your name as a lawyer. We have a dispute over the rights to a railroad spike patent. It seems that Erastus Corning in Albany has copied the hook–headed spike that a man named, Henry Burden, invented and manufactured. Burden sued him and won, but we have been asked by the Supreme Court to assess the damages. This may take a few months, maybe three or four, but if we get your name around enough on this case, you will be a power. You know, with that speech you gave today and a well–publicized case, you just might be able to enter politics. Well, give it a thought. Nice to know you can do what you want."

As they were getting ready for bed Ellen asked the question that had excited her imagination ever since the Chancellor had raised the thought.

"Do you think you would want to be in politics, Manse?"

"No," he said flatly.

"It would be exciting though. If you were, I would somehow feel that in a small way I was carrying on my father's life."

"Don't be a goose, Nelly. I still have dreams of being able to support my family by writing. I just want to see how much I can do. Eventually, I want to get out of law."

"But, Manse, look how good you are and what it has brought you already."

"Nelly, I don't want law, and I have no ambition for politics."

Ellen said nothing as she turned the blanket down on the bed and arranged the pillows. Something was stirring in her, a frustration borne of her own passiveness and Mansfield's indecisiveness, a frustration of being carried along on a current of someone else's choosing.

"Manse, we must begin thinking seriously about our lives. It is impossible for us to carry on a married life in our parent's house," Ellen declared with finality. "One has such an unsettled feeling while living anywhere else other than in one's own home. If we had our own home, then you would be free to write without your father reminding you that your duty is to the law. As a starting point, why don't we just rework one of the small homes Father gave us and move into it?

"Nelly, those houses need work, more work than you would want to put into them. They're all right, but they are outside of the fashionable district."

"We can't entertain here without first asking permission, and we never have a meal alone together, just the two of us."

"I would have to come back to Pine Grove every day to the court-room," Mansfield stated wearily, "we'd have to find servants...." his voice trailed off into silence.

"Don't go to any trouble, Manse," Ellen said coldly. "Wait until Father tells us what to do. It is getting rather difficult in our family to tell just who the children are and who are the parents!"

"Right now," Mansfield said with a smirk, "I'd wager you're one of the children."

"Do you know what happened the other day?" Ellen pleaded. "I slapped Frank's hand because he kept poking his fingers at Johnny's eyes, and Mother said, 'Ellen, I won't have you reprimanding the children in that manner in this house.' I can't even raise my own children!"

"Look, Ellen, if you want me in politics to carry on your father's image, you're going to be awfully disappointed. And if you are angry with your mother, tell her, don't take it out on me."

He reached into his wardrobe then and pulled out a bottle of bourbon. "Want a drink, Nelly?" he asked with a sudden grin. "It will relax us, and I think we could use it."

"Manse!" Ellen said shocked. "You know your father doesn't allow liquor in this house. Don't you dare drink that!"

"I do not have to abide by the rules of the American Temperance Union even if Father is President," Mansfield said, pouring the amber liquid into a glass. "You see, Nelly," he said holding the glass out, "I can do what I want, even in Father's house. As for you, be careful you don't become a shrewish wife, for that kind of woman can drive her husband to drink." He downed the liquid, made a face, and crawled into bed.

Ellen, shocked, sat down in the chair by the window and stared unseeingly into the park across the street. She listened to the wind blow the rain from the pines, hurt and confused by the abyss she felt open under her.

49

Chapter 11

Ellen's eyes watered with the effort to suppress a yawn, while all around her voices were lifted in conversation and laughter. Mansfield was at his best, holding forth on stories, every story funnier than the one before it. He sat with a careless elegance, one elbow on the table, some of his dark hair falling over the corner of his forehead. A study of casual indifference. He spoke lightly, pausing in all the right places for effect, so that his listeners were aware of the nuances as much as for the contents. Ellen listened to Mansfield hold forth and watched as Isabella Whitney, seated across from him, sat mesmerized, her eyes shining, now and then convulsed by laughter. Mansfield finished his tale, paused for effect, and as he did Ellen caught a glance between him and Isabella, a glance that for just a brief moment seemed to be a caress, then the moment passed and Mansfield turned to Kathryn Batchellor on his right to say something. Ellen felt a sensation like a cold fist in her stomach, a tightening of all her senses. She was acutely aware of her own bulk, of the green taffeta gown which strained at the seams. Worse, she felt weary inside, weighed down by motherhood and the conflicts of being a child in her mother's house. Still in her early twenties, she could no longer remember the quick laughter, the eagerness of youth.

Isabella Whitney was lovely, with chestnut hair piled dramatically high, candlelight glinting off her diamond earrings, her low décolletage showing as much creamy white skin as she dared. She was always elegant with a sensuousness that seemed to smolder just below the surface. Married to a close friend of Mansfield's, Wade Whitney, they lived in the fashionable Franklin Square district, and when Isabella wasn't attending a party, she was giving one. Isabella and Wade had no children yet, but Ellen was certain that when they did, Isabella would conceive a party for every child. Mansfield had known Isabella most of her life, and indeed, she had been one of the prolific letter writers he had delighted in at Union College.

"Do you think the Southerners will be coming North this year with their darkies?" Wade asked Mansfield.

"They can't resist us," Mansfield laughed.

Tensions were growing in Saratoga between the Northerners and the southern visitors who always came with a full coterie of slaves. Because of its reputation as the South's favorite northern resort, the abolitionists had targeted Saratoga also, and the resort, which had reveled in the courtly charms and money of the Southerners, now became the site of bitter debates over the slavery question.

"The South knows that its only salvation in the Union is in the rule of a national administration patriotic and sagacious enough not to drive them to a separation," Wade continued. Wade loved politics but deferred to Mansfield on such occasions, as did others, thinking that the son of the esteemed Chancellor of New York should know more about national problems and solutions than they themselves did. If they only realized, Ellen thought, how little he cares about such things.

"All this talk about the North and South is complete balderdash," Ellen said, her soft, slurring voice rising. "Some slaves have been badly treated, I'm certain, but for the most part, everyone on a plantation knows their place, and they're all needed and loved. These abolitionists are just fanatics trying to stir up hatred and trouble, and most Yankees just love trouble." Mansfield frowned and said nothing, and Ellen imagined that she felt a coolness in the room, but she didn't care. Yankees were just a little too all-knowing to suit her.

On the way home Mansfield was silent, the silence broken only by the staccato sounds of the horses' hooves. Finally, Ellen broached the only subject that was presently disturbing her. "Isabella looked pretty this evening, didn't she?" As soon as she said it, she wished she hadn't. Mansfield glanced at her sharply, then turned back to his driving. His only sound was indistinguishable and noncommittal, as disinterested as though Ellen had simply mentioned a stranger's name.

That night, as tired as she was, Ellen lay awake until she heard Bessie cry as the first slants of dawn washed their bedroom with a pale, useless light.

Mary Elizabeth had been born just three months ago on November 2, 1856. She was a good baby, but Ellen was so exhausted chasing Frank and Johnny that she could hardly enjoy Bessie. There were times when she wished desperately that she could just let Frank and Johnny do what they pleased, but Sarah insisted upon decorum, so Ellen had to be constantly at their heels.

As she undid the blankets that held Bessie tight, Ellen's heart felt a tug of joy as it always did when she looked at her daughter. Bessie was blond, like Ellen, with the same strong blue eyes Ellen possessed. She held the child to her, enjoying the warmth and love of this creature Ellen felt to be her secret self. All night she had lain awake thinking that she and Manse must have their own home. "And we are going to have our own home, my little Bessie, and soon," she promised herself firmly.

51

There could be no talk of moving West with the spike case going on, but Mansfield assured her that as soon as the pressure on the case lessened, they would begin building their own home on the land they had bought in Saratoga. "Then," he promised, "when this case is over, we can sell the home and move West, where you belong, Nelly."

But the spike case was going on much longer than anyone had anticipated. It was more complicated and more boring than Ellen cared to understand. Just the other evening Sarah had said to William Seward, one of the lawyers involved in the case, "I wish you would explain what this everlasting spike case is about, I don't understand." Mr. Seward had looked at her with amusement playing about his lips and replied, "Indeed madam, I should be very much ashamed if you did. I have been engaged in it for quite a while, and I don't understand it yet."

Ellen felt, rather than saw, Mansfield's frustrations. The Chancellor also, for the first time in his career, had lost control of a case and was carrying a whole gaggle of lawyers along with it. Communication between the Chancellor and Mansfield seemed to be limited to railroad spikes or to silence. Many evenings his father would ask Mansfield to come back into the courtroom for a while so the two of them could go over documents in private, without the endless daytime interruptions that were beginning to plague them.

Ellen wondered if Mansfield had given up his dream to be an author. There were a few evenings when he had sat at his desk, but Ellen thought he had done very little work, and when she asked him about it, he dismissed the question irritably. He seemed strangely on edge, and on evenings when he wasn't in the courtroom, he wanted to be out with other people. If Ellen was unable or unwilling to go, he went anyway, as though constant movement and company would brighten the dark side of his spirit.

The pessimists were right. Saratoga did not seem to possess the same gaiety that summer of 1857, when the lack of southern visitors was noticeable. Just a year or two before the Southerners had been catered to and courted by many of the important northern visitors. Now the few who had come to Saratoga were ignored and treated as though they were criminals by the Northerners who had made themselves victims of the bigotry they so vocally despised. The Southerners were vacationing at the Gulf or in Charleston or Virginia, and their graciousness and vitality were missed by Saratoga society.

Unable to sleep one hot night, Ellen went outside to sit on the front porch. Music from the hotels floated on the air, and street lamps illumined the occasional couples who strolled down the street and into the

52

park. Mansfield had gone out for an evening of whist, irritated because Ellen refused to go with him. She had felt too exhausted by the heat and the children to be able to concentrate on a card game, and what she wanted was a cool, quiet corner all to herself. She was tired of the same company, the predictable conversations. What she longed for were ideas, but everything anyone said seemed to be just surface conversation. She wondered if anyone else felt this way. It was this thirst for ideas which had first drawn her to the Catholic Church, and now she longed for an object around which to wrap questions. It was impossible to read Carlyle and then engage in an evening's conversation about the children or, she thought with a slight bitterness, about the home she didn't have.

As she watched, Mansfield with Isabella and Wade Whitney emerged out of the shadows of the park, their low voices punctuated by Isabella's throaty laugh. They stopped in front of Pine Grove, and Mansfield, bowing formally from the waist, took Isabella's hand and lightly kissed it. Then saying goodnight to them both, he walked jauntily across the street and up the steps of Pine Grove.

"Manse?" Ellen asked out of the darkness. "I'm here."

"I thought you would be in bed, Nelly. What are you doing out here?"

"It was too hot to sleep, and I thought the cool air would relax me. Did you have fun?"

"It would have been nicer if you had been there."

"I just can't go out every night." Still, in spite of herself, she wondered what had gone on, who had talked to whom, and most importantly, if Mansfield had looked at Isabella again the way he had last winter.

"Let's go upstairs, Nelly, and get you to bed."

As they lay in bed, his kisses awakening her body, Ellen wondered for the first time just who, in his mind, Mansfield was making love to.

Ellen sat on the garden swing, idly rocking Bessie back and forth while Frank and Johnny ran all over the yard. Suddenly, Johnny took a handful of dirt and threw it at Frank's face. "No, Johnny," Ellen reprimanded him, quickly getting up from the swing. With her free hand she took Johnny's chubby arm and looked at him sternly. "No!" Wailing loudly, he struggled to free himself of her grip as Frank ran around to the front of the house. "Miz Ellen," Dolly called from the back porch. "Miz Ellen, Miz Mary's here to visit you."

"Oh, Dolly, would you get Frank and watch these children?" She irritably handed Bessie to Dolly and went into the kitchen. She paused a moment to smooth her hair back from her face and then went into the parlor to greet Mary.

53

"Do you have a minute, Ellen? I haven't had a visit with you in so long, I just decided to stop by. You're so busy, I'm never certain if I'm intruding or not."

"Mary, you know you're always welcome, and besides, you've just rescued me. We'll stay right here in the parlor. My children make being outside a little distracting."

Ellen felt slightly self–conscious of her own disheveled self as she looked at Mary, cool and lovely as sunshine in a light lemon organdy dress tied with a matching sash. Her eyes danced from under a straw hat decorated with yellow roses. "You look like lemonade," Ellen exclaimed delightedly. "Let me see if Dolly will make us some as soon as she has a free hand."

They sat and chatted lightly, Ellen happy to be rescued from the children for a few minutes and to hear some news outside the walls of Pine Grove. There was a subdued and nervous air underneath Mary's usual vitality, and it was a few moments before Ellen began to wonder why Mary was really here.

"Ellen?" Mary questioned suddenly as she finished her lemonade. "I hope you won't take offense, but I really came here to tell you something I think you should know." Ellen's heart skipped a beat, and Mary was silent for a moment. Then nervously, she said, "Ellen, people are beginning to talk about Mansfield. I mean him and Isabella. He had tea with her the other day when Wade wasn't there. That's not really so bad, and plenty of men and women are alone together in Saratoga, but, well," she said resolutely, "I don't want to hear people talking about you when you don't deserve it. And I do think you should know what they're saying."

Ellen swallowed hard, then sat on her hands so Mary wouldn't see them shaking. "Mary, Manse is well–liked," she laughed, "and has lots of friends. Wade's a good friend of his also. Saratoga is always full of such ugly rumors. However, if I were to worry every time a woman finds Manse handsome ... "

"It seems as though Isabella doesn't mind telling a few people he was there. The other night she said loudly enough for everyone to hear, 'Mansfield Walworth is the most exciting man in Saratoga.' "

"Mary, if Wade hears the rumors and isn't jealous, why should I be? Now let's not discuss it anymore."

Ellen could not ignore Mary's visit, and jealousy coiled around her heart like an ugly fiend choking out reason and love. She could not submit to Mansfield's embraces, and yet demanded he spend more time with her.

"Mansfield, you have a family. Can't you just tell your father you would like to spend an evening with us instead of in the courtroom? That's a ridiculous case anyway, and it will never be finished!"

One evening as they were dressing to go out to dinner, Ellen looked at her reflection in the mirror in exasperation. Her face was puffy and the dress of ivory cambric with the short bishop's sleeves made her feel like a lace balloon. In contrast, Mansfield looked elegant in a cream–colored waistcoat and pearl gray trousers set off by shiny black boots.

"My, you will cause quite a stir this evening, Mr. Walworth."

"Thank you, Nelly." He looked at her for a moment and then said, "just a little word of warning. Don't spend the evening talking about the children, or worse, don't take up the Southern cause."

"All right, Manse. I shall only speak of fashions and parties, like Isabella."

"Isabella does deserve credit for knowing what not to say."

Irritation and anger flared within Ellen. "Then why don't I just stay here so you can have a proper evening's conversation with her?"

Mansfield turned to her then, a look of incredulity on his face. "Ellen, don't be ridiculous."

She couldn't stop. All the fear and jealously she had been holding within her bubbled to the surface, demanding to be let out. "Mary was here last week. She said everybody is talking about you and Isabella. She said you were at her house when Wade wasn't home."

"I was," Mansfield said solemnly. "I went to see Wade, he wasn't there, and Isabella asked me to have tea. We just talked about nothing, then I left."

"Manse," Ellen said softly, "I would just love to sit with you and talk about nothing. Sometimes I look across the park and think how much I wish you would come to me and ask me to go there with you, like you used to do when you wanted to escape your studies."

"And if we just sat and talked about nothing, Nelly, you would end up with another baby."

"Is that what it leads to then?" Ellen asked, her voice rising. "If you were so innocent, you wouldn't think that. Is that what you think with Isabella?" Tears stung her eyes. "I've seen the way you look at her."

"Every time I look at you, Ellen, you're holding a baby. And every time we talk it's about the children or the house you want. We can't just talk about nothing."

Rage choked her then, and she flew at Mansfield, her fists pummeling his chest. "Don't, Manse, don't do this to me."

55

He hit her then, a stinging blow to the side of the head which made her ear ring and left a faint pink imprint on her face. "Leave me alone, Ellen," he warned coldly as he walked toward the door. "I've had enough."

The heat of summer gave way in September to cooling rains, and then suddenly, it was as damp and cold as it had been hot. Ellen lingered with Bessie for a while before putting her to bed, putting her face on the baby's neck and blowing softly. Bessie grinned and gurgled, her eyes shining with joy. Sitting down to rock Bessie, Ellen thought she needed the baby as much as the child needed her. She held one finger out for Bessie to grasp, and with the grip she felt an unbreakable bond between them. As darkness enveloped the room and Bessie fell asleep, Ellen laid her carefully in the crib, making sure the draft from the open window wasn't too strong.

The next day Bessie was fussy, now and then pulling up her legs and wailing furiously. She developed dysentery that couldn't be stopped, and Dolly and Sarah took turns with Ellen comforting Bessie and watching Frank and Johnny.

When she had not improved by the third day, Dr. Allen was sent for, and after examining the child and prescribing medicine for her, he told Ellen to keep a close watch on her, and send for him if she worsened.

The following day the vomiting and dysentery increased in intensity, and in spite of Dr. Allen's best efforts, Bessie died in Ellen's arms that night, just six weeks short of her first birthday.

"I don't believe it," Ellen sobbed in Mansfield's arms, "just a few days ago I played with her, and she was so happy and well. I won't ever believe it."

The dim gloom of a rainy autumn and drawn blinds closed about Pine Grove. Martin D. and Lemuel arrived home from school, much to the delight of Frank and Johnny who couldn't understand the stillness. Clarence arrived, along with Bessie's godfather, Archbishop John Hughes of New York City. Their voices made efforts to comfort Ellen and Mansfield, but Ellen could hear nothing. Grief cut into everything she said and did, and holding Frank or Johnny would only bring about a flood of tears and sobs.

The night after Bessie was buried, Ellen and Mansfield sat in their bedroom, the empty crib in the corner a focus of their grief. Ellen sat in a chair sobbing, holding her arms across her stomach as though to hold herself together. Mansfield, his eyes red, said nothing as he sat on the bed, a glass of bourbon in his hand.

"Crying isn't going to help," he said finally.

56

"I can't help it, Manse, I can't stop. There is so much emptiness ... where do you think she is now?"

Mansfield didn't answer for a moment, then finally with a slight slur to his voice asked, "What difference does it make?"

"Manse, you can be so selfish. It makes all the difference to us. I know she is with God. If I didn't think so, I couldn't go on."

"Maybe, Ellen, maybe God is punishing us."

"Why? I haven't done anything wrong."

"Are you saying that I should be punished?" Mansfield asked.

She looked at him for a moment, wondering if he felt the empty grief inside himself that she did, and for just a brief moment, a stab of pity for Mansfield pierced her heart.

"I didn't mean that, Manse. It's just that nothing has gone right lately, and now this. This is the worst that could happen to us."

Unable to sleep, Ellen lay in the shelter of Mansfield's arms, feeling nothing but numb emptiness. Inside herself something had splintered, an idealism that only innocence can breed, and innocence had suddenly left.

Chapter 12

Motherhood was no longer a miracle, it was an endless cycle of reproduction. On October 2, 1858, Ellen's namesake had been born; and now in this summer of 1859, Ellen was again confined to the house, the new baby expected in late October. When Ellen had announced to Sarah that she was "in a fix" again, Sarah pursed her lips and a slight frown of consternation passed over her face. "Really, Ellen," she sighed. "This is simply too much. It's too hard on you, and too hard on the babies. You and Mansfield are just going to have to decide not to have your children so close together."

Ellen was embarrassed to be pregnant again so close on the heels of little Ellen's birth, and she didn't see how she would possibly have the energy to care for two babies at one time. Even though Frank was only six years old, Ellen could hardly remember a time when she hadn't been besieged with children. Constantly tired, weariness dogged her until she wondered if it was possible to feel any older. She spent a part of every day reading earnestly to Frank and Johnny, encouraging them to learn new jaw–breaking words and had them make sentences of those words which she expected them to repeat to her at intervals throughout the day. She held Ellen as much as possible to assure the baby of her love. But every few nights it seemed at least one of the children was awake and needing her, and between sleepless nights and busy days, Ellen began to feel she was no longer a person, she was simply there for everyone's use. Her blue eyes, once clear and piercing, were now dulled by lack of sleep, and the downward curves at the corners of her eyes were more pronounced than ever. She went about her duties with a smile of determination and a sigh of resignation. At night, she submitted to Mansfield's embraces when she had to and fell asleep having satisfied everyone but herself.

She yearned for time for herself to develop her own intellect, and often complained that time that once might have been spent on her personal pursuits was now completely absorbed by the children.

Only her letters to Mary gave her the close companionship she longed for and the creativity that demanded an outlet, and she cherished those quiet times she could steal and poured out her heart to her friend.

One night, when the children were asleep and the only sound in Pine Grove was an occasional creak as the house settled in the stillness, Ellen sat at her desk giving Mary an account of the events of her days. The happy sound of music from the hotels and occasional laughter drifted like a coverlet on the warm summer night. And suddenly, Ellen realized that here in Saratoga she was home. She had given up all thoughts of moving West. "Even if I did move back to Jacksonville, Molly," she wrote, "it would not be the Jacksonville of our girlish days to me for all is so changed. Though there is very little of the society here that I care much about, it is such a free and easy place where everybody can do just as they like without being meddled with. So I have become quite a Saratogian and given up even the inclination to go West to reside; and then it would never be the West of our girlish days to me for all is so changed that it would be a sorrow to me to go back to stay." The lamp-light blurred as her eyes filled with tears of regret and acceptance. Things did change, she thought, and change could shut the door on dreams and longings. She had accepted Saratoga as her home, but her regret would always be the loss of her girlish heart and her dreams in Jacksonville. She wiped her eyes hastily and glanced toward the bed where Mansfield lay sleeping, his even breathing filling the room.

She longed to tell Mary of her problems with Manse, how he seemed to avoid her, how they couldn't talk without arguing. But she needed more than just to tell Mary, she thought with a sigh, she needed answers too. And even if she could talk to Mary face to face, she would never be able to bring up the horrifying incident of a few days ago. She had been wrong, she knew, to force the old subject of a home when Mansfield was tired after a long day. Like her, he was often tired, his creativity and time sapped by that interminable spike case. He had not published a book since 1853, that happy year Frank was born, nor did he seem to have any ambition anymore to write another. Ellen, fed up by the lack of privacy here at Pine Grove, fed up by Mansfield's absorption on the case, complained one evening how little she saw him, how seldom he paid attention to the children.

"Manse, I don't feel like I have a husband anymore. I see you only at suppertime, and then we converse with the entire family, and we don't see each other alone until bedtime. That's the only time we're together. We hardly speak to each other anymore."

"At bedtime, Nelly, we might talk more if you weren't so busy avoiding me."

For a moment she paused, while she searched for the right words. She knew that if she spoke harshly or even tried to explain her feelings of entrapment, she would burst into tears and cry until she was sick. And Mansfield was disgusted every time she shed tears.

"I love you, Manse," she began haltingly. "But I just don't think I can handle any more children. Manse, I want to be the best, most loving wife I can be, but we don't have a home of our own. I'm trying to raise a family in someone else's house, and you don't seem to care!"

"I'm busy, Ellen. I have this damnable spike case to spend my life with! Because I'm working with such an esteemed lawyer, I must do exactly what Father requests when he requests it."

"Look at our friends, Manse. They have their own lives. They have their homes and families and friends and work they're proud to do, and they have a complete life! Why can't we?"

"For a lawyer, Pine Grove is the best place to live. The most important people in the state come and go here."

"Manse," Ellen said accusingly, "you know you don't care one whit about being a lawyer. You promised that when you passed the bar, we could have our own home, and that's been a long time ago."

"Where shall I find the time to build a home, Nelly? This case has me tied in knots, I can't find time to write, I, who have published a novel can't find the time to even begin another one!" Mansfield confronted her, his hands on his hips. "May I remind you, Ellen," he said coldly, "that you aren't exactly suffering. You are living in one of the most notable homes in New York State, you are married to a man who happens to be a published author, a respectable lawyer ... "

"And a very weak man," she added contemptuously. "I would like to be married to a man who wants control of his life, not a spineless ... "

He rushed at her then, grabbed her shoulders, and shook her until her neck snapped, and then his hands were on her throat. "So help me, Ellen, if you ever call me weak again, I'll kill you!"

"You are!" she gasped and his fingers tightened until she felt a suffocating, sharp pressure. She tried to breathe but couldn't, and he held her at arm's length so she couldn't fight back. His eyes, not just angry but maniacal stunned her as much as the pressure on her throat, then suddenly they softened, and Mansfield had her in his arms. "Oh, Nelly, forgive me, forgive me, I love you." He kissed her face, the murderous red marks on her throat, and then pushed her onto the bed. "Nelly, Nelly, I need you," he whispered hoarsely as he began pulling up her dress. "Please, Nelly, please."

Ellen got up from the desk and went to the window and gazed into the soft summer night. The street lamps below shone on an empty street, and her heart felt as cold and empty as if it were mid–winter. The soft air made her feel lonely and sad, she felt not only unwanted but totally rejected.

She had loved Mansfield with all the fervor and idealism of youth. He had seemed to her the most handsome, most romantic figure she had ever known. He had wooed her with ardor and impetuousness. She believed God had meant them to marry, that coming to Saratoga as Mansfield's stepsister had been by some preordained divine design. She had loved him, and loved him still. Yet a veneer of fear was spreading over her love for him, a shadow smothering love and tenderness and desire, threatening to blot out love itself. Mansfield had hit her often, once bruising her eye. Another time he had grabbed her by her long hair and hit her head against the floor, raising an ugly goose egg on the back of her head. For days afterwards her hair came out in handfuls, and her head was so sore she could hardly brush her hair. If Sarah and the Chancellor heard the noises and noticed her tear-swollen eyes, they discreetly said nothing. Yet for days, sometimes weeks afterwards, Mansfield would be tender and kind and loving, leaving her wondering what a hideous creature she must be to provoke these attacks. She would vow fiercely to be kinder, more loving, more spirited, and then all of a sudden the heartbreak and terror would begin again.

To Saratoga, they presented a united front, Mr. and Mrs. Mansfield Walworth. For to Saratoga, Mansfield was a success—debonair and handsome, courtly and charming. Ellen had seen Mansfield's charms and been captivated by them too, but she had loved him because of what she had believed to be his integrity. Now she knew that the inner quality she had perceived as integrity had simply been obedience to his family, an obedience he couldn't break with his own strength because there wasn't any. The inner qualities he lacked were covered by his wit and his courtly, charming manners.

My whole life is my marriage, she thought. Without it I am nothing. In despair, she looked out at the black night as though it were an unexplainable void. She had a husband, she had children, but it was all turning out so wrong, and she was helpless to know what to do.

It was difficult to find a Southern accent anywhere in Saratoga that summer, and perhaps, it was just as well, for the angry voices of the abolitionists clashed with the music and the gay laughter of the visitors.

The slavery question was debated hotly in every home, and nowhere was it talked about more than in Pine Grove. The Chancellor loathed slavery and supported African colonization but had long viewed abolitionists as "incendiaries," who would arm one part of the nation against the other and light up the flame of civil war.

Hatred was sweeping the country like a brush fire gone wild. "Is President Buchanan helpless," Ellen questioned one evening at supper, "or just plain ignorant? It seems to me the President of the United States should be able to appeal to the people more than these street corner lunatics."

"It's a free country, with free speech, Nelly," the Chancellor reminded her. "We shall just have to hope intelligence and reason win over slander."

There was no refuge from anger, Ellen thought. Like a contagious disease, it was everywhere, in her own home, on the street corners, and now it was sweeping the entire country.

The only thing that could be relied upon was the cycle of the seasons, and warm summer slid into the crispness of late September and early October. The inevitable rains of early autumn cleared with Indian summer skies, and the autumn air grew lazy, and the last of the wild asters and goldenrod still lingered in the park.

Ellen counted the days and weeks, and at the beginning of October, she was buoyed by the fact that there was only a few more weeks until the birth of her baby, and she could be rid of this cumbersome burden. Then on October 12th, one day after the fact, Saratoga was jolted by headlines that blazed from newspapers, Negro Insurrection at Harper's Ferry, Virginia! And on the 21st of the month, in the midst of all the excitement, Clara Teresa was born.

Chapter 13

Insurrection! The word burned on lips all over the nation in a spirit of excited anticipation. The quiet storm of dread that had been hanging over the nation had not imploded in stark fear after all, but was found to be a fervid antidote to the dull routine of everyday life. An electric excitement hung in the air, heightened by a sense of national mystery.

"It's such a shame that Martin D. is stationed all the way out in Oregon," Sarah lamented after supper one evening, "when so much is going on close to Washington." Martin D. had recently been commissioned a brevet second lieutenant at West Point, and immediately upon graduation had been assigned to Ft. Umpgrea in Oregon.

"He might as well have some excitement," the Chancellor agreed, "before he settles down to study law." Martin was planning on staying in the Army for only the prerequisite three years before resigning and returning to Saratoga to study law. West Point had been a necessary bore to him, Army life a recusant routine to his contemplative nature, and Army service a necessary payment for his education.

It was he who had been intrigued by the law books and court records in Pine Grove's courtroom. It was he who was fascinated and felt born to carry on the tradition of law started by his grandparents and carried on by his father and practiced so brilliantly by his stepfather.

"If it weren't for the abolitionists, there wouldn't be any trouble to come back for," Ellen remarked. "When they opened the federal arsenal, I wish they had done it for the purpose of shooting those troublemakers. I remember the abolitionist I heard last spring by Mr. Stewart's store shouting like a crazy person. I never heard such vile, pusillanimous words in my life! I hope winter will freeze them out!

The Chancellor lowered his paper and looked beyond his family as though he could see all the way to Washington. "I regard the law with as great a reverence as I do religion, but laws mustn't chain humans. Washington, that great man—honored at home and abroad more than any man on earth ever was honored—did he go for enforcing laws? No, he resisted laws that were oppressive against a free people and against the injustice at which they rebelled. Enforcing the laws right now will splinter the country."

"I do hope Mr. Lincoln is elected President," Sarah said wistfully. "It would be so exciting to have someone we know in the White House."

Abraham Lincoln had been a close friend and colleague of John Hardin's, riding the circuit with him and was often a guest in the Hardin home. Ellen remembered him only as a tall man, so tall he had to stoop to walk through doorways. Mary Todd was John Hardin's cousin, and she and Sarah had been friends before Mary met Abraham Lincoln. Now Sarah saw the exciting possibility of renewing close ties with old friends in a sumptuous setting like the White House.

For her part, Ellen cared very little about what was happening in Washington. She had her own problems right here in Saratoga just trying to keep up with her family. After the birth of Clara, Sarah had sat on the edge of Ellen's bed one afternoon and, taking her hands, had said, "Ellen, you and Mansfield must stay away from each other once in a while. You cannot keep on having children one after the other. It's too hard on your body." She paused a moment before continuing. "It's hard on your marriage also. I'm certain Mansfield is getting a bit tired of always having a pregnant wife."

Mansfield tired of a pregnant wife! Ellen thought indignantly. Didn't anybody consider how she must feel, least of all Mansfield? She didn't want any more babies! And on the heels of this thought came guilt, for the Church taught that the reason for marriage was procreation, and to deny a child entry to this world was to deny life to God's kingdom. In not wanting children, she was denying God's plan for her life, but she couldn't help it. She was weak; she just couldn't handle any more babies. She wanted to be a wife to Manse, to be alone with him and laugh with him, and instead, she was a tired burden. Self–pity and guilt became her quiet companions, stealing in to keep her company in the hours she rocked the children, or nursed Clara, or spent sleepless time waiting for Manse.

Mansfield took her for granted, she knew, and acted like he could hardly stand her. This life wasn't what they had intended, not at all, but it was what was given to them, and neither one of them knew what to do with it.

Fear of pregnancy had made impossible any real intimacy between Ellen and Mansfield. And without intimacy, the tensions between them escalated. They avoided each other, Ellen longing to be with Mansfield alone, but they were rarely alone. After breakfast with the family, Mansfield shuttered himself in the courtroom for the rest of the day, shouldering the hopes and wishes of those who mistakenly took him as heir of the Chancellor's intellect and ambition. Only the Chancellor no longer saw him as the rightful inheritor of all he had built. He watched Mansfield carefully, questioned his decisions, and acknowledged to himself that in practicing law Mansfield was only fulfilling a familial obligation, an obligation which Mansfield obviously saw as the dullest possible. He and Sarah had often spoken about the marriage of Ellen and Mansfield, both of them empathizing with Ellen's plight, both of them suspicious of the signs of abuse they saw on Ellen's face, the mute pleading in her eyes. And both of them helpless to deal with the situation.

Ellen was certain that their lack of a home of their own was the root cause of their troubles. They needed a haven, a chance to talk of themselves and their family away from Sarah and the Chancellor's mundane talk. If she and Mansfield could be alone for more than an hour, Ellen thought, he might drop his mask of impersonal courtesy that he so often wore around her. They would be able to get back the feelings of their early days together, even of the years after Frank and Johnny were born. Bessie's death and the subsequent pregnancies had shut a door on love, and she longed to warm her cold and lonely heart in the glow of Manse's love in their own home.

The winter of 1860 was calm and peaceful, and if Mansfield was distant toward Ellen and his children, at least there were no vicious flares of temper. The children were safe and secure in the family life of Pine Grove, and Ellen vowed that what was missing in her marriage would be made up in motherhood. After all, God had given her these children to love and raise, and until she found a solution to her problems, she would concentrate on her family.

Frank and Johnny were healthy, happy, and active, and frolicked with each other like spring colts. Frank had dark, curly hair like Mansfield, and also showed signs of introspection. There were times when Frank would ask incessant questions and then quietly withdraw into a contemplative mood. Johnny, on the other hand, was more active, always cheerful and the noisier of the two. He was fair like Ellen and seemed afraid of nothing. Ellen often compared him to her father, and now and then, she would wonder just how much there was in a name. They both shadowed Mansfield when he was around, but when he wasn't, they seemed to take it for granted that he was busy. Ellen was a blonde delight, smiling widely at anyone and everyone, a bouncy, happy child who could light up the gloomiest of days.

Winter was a time of abandon for the citizens of Saratoga, for they could move about their town freely, unencumbered by the crowds of summer. They entertained constantly, their social life as structured and unremitting as the society of New York or Washington. Ellen and Mansfield were busy through all the cold nights with sleigh rides and dinners and dances. After two confinements so close together, Ellen felt like a door had been opened for her, and she felt gayer than she had before Bessie's birth. Perhaps problems will work themselves out, she told herself a dozen times during the day, maybe she just needed patience.

As the deep snows of winter melted under the sun's warmth once again, rumors circulated daily that Black Republican invasions were multiplying over the South, and delusions of persecutions and impending disaster flourished. From Texas came shocking reports that incendiary fires were blazing against the night, that abolitionists were plotting with slaves to incite a full scale race war, such as John Brown had tried to ignite at Harper's Ferry.

When they were alone in their bedroom one night, Mansfield stretched out on the bed fully dressed, his arms under his head and stared at the ceiling.

"I should join the Army, Ellen. I thought of doing that years ago, and I should have."

"Don't be ridiculous, Manse," Ellen said shortly. "You may not like being a lawyer, but why throw all that effort away?"

"There's a lot going on now," Mansfield continued. "There would be a lot of excitement, and there certainly isn't any of that now."

Ellen felt a hollow sensation in her stomach as she realized Mansfield would like to be away, not only from his daily routine, but from her. She rushed over to him and put her arms around him and laid her head on his chest. "No, Manse. Please, be a husband to me and a father to our children and let's build a dream together. Oh, Manse, I know we could be so happy."

He kissed her cheek perfunctorily and said nothing. Dear God, she inwardly cried, how can I reach him?

The gaiety of the winter had abruptly disappeared with the spring, and Mansfield often went out alone in the evenings. Unless they had a formal invitation, he never asked Ellen to go with him. After supper he would excuse himself with the words, "I'm going out for a while. I'll be back later." He never said where he was going and Ellen was afraid to ask, but when he came back, there was often liquor on his breath.

One night he came home later than usual after everyone was in bed. Ellen lay awake, sickened by the familiar feeling of rejection. She had been abandoned, first by her father and now by Manse. Something was wrong with her, she knew that, but she didn't know what it was or what to do about it. Her thoughts tumbled as though they were in a basket rotated by handles, and she became so tired of thinking she was afraid she would have a headache. Now, as she heard Manse come up the stairs, she hurriedly tried to pretend she was asleep, but hearing him she

66

felt relieved and hopeful. As he came into the room, she called out softly, "Manse?"

"I'm home, Ellen." He came to the bed and put his arms around her and kissed her. She smelled the familiar odor of whiskey and tobacco, but she didn't care and kissed him back. "Where were you, Manse? I missed you."

He gave no reply but took off his shoes, went over to the chair by the window, and sat down heavily.

"How awake are you, Ellen? Can we talk?" His voice was thick with whiskey, but he didn't slur his words. Ellen was starved for his companionship and thrilled that he wanted to talk. "Of course, Manse," she replied as she sat up in the bed.

"Ellen, I've made a decision." Her heart leaped toward hope at his words. "I'm going to sell our property."

"Manse, no!" She almost screamed the words.

"With the money, you and the children will have plenty to live on. I am going into the Army."

An hour ago she thought she would do anything Mansfield asked if they could just have a decent marriage, if he would just love her. Now she stood in front of him in her nightgown, barefooted, her long hair streaming down her shoulders, and fire in her eyes. "Manse, a year ago you said you would kill me if I every called you weak again. Well, if you sell that property, I really believe I could kill you." And for one brief murderous second she thought she might really be capable of such a heinous crime. Mansfield threw his head back and laughed. "How, Nelly? Nag me to death?" Shaking, she slapped him. He rose slowly, outrage on his face, then in movements like a panther he had her arms twisted behind her back, tightening his grip until she screamed loudly in pain. He dropped her arms and made a kicking movement toward her with his foot. It was that moment, more than the pain, which tore her to anguish. She began to cry great sobs that felt like they were coming from someplace deep inside her and moving through her body. She loved him, and he was treating her like a mangy dog. She loved him, and he was going to sell her hopes and dreams. She cried until she was sick, and as the sky began to lighten, she fell asleep exhausted. When she awakened with Clara's cries, her eyes were so swollen she could hardly see.

There was no use hiding her anguish. It was written not only in her eyes, but in the stoop of her shoulders, in her walk. That evening they all sat at supper quietly, awkwardly. As Dolly passed a bowl of potatoes, Ellen looked at Mansfield with a beaten but defiant look on her face.

67

"Manse, did you tell your father that you are selling our property so you can join the Army?" Mansfield flashed a murderous look at her, then looked down at his plate, his jaw tightening. "No, I haven't. I thought the Army could use me, Father, and I want Ellen and my children to have a good income while I'm away." The Chancellor sat still, the skin on his neck growing red and the color rising in his face. He looked as though he might choke on his rage, but instead his voice was controlled, quiet. "I would like to be informed of your plans, Mansfield. Why don't we adjourn to the courtroom after supper where we can talk?"

The next morning Ellen poured out her heart to Sarah. "We need time alone, Mama, we need our own home. That's the only chance we have for our marriage." Then she burst into a flood of tears. "I don't know what went wrong. He knew me when he married me, what is it that I did so wrong?"

"It isn't you, Ellen. It's Manse. He has always used the Army as a threat. He probably expects that with his father's name he will be received into the Army like a prince and be given a high rank! I don't know what went wrong with Mansfield, Ellen, but it definitely is not you!" Sarah fluttered helplessly for a moment, twisting her handkerchief in her hands, her brow lined in consternation. "We were so happy, the Chancellor and I, when you and Manse announced your engagement. We thought you would settle him, that with you as his wife he would take to responsibility. But we never expected this," she sighed as her eyes filled with tears. "I shouldn't degrade another woman's efforts, but Manse was just plain spoiled from the time he came into this world."

The lonely spring turned into a lovely summer, and Ellen thought she had never seen a softer, more fragrant June. Sarah and the Chancellor were taking an extended trip for the summer, first to Kentucky to get Lemuel from school and then to Maine, New Hampshire, and Massachusetts. The Chancellor, no matter how much he had to be away during the year, always made it his business to be in Saratoga for the summer months, but no one questioned this trip. They were leaving so that Ellen and Mansfield could have some time alone. "Now, dear," Sarah said to Ellen, hugging her, "make Manse more important than the children. And take care of yourself. Let Dolly take care of the children, and you rest and get out a little more."

Ellen was full of fear and excitement. Excited that at last she and Manse would be alone, and she could be a real wife to him for the first time in their marriage. And afraid that he would no longer want her, afraid that it just might be too late.

The warm, somnolent air of early summer crept over a Saratoga empty of Southern visitors. Even though the soft, sensuous accents were missed, there were still people and music and laughter. Ellen tried to create a marriage out of the fantasies she had lived for all these past years. She and Mansfield breakfasted together in the mornings, taking their time. She planned quiet suppers for him in the evenings, sometimes including Frank and Johnny, but often just the two of them alone. In the warm evenings they often strolled the streets or the park, seeing Saratoga with a visitor's eye. Twice, she planned dinner parties, and with Dolly's help and Mansfield's admiration, rendered them graciously. Without the Chancellor around, Mansfield didn't stay in the courtroom as much, and one afternoon they rode out to the lake and had a picnic. Ellen bought a few new dresses, and by August, there was a sparkle of youth and hope and expectation in her eyes. When Mansfield occasionally had a drink, she didn't upbraid him. She didn't bring up the subject of writing or of their own home. What she wanted was Mansfield, and what she wanted Mansfield to be was a husband and father. Then, by October, she knew she was pregnant again.

All her feelings of youth, of lightness, and of hope, were gone. Hopelessness triggered a listless depression that she was powerless to fight. She kept the secret to herself. She would not tell Mansfield and ruin what they were beginning to feel again. Out of embarrassment, she vowed to herself to keep it a secret even from Sarah. Poor baby, she thought over and over again, poor baby that's so unwanted its mother can't even admit to it. She stopped eating, hoping that if she lost weight it would be a long while before she would appear pregnant. By February, she realized she had to tell Mansfield, but she couldn't face him alone. First she had to tell Sarah.

To her surprise, Sarah took the news calmly. "Well, Ellen, if you insist on having babies, we must be happy about it. How does Mansfield feel?"

"I haven't told him yet." She paused. "When Manse finds out, he'll want nothing more to do with me."

"What makes you think that?" Sarah asked, her eyes narrowing.

"He said this summer that he was fond of me, that he wanted to be with me, but that he needed a woman without a pack of children running around. 'Women and children together,' he said, 'are nothing but total misery.' I don't know what he expects," she stated angrily.

And always, in her mind, was the picture of Isabella who had only two children, who still seemed as gay and young as ever. She, too, had had that feeling of lightness last summer, Ellen reflected, but now, in the quiet of winter, she felt as heavy and oppressed as if she would never have the energy to walk or even breathe again. She did not feel pretty, she felt like a rickety delivery wagon.

"Ellen, you are going to have to find strength," Sarah stated firmly. "Not just physical strength, but strength in your soul. We can no longer make excuses for Mansfield, we must see him as he is. Your husband," and Sarah drew a deep breath, "is not a responsible person and is never going to be. Until you face that fact, you will never be anything but tied in knots."

This was a surprising speech from a woman who had always had others to care for her. As the youngest child, Sarah had been the pet of her family. Marriage to John Hardin had been gay and financially secure, as had her marriage to the Chancellor. Yet she knew how fortunate she had been as she watched other women floundering helplessly in unfortunate marriages. Now she was watching her daughter struggle to make a marriage work with Mansfield, whom Sarah had never fully trusted. "Unfortunately, Ellen, you are the one who will have to be responsible."

But how, Ellen wondered during the sleepless nights, how does one become responsible enough so that one's husband loves her? Will responsibility erase the need to be loved by the man one loves?

When she finally told Mansfield she was expecting another child, he only said, "I'm sorry." And as she knew he would, he started avoiding her again. Then one night he came home late, whiskey heavy on his breath, and without any other preliminaries told her he had sold their land.

"No!" she screamed, and then clutching her stomach she began to sob. Great gusts of anguish and anger consumed her, and the harder she cried the angrier she became. Now there would be nothing to share together, not ever.

"I hate you, Mansfield Walworth!" she cried. "I hate you!" Hardly aware of what she was doing, she grabbed the pitcher on the washstand and hit him on the side of the head before he knocked it from her hands to shatter on the floor. She felt a surge of savage satisfaction as a thin trickle of blood appeared on the gash, just a brief moment of satisfaction before he kicked her hard in the stomach. Then he turned and left the room.

The next day intense cramps started, cramps borne of violence and anger and fear, fear that Mansfield had killed this child.

Sarah was beside herself. She sat by Ellen's bedside, holding her hand and placing damp cloths on her head. She paced the room as Ellen dozed. Finally, as evening was darkening the bedroom, she issued the ultimatum that had festered in the back of her mind for the past year as she had watched her daughter grow more distraught and unhappy. "You must leave Mansfield for a while, Ellen. As soon as this baby is born, you will go back to Kentucky. This situation must not continue under any circumstances."

Ellen listened to the words in a gathering cloud of amazement. If Sarah had ever made a decision before, Ellen was never aware of it. And now Sarah, who had been so distraught and terrified of being alone after John Hardin's death that she had reverted to an almost childlike dependency upon her own family, was sounding like a judge in the Walworth courtroom!

"Bird's Nest in Louisville was bequeathed to you, Lemuel, and Martin D. by my family. You and your children will go there, Ellen, until things work themselves out."

Ellen lay in bed, too weak to protest. Her hopes and dreams shattered, she felt the sand in which she had firmly planted her feet begin to shift imperceptibly under the weight of her confusions.

Chapter 14

Once it was decided that Ellen and the children should go to Kentucky, the family seemed relieved, and life at Pine Grove took on all the appearances of a return to normal. The Chancellor promised to find Mansfield a position in Washington under the new administration until the marital storm blew over. That way, few explanations would be needed as to why Ellen and Mansfield had separated. No one in the family was to know of this development, including Clarence, so that talk and, therefore, ill advice could be disregarded for the moment. It was, Sarah announced to Ellen, the most sensible solution.

Sarah was all atwitter with plans to attend Abraham Lincoln's inauguration and with the excitement of finding herself in the Washington inner circle. The Chancellor, a lifelong and noted Democrat, was staying home to prevent any personal or political embarrassment to Sarah's friends. He had always opposed Republican policies, but, alarmed by the boiling cauldron of dissension in the nation, felt that Lincoln's election was the only hope for survival of the Union. "Now," he said over and over, "we have the prospect of a peaceable solution to our internal difficulties."

Evenings in the parlor after dinner took on an atmosphere of anticipation. Ellen felt strange, as if she was an onlooker, an onlooker far away from Pine Grove itself, with the ability to peer through roof and walls and observe the incongruity of a peaceful evening with a splintering family. The parlor glowed warm and cheerful in the firelight. Lamps cast a quiet light on the Chancellor in his rocking chair, while Sarah's fingers flew excitedly on a basque she was embroidering. Frank and Johnny giggled on one side of the room, their playful voices coming to Ellen's ears with a dreamlike quality, as though from another far–off, unremembered time.

"Sarah, why not invite Mrs. Lincoln for a friendly visit in June or July?" the Chancellor suggested. "I'm certain Mr. Lincoln will be in a position by then to spare her for a while."

"And she may be tired of the routine of official visits and wish a short time of quiet," Sarah agreed delightedly. "If she comes, we will not let her be surrounded by a crowd, but offer her as much quiet as she pleases."

June or July. I'll be gone by then Ellen thought dully. This pregnancy and the uncertainty of her life had rubbed her nerves raw. Sitting on the edge of sanity, Ellen wanted to scream. The Lincolns! She wanted to talk about her own future so she could ease her fright. How could

72

they be so calm in thinking about themselves, when she, their own daughter, was facing an abyss. They weren't even displaying common courtesy in denying her the relief of talking about it. And Mansfield seemed oblivious to it all.

Ellen moved through the days now like a sleepwalker lost in the midst of confusion. She passed endless days feeling like an inanimate object, heavy and numb, in a haze of shock at this turn in her life. Then there were days when she felt strong, excited, and curious about the journey and the life they would lead at Bird's Nest, delighted at the thought of being close to Mary and to the soil of her childhood once again. This was not what she had expected for her life, not what she had wanted. But she would show Mansfield how capable she could be!

She barely remembered Bird's Nest, having been there only once during a visit to her father's family in Louisville. She would have money from the sale of the property in Saratoga, and with the produce she could raise she should be able to manage. In her good moments, Ellen, who had never planted a seed in the ground in her life, pictured vast fields filled with a bounty of vegetables and darkies who would obey her every command. Experienced in the fields, they would tell her what needed to be done and when. In her worst moments, panic and fear attacked her as she wondered how she would manage the train ride to Louisville with four children and a new baby. And in her very worst moments, she wondered how she could ever say goodbye to Mansfield.

Yet hope still beat in her heart like an army on the march, hope that Mansfield would say he needed her, that he couldn't and wouldn't live without her. For despite the physical abuse, despite the anger and the anguish, she still loved him. These days he acted as if she were no more than a distant cousin, and he ignored her because she was carrying his child. These days brought a particular grief, an anguish too deep to be borne, but she had no choice except to bear it.

Under gray leaden skies and with a cold rain falling, Saratoga welcomed spring with the news that Fort Sumter had been fired upon. Ellen, lost in her personal fear of the future, lost within the confines of herself and this child she was carrying, hardly comprehended the impact of the news. Mansfield was excited, though, and for the first time in two months opened up to her. "It looks like there really will be a small skirmish. My going to Washington won't look strange at all now."

Overnight Saratoga was filled with excitement. The air echoed with intense murmurings of who was joining the Army. Militia drills in Congress Park became entertainment. Everyone agreed that the Southerners, only farmers really, with no factories, no iron-works, could be beaten in a matter of a few weeks. Once the slaves were freed, life could return to normal, and the Northerners could feel justified in their noble Christian effort to better mankind.

Sarah remained in Washington, unable to tear herself apart from the excitement. The afternoon Fort Sumter was fired upon, she wrote to her family. She had been out riding with Mrs. Lincoln, and her little boy had given her his picture. With a mixture of awe and disbelief, Ellen read Sarah's letter over and over again:

> "I can scarcely realize the strange situation I find myself placed in, or think I am in the capitol of a great and free nation. Here is the President, the Cabinet, with the great Chief of the Army, shut out from the rest of the world. All communication cut off by mail, an army checked in their march to protect the Capitol, and yet everything seems so quiet here as a Sabbath Day. I would not be anywhere else for the world. I have not felt the first sensation of fear as yet. As for this city being attacked, they are prepared for it, but it will not be done yet."

Washington under siege! Ellen could neither picture it nor believe it, and she envied Sarah being in the center of all the excitement. Manse will soon be there too, she thought. Her envy turned to a burning flame of antagonism toward Mansfield and his freedom, and then to distress and self–pity for herself and the children, shut away on a farm, lonely and alone.

The terrible beauty of spring underscored Ellen's loneliness and fright. May was warm and dry, the forsythia blossoming in great yellow fountains and the delicate pink of the dogwoods opening like gracious umbrellas of gentility. Tulips nodded their bright heads of red and yellow in the side yard of Pine Grove, and the faint scent of lilacs was just promising to perfume the air. Ellen was overcome with nostalgia for her first spring in Saratoga when she had just met Mansfield. She tried to keep a detached calmness around him, a measured politeness, in hopes that her vulnerability and fear would recede into a strength she did not yet possess. She refused to weaken herself in front of him with tears, even though they were a constant threat.

One sunny afternoon she went into the backyard with Clara and Ellen and watched as Mansfield pushed Johnny on the swing. Johnny's cries of delight pierced her heart as she thought of the children growing up without a father. When Frank ran over to Mansfield and threw his arms about his legs, she abruptly turned to the kitchen door and blindly asked Dolly to watch the children. She hurried cumbersomely upstairs and dissolved into the tears she had vowed not to shed.

"Have you thought," she asked Mansfield later that evening, "how your children will feel growing up without a father? They're going to miss you, Manse."

"Ellen, it's not forever. I do intend to join you and the children in Kentucky in a few months. This situation is only temporary."

Ellen, stunned, said nothing. This was the first time Mansfield had mentioned it casually, almost in passing, and she wondered just what his plans were.

Again and again she thought of the remark. She needed loving reassurance, comforting, but Mansfield said nothing more, nor did he touch her. There were times when she would have preferred a stormy scene, anything but the casual indifference with which he treated her. His buoyant spirits, such a marked contrast to her own, caused her to rage inwardly at her own entrapment.

The weeks were packed with worry, the handicap of pregnancy, and withdrawal from friends. The family was increasingly solicitous and kind but completely blind to her fear.

Yet, beneath the fear was a measure of hope that Mansfield would be joining her. It was this hope that enabled her to withstand his casual indifference. And when their son was born on the nineteenth day of June, it was this same hope that caused her to name him after his father, Mansfield Tracy Walworth.

Chapter 15

A s the train rocked and swayed through never–ending miles of hills and rivers, by country towns and pastures yellow with flowers, Ellen felt grateful that Lemuel and Dolly were with her, for it was an abrupt shift of security to suddenly be responsible for herself and her family. As she looked out the window and watched barns and homes flash by, she thought about the love and happiness and security that they represented. "This summer is just another transition," she thought, "a revolution in change. I have always been dependent upon my parents or my husband, but now, for the first time, I will by alone and responsible for my little children."

"Here, Miz Ellen," Dolly said, "let me bathe Clara's face, then I'll hold the baby for a spell." Ellen was wrinkled and damp with perspiration from holding little Manse, and frequently she would pass him to Dolly to gain some relief from the warm bundle. The dust and heat threatened to smother them all. From time to time Dolly would go to the washroom and bring back cool, damp cloths to wipe the children's faces.

Lemuel kept Frank and Johnny busy playing word games and encouraging them to make up stories about the people who lived on the farms.

The green land billowed beneath a brilliant sky, and Ellen leaned back against the red plush cushions thinking of Mansfield. She bit her lower lip hard, as though the pain she caused herself would obliterate the growing emptiness within her.

"Lem, do you think Manse really is planning on joining you in your law practice in Louisville?"

"Why, I suppose so, Sister. He said he would."

"He hates it so. If he likes Washington, I just don't know if he will try practicing law again." Lemuel's gaze shifted to the window, and he said nothing.

Parting from Mansfield had been so strange, Ellen reflected. He was jaunty and happy with the prospect of adventure that he believed lay ahead for him in Washington. He had kissed her goodbye perfunctorily and hugged the children.

"Don't worry now," he admonished them lightly, "Daddy will come to our new home in Louisville soon."

He left, and Ellen turned to her duties with the children and occupied her mind with the move to Louisville. There was no more feeling of abandonment on her part than if Mansfield was going on an overnight journey. If anything, a sense of relief and expectancy pervaded her days. But now, watching the countryside flash by, an acute ache for her lover and the family life she wanted joined the dust and heat and threatened to submerge her.

"Kentucky is sure far away," Johnny said as he pushed against Ellen. "Our Uncle Mark is going to meet us?" he inquired for the umpteenth time that day. "My grandfather's brother?"

"Yes, yes," Ellen answered impatiently.

"It means 'Land of Tomorrow,'" Frank said proudly, "that's what the Indians called it."

They were going into the land of tomorrow, reluctantly carried there on a rhythmic clatter of wheels on rails, but for Ellen it was a blank tomorrow, stretching into infinity.

Uncle Mark greeted them enthusiastically and made quite a fuss over the children. This was the first he had seen his brother's family since they had moved to Saratoga. His niece, who was still a child when they left, was now married with children of her own.

As Ellen alighted from her Uncle Mark Hardin's carriage, she thought she would cry in relief and gratitude. Instead, only a soft, "ohhh," escaped, filled with wonder and gratitude. The house was beautiful. The old house had been replaced by a new one. Only seven years old, it sparkled like a jewel in the midst of thirty–six acres graced with stately beeches and evergreens. Three hundred peach and apple trees flourished, and a fine spring bubbled close to the house affording a constant supply of pure water. The former owner had hired a landscape gardener to design colorful flower beds, slightly formal and greatly inviting. Here hollyhocks, four o'clocks, and delphiniums bloomed next to a garden of fragrant, rare roses; a spacious vegetable garden gave way to outlying meadows and hills covered with trees of the kind that enhanced the character of the blue–grass region of Kentucky.

Holding little Manse, Ellen excitedly hurried up the twelve long front steps leading to a broad piazza framed with vines and choice roses. "Oh, Lem," she cried, "can you believe how beautiful it is?" Once inside they hurried to and from every nook and cranny, charmed by the commodious rooms, the shiny woodwork and floors. "There's every modern convenience here we could want," Ellen exclaimed delightedly.

Later that night, when the children were quiet and in bed, she stole out to the piazza and breathed in the scent of fresh, cool air perfumed with roses. She felt that the world was brand new, that after years of heartbreak and tears she had been granted an offering of serenity and

77

beauty. "Bird's Nest," Ellen thought. "A beautiful nest for our family, all enclosed with vines and roses, a perfect name." She breathed a silent prayer of thankfulness and her eyes filled with tears. "Bird's Nest will be a home for all of us, a real home," she vowed. "Here we'll have a simple life, full of simple happiness."

The first days in a new home are like a new love. Somewhat strange in the aftermath of being jolted from familiarity, everyday tasks take on a glow, fueled by the certainty that perfection will be awakened in one's being and in one's actions.

Ellen was happy getting settled, and she bustled about buying furniture and household supplies and finding help which she would need when Dolly left for Pine Grove. From Lemuel, she borrowed $1000 to help defray their expenses. "You can ask Mother to reimburse you, Lem, I'm sure she will. We have to have these things, we can't very well get along without coal or a few pieces of furniture, can we?"

Lemuel rode into town every day looking for space for his law office, and in his shy, sincere way tried to get acquainted with the merchants, lawyers, and doctors. Every evening he brought back funny tales as well as stories of the town's suspicious attitude toward strangers.

Louisville did not have a right or wrong side in this war, and every newcomer was greeted with an air of uncertainty. After Ft. Sumter was fired upon, a resolution had been introduced that "the proper position of Kentucky is that of a mediator between the sections, and that as an umpire, she should remain firm and impartial in this day of trial to our beloved country, that by her counsels and mediation she may aid in restoring peace and harmony and brotherly love throughout the land." Governor Magoffin had refused to send militia when ordered to do so by the Secretary of War, reminding the nation that "Kentucky will furnish no troops for the wicked purpose of subduing her sister southern states." The Confederacy had also requested that Kentucky send troops, but the Governor stated that she would arm only for her own defense, and that it was her firm intention to remain neutral in the conflict between the Federal Government and the Confederate States. Still, men with Confederate sympathies were leaving the state in large numbers and "joining up" as soon as they crossed the border. Reaction blazed against this breach of neutrality, and numerous public meetings were held at which the expression of Union sentiments was most emphatic. Humming with discontent and the frustration of being unable to openly declare allegiance, either the Stars and Stripes or the Stars and Bars flew from homes and public buildings silently shouting their owner's allegiances.

Carried along by the exuberance of being on her own and head of her household, Ellen was full of enthusiasm for her home and her family. Her gardens were productive, and the fruit trees were mature enough to bear bushels of fruit for eating and preserving.

As much as she abhorred the war, as much as she regretted and feared Martin D. being on the battlefield, Ellen realized that the hungry soldiers flooding into Kentucky would provide her with an income. They needed food, and if she worked hard, she could turn a tidy profit.

One morning, standing in the damp garden before the world was quite awake, Ellen looked at the back of the lovely house then out toward the vegetable garden and the trees and hills beyond. "So help me, I will have a happy family," she vowed. "And when Manse comes, he'll see what joy there is in a loving, domestic life. Manse has to be shown, and I will show him!"

Chapter 16

"**M**a, we got comp'ny!" Johnny ran into the kitchen, his eyes wide and sparkling. "Come on," he urged excitedly.

Ellen smoothed her hair back from her forehead with one hand while cradling baby Manse in her other arm and curiously entered the parlor to find a rather plump woman of about thirty with an open, cheerful face. "Mrs. Walworth? I'm Harriet Gray. I just wanted to call on you and welcome you to the neighborhood." Her voice was southern soft with a curious mixture of the backwoods and Southern gentry drawls.

"Why, I'm so glad you came," Ellen exclaimed. The woman extended a gingham–wrapped package toward her. "It's ginger cake. I hope you will like it."

"My children will be more than happy." Ellen smiled at Johnny who was sprawled over the arm of the sofa. "Please sit down. If you don't mind waiting a moment, I'll get us some coffee. Johnny, you run upstairs now and play with Frankie."

"I'm very happy you came," Ellen offered as she sat down a tray containing two cups and saucers, a creamer and sugar bowl, and a silver pot of coffee. "We haven't had many visitors."

"I'm afraid this war has made many Kentuckians lose their manners," Harriet apologized.

"My family is from Kentucky, but we had been living in New York," Ellen explained, although she imagined her visitor already knew. "Saratoga Springs. My brother has come here to open a law practice."

"By himself?" Harriet asked genially.

For a moment Ellen paused. "Well, my husband—my husband will be practicing with him, but he's been detained in Washington. He's on the staff of the Adjutant General."

"It must be difficult, having to be separated. Your children must miss him very much."

At the mention of the word "separated," Ellen froze, then decided the woman couldn't possibly know her circumstances, particularly when she herself wasn't too certain of them.

"This war is so cruel. We're fortunate here in Louisville that so many of our men are still at home. Yet," Harriet sighed, "many have gone to fight for the Confederate, and their wives are glared at by many of their neighbors who are Union sympathizers." She paused and took a sip of coffee. "My husband says you can smell the army coming before you see them—doesn't matter if they are Yankees or Confederates."

"No, I guess it doesn't matter," Ellen said. "I can't take sides. My father was a Hardin from here in Kentucky, and until he was killed in the Mexican war, he and Abraham Lincoln were good friends. I have an uncle and friends in Mississippi. My stepfather was the Chancellor of New York State, and my husband was born and raised in New York. My brother is a West Point graduate serving in the Union Army."

"My husband is a doctor," Harriet said, "and says both sides hurt alike. All we can do during this time is to be as civilized as possible and look for the good in one another. Still, Louisville knew the moment Lincoln was elected that it was a catastrophe. He didn't get many votes here in Kentucky, I can tell you."

A loud thud resounded from upstairs, and Ellen rolled her eyes in mock exasperation and gave a rather self–conscious laugh. "I'm afraid my children are rather lively."

"How many do you have?" Harriet inquired, looking at the ceiling.

"Five. They've been blessedly quiet while you've been here, but normally we're a rather noisy bunch. Frank is eight, Johnny's six, then Ellen, whom we call Nelly, is three, Clara is two, and," she said, indicating the baby she was holding, "Mansfield Tracy is just eight months old."

Harriet laughed with genuine good–nature as she rose to her feet. "I'd like you to call on me, Ellen, when you have time, and bring your children. William is eight and our only child, so our household could do with a livening–up."

Ellen, who rarely left the house even to go into Louisville, watched as her visitor drove off down the road. "I didn't realize how much I've missed society," she thought. "And Mansfield's absence wasn't difficult to explain. I guess I just haven't been able to explain the situation to myself."

Over six months passed, and Mansfield didn't come. Ellen had not heard from him since he said good–bye in Saratoga, not even at Christmas, and when Frank or Johnny would inquire about him and ask when he was coming to live with them, Ellen would hug them tenderly and mutter something about the war keeping him in Washington. Johnny eventually quit asking and became quite attached to Lemuel, but Frank plainly missed Mansfield. Now and then Ellen would catch Frank looking at her questioningly, as though she was withholding information from him. At such times, her heart ached with longing. She tried to be more gentle with him, for Frank had been close to Mansfield and idolized his father.

Ellen finally received a letter from Reuben on a cold February day, a fine drizzle dripping from a leaden sky. She sank gratefully into a chair to read it; her back, which always ached these days, felt as though it would break in two at the waistline. Eager for news of Saratoga and the family, she opened the letter quickly and scanned its contents. Then, suddenly sitting bolt upright, she started again at the beginning reading carefully.

> Mansfield had been arrested at four a.m. on February 14 in Brown's Hotel in Washington on charges of spying for the Confederacy. In his company was a Mrs. Augusta Morris. No evidence of disloyalty had been found against Manse, but a few days before his arrest he had paraded in a Confederate uniform before his cousin John Barbour and announced he held a Confederate Captain's commission. John had reported Mansfield to the Secretary of State, and at the time of his arrest, a Confederate uniform had been found in his trunk. No other evidence of conspiracy had been found, however, and the government report concluded that he was simply mixed up with Mrs. Morris socially, like several other parties. He had been rounded up with eighty other prisoners and put in the Old Capitol Prison.

Ellen read the letter incredulously, including Reuben's offer to pay her travel expenses if she wished to go to Washington. She sat rock still as a dull numbness spread through her. Manse arrested on charges of spying for the Confederacy! And in the company of another woman! She tried to picture him in prison, in the squalid cold and loneliness. Then she wondered if Mrs. Morris was with him and thought jealously that perhaps he wasn't lonely after all.

'Suddenly she wanted to stamp both feet and roar in anger. Instead, agitation forced her to her feet, and she began to pace back and forth across the broad expanse of the parlor, coiling inwardly and seething. She wanted to utter blood–curdling threats of retaliation. Her anger propelled her relentlessly back and forth across the parlor until dusk began to envelop the room.

Dolly, sensing that Ellen should be left alone had not intruded, but now as dusk began to dim the room, she entered timidly. "Miz Ellen, would you like a cup of tea?" This friendly gesture broke the tide of anger within her, and Ellen's face crumpled in sorrow. "Oh, Dolly,

Manse is in trouble." Tears began coursing down her face, and she held her fist to her lips as though to stop the threatening flood before she drowned. "I'm going upstairs. Take care of the children, will you? I need to be alone."

Throwing herself down on the bed, Ellen sobbed in sorrow and anger. All this time, while she had been alone with the children, Manse had been with another woman! He was gaily courting disaster while she tried to support their family and stave off loneliness. She hit the pillow with her fist. No, she would not go to Washington. Let him rot for all she cared!

Exhausted by her fury, she tried to sleep, tried holding her eyes shut, willing her body to relax. But her head ached, as it had through many familiar nights in the past; too many thoughts crowded her mind and always the one question—why?

How had she failed her husband? They had joined the Catholic Church together believing passionately that God's grace would bless them and their children. Did Manse even remember or think about that? Did he ever think of his children, lonely for him, and miss them? Did he ever think of her? The half–formed questions jumbled into each other. Each path down which her mind now reeled ended with frag-mented images, both familiar and haunting, of their life together, sun-shine and deep shadows. What had gone so wrong, what was she doing alone in this house with her children, why wasn't Manse with them?

She felt desolate. "Confess your sins and do penance for them in sorrow and contrition." Clarence would say. But what sins? Of what was she guilty? Had she expected too much of Manse? All she had done was love him. He had splintered their life and shattered that inner peace she longed for. She felt enveloped, even this far away, by his tar-nish of shame and guilt. Resolutely, she tried to fight off this thought, but it only made her cry harder.

The next few days passed slowly, her mind exhausted by the relent-less question of whether or not she should go to Washington. And what if she had to face Mrs. Morris? She realized, with surprise, how much she had been hoping Mansfield would follow her to Louisville, and as always, she felt angry with herself for her hope. She and Mansfield were separated, she reminded herself sternly, because he had found it impossible to have a wife and children. She would remind herself of that fact often, she promised, and never again let hope rise so high it could engulf her in sorrow. She was alone and would likely remain alone. She hardened herself to that fact.

In another week, she had a letter from Mansfield.

"My dear wife," he wrote, "I am imprisoned here for unknown cause but am allowed to write to you, the letter being first read at the Provost Marshall's Office in this city. Do not be concerned about me—I am well and hope to be released. I hope that you will inform me soon that you and Lem and the children are well—write to Mother for me. Endeavor to manage or act, under the circumstances, regarding your matters according to your best judgment, for you know I can be of no assistance to you now, and I don't want you to worry about me—I have never acted from my sense of duty to my country, and my only anxiety is that you are so unfortunately situated— God protect you, those who are dear to me. I have struggled hard, but it seems in vain. In this dark hour, when I cannot struggle for you, I expect you to be strong, firm in faith, and assured of my constancy to truth in the end— Put on that character which belongs to you from a nobel and faithful ancestry, and leave me in your prayers to the eternal God of truth—No services of religion are heard within the square bounded by the tramp of the sentinels, but the heart conscious of noble purpose communes with its God and feels that he ordereth all things well. I long to say pray for me, and speak of me daily. Give my love to Lem. Tell Frank that I think of him every day, and that he must love you more while I am detained away. Write to me and direct to the Confederate Prison in the Old Capitol, Washington.

> God Bless You,
> Your
> Manse T. Walworth"

Ellen put the letter down wearily. How cleverly it had been composed, how careful he had been to avoid any doubt by the Provost Marshall's Office. The writer of gothic fiction had written a proud, if melodramatic, letter, obviously aware that the officials in the office would read every word.

Mansfield had never intended to join them in Louisville of that Ellen felt certain. He no more wanted a wife and family than he wanted a law practice. She scanned the letter again. He had offered his love to Lem and Frank but not to her. She furiously reread the line that he could be of no assistance to her. When had he been? She and the children had received no word, no money from him in months. Still, he did seem to long for religion and desire prayer. Dear God, what should she do? In God's eyes she was Manse's wife and always would be. From upstairs came the playful voices of Frank and Johnny and the shriller voice of Nelly. Their children. By loving their children, she was loving Manse, and from this distance, that was all she could do. She would not humble herself by going to Washington, she would wait and see what Mansfield wanted. All she could do was pray. She would pray for Mansfield, and let God do the rest. Weariness engulfed her, and in her loneliness she longed for Sarah. She did not feel like a woman of twenty–eight, but like a perplexed and bewildered child who had no place in this world.

Chapter 17

It was the middle of March when Sarah came to visit, and Ellen thought she would burst with happiness and love having her mother with her again.

"I just can't stay away from my grandchildren," Sarah exclaimed, but gratefully Ellen knew that this visit was to reassure Sarah of her daughter's comfort.

Sarah's presence was like a healing balm to the household. She moved in with bustling efficiency. Her ability to anticipate and divert a crisis when it was just beginning to brew astonished Ellen. When the children's noisy activities stretched her nerves to the breaking point, Sarah would intervene. Her mother radiated love and caring, and to her Ellen could pour out her heart.

"The poor Chancellor is completely humiliated," Sarah remarked to Ellen one evening as they sat in the lamplight sewing. "Mansfield's actions have been so embarrassing. The Chancellor goes about the house now so silently, completely preoccupied; and you know how he talked constantly. He is hoping to come down here next month to accompany me back to Saratoga. I hope he does come. He needs to get away. I don't think he feels well, and it has been such a cold winter." Sarah put her sewing in her lap and looked at Ellen. "It seems as though Mansfield offered his services as a spy to Major General John Fremont. Mansfield told him he had news of a coming attack on Washington and had perfected two avenues of intelligence from the South. He meant your Hardin relatives and you, Ellen."

Ellen said nothing for a moment. "Manse surely doesn't know what my life is like down here. I'm so secluded I don't even know there is a war. Louisville might be as far away as Saratoga for all I know." She angrily jabbed a needle into the cloth she was holding. "Evidently, there's so much activity in Washington, Manse can't conceive of seclusion."

"Washington is hysterical now, Ellen. Everybody is accusing everybody else of treason; the poor President can't trust a soul." Sarah picked up her sewing once again and squinted as she threaded her needle. "I'm glad you didn't run to Manse in Washington, Nelly. You know he could be released if he would just take the oath of allegiance; but, of course he won't do that. I don't know how he ever got it into his head to support the Confederacy. With his father's position and Mansfield being born, raised, and educated in the state of New York, wouldn't you think his allegiance would be to the Union?"

The children were delighted with Sarah being at Bird's Nest. Cries of "Grandma" reverberated from every corner as Frank and Johnny exhorted her to watch them or listen to them. Johnny was just learning to read, and every time Sarah sat down he was waving a book at her, begging her to listen to him. Clara would toddle to Sarah and put her head in her grandmother's lap and beg to be held. Nelly, in her quiet, timid way, would follow Sarah's every step through the day, often imitating her actions.

With the crisis of Mansfield's imprisonment, letters flowed regularly between Saratoga and Louisville.

"I think Father thinks it his duty to keep us informed of Mansfield's every move," Ellen remarked to Sarah, "but I'm glad he does. The children need news of their father." Ellen had said very little to them about Mansfield, but she had reassured them that when the war was over, they would see him again. She did not tell them he was in prison, or that he supported the Confederacy. Nor did she any longer reassure them that some day they would be a family again.

At the end of March, her stepfather forwarded a letter to Louisville that Mansfield had written to his sister, Ann Eliza. Mansfield was ill with measles when he wrote the letter, and as she read it, Ellen felt he must have been almost delirious. He recalled their dead mother's devotion:

> "With the freshness of yesterday, especially during this past week of sickness and pain. It seems to me one touch of her hand upon my throbbing temples would restore me to health. I fear Johnny is dying, and I cannot be near to the little sufferer. All is sickness and sorrow and there is no night but his still small voice will whisper of Heaven, and I am not alone."

On a separate piece of paper Reuben had scrawled that "Secretary of State Seward had no serious objections to Mansfield's release, providing he left Washington. Clarence had visited Mansfield in prison, and Secretary Stanton was very friendly with Father Walworth, giving him a general pass to visit his brother whenever he wished."

A sense of despair washed over Ellen as she finished reading her stepfather's letter:

"I am broken down and desperate," he wrote, "over news of my country and the troubles of my own family, and I fear that my mind will give way under it before too long. But I shall endeavor to hold up my head before the world as long as I can, although I cannot see any bright spot for the future this side of the grave."

87

"Oh, Mama," Ellen said quietly when she finished reading the letter, "this doesn't sound like the Chancellor Walworth of even a year ago."

Sarah's mouth tightened, and her eyes glinted angrily. "He has been broken by Manse. We all have, Ellen. When I think of you and the children all alone here when you did nothing wrong, practically banished from home, then I hate Mansfield. His father still worries about him, of course, and still wants him in his rightful place with you and the children. Now he is no doubt worried about Mansfield ill with measles."

Frank came running in brandishing a stick. "Mama, Johnny's being real mean to Clara. He just pushed her down."

"Did she get hurt?" Ellen asked with a sigh. "Frank go in and tell Johnny I'll have to spank him if he hurts his sister, will you? And tell him I told you that."

When Frank left the room, Ellen asked Sarah the question that had been playing around the edges of her mind for some time. "Mama? If Manse refuses to take the oath and is released from prison as a Confederate, do you think he'll come down here?"

"I certainly hope not," Sarah answered with vehemence. "I'm sorry, Nellie, but if he disappeared off the face of the earth, I'd be happy. My husband would be happier and so would my daughter. The trouble he has caused!"

Soon, spring warmth began to envelop Bird's Nest, and tulips and daffodils began to brighten the garden. Ellen received word from her stepfather that Mansfield had been released from prison and into his father's custody. Reuben wrote apologetically that he was perplexed why Mansfield wasn't allowed to come to Kentucky to see Ellen and the children or even stay there if he wished. Since his son had come home, Reuben wrote, he felt he should cancel his plans to visit Bird's Nest. He urged Sarah to return home and bring little Nelly with her. He also prayed God would "relieve us from the troubles that this unnatural and horrible civil war and unprincipled politicians and demagogues have inflected upon the country and enable us to bear the evils that it is inflicting upon families everywhere."

"He sounds more like his old fighting self now," Ellen commented. "There isn't the note of despair in this letter that has been in the others. I'm disappointed he isn't coming though, I did so want him to see the gardens. Now I guess it will be quite a while before he gets down here. Mama," Ellen said pleadingly to Sarah, "I know it's selfish of me, but I hope you aren't going to leave just yet since Father isn't coming down. I need your company a while longer, and I want Dolly to teach me how to make preserves. I've been so lonely."

"I'll stay here, Nelly, until we can find good help for you. I don't know how you are going to manage your children, a garden, and an orchard by yourself."

"We'll manage," Ellen said with tentative confidence. "We'll even make money."

So many men had already been swallowed by the armies and war work that good help was hard to find. Ellen finally found a young girl, Mary Fair, to help her, although the wages Mary requested were higher than Ellen felt she could pay. "Don't worry, Nelly," Sarah reassured her, "we'll send you enough to cover the helps' wages. You know the Chancellor feels strongly that good wages and dignity go hand in hand." Mary's brother would also be available to help part–time, and with Lemuel's help in the evenings, they should be able to manage.

The fruit trees were beginning to blossom when Sarah decided she could no longer extend her stay at Bird's Nest. "Do you mind if little Nellie goes home with me? The Chancellor would be so happy to have a child back at Pine Grove again, and it would make your summer easier, Ellen."

Ellen often longed for some relief from the children's constant demands, but sending her three–year–old child back to Saratoga was difficult. "She should be able to see her father," she reasoned to Sarah, "she doesn't even remember him." With a pang she thought of Frank who would be beside himself with joy if he were to visit Mansfield, but at eight years of age, Frank was needed to help her.

Ellen hugged little Nellie to her as she adjusted the child's bonnet. "Give your grandfather a hug for all of us," she petitioned cheerfully, "and we'll have a big party for you when you come back this summer." She kissed Nellie's soft cheek, then hugged Sarah. "Thank you, Mama. Write to me now, you hear? And take good care of Dolly. I need you all."

She watched as the three struggled down the steps and into the waiting carriage. They waved as they started off, and when Ellen could no longer hear the horses' hoofbeats, she sat down on the front steps and buried her face in her arms.

As the days grew warmer, the tempo of the hours increased so that between awakening in the morning and falling into bed at night, Ellen raced at high speed from chore to chore. The vegetable garden miraculously began to yield soft, green shoots where she had planted small seeds a short time ago. She and Frank and Johnny went out every day to weed and hoe; both boys puffed with importance that they were needed. When they tired of the garden, she would dispatch them to the shade to keep Clara company or to watch little Manse. She strode between the rows every day in her high boots and cotton skirt, a straw hat shading her face. Even Lemuel would help when he came home in the evening. They were all fascinated by the reward of tiny green plants. There were going to be good crops to harvest, and in this, her first efforts to use the earth for the goodness it offered, Ellen felt an inner thankfulness to God and a primal peace that filled her soul.

She and Mary kept the house and the clothes clean and in good order. They preserved vegetables and fruits for the family's use. Lemuel drove into Louisville every day with vegetables to be sold to the merchants, and although it did provide a small income, Ellen found that it barely met expenses. Undaunted, she kept at her efforts.

"When I'm practicing law, Sister," Lemuel reassured her in his slow drawl, "I'll be able to help us out. I am working as hard as I can to get my studies over with." He was, Ellen knew, pressuring himself to start practicing as soon as possible. Lemuel saw law as a cornerstone of civilized life and found farming a fascinating challenge, and the energy these two disparate activities generated in him produced a cheerful, almost euphoric presence. By August, when it seemed there could never be enough time if she had the world's lifetime, Ellen was shocked when Lemuel announced plans to visit Saratoga.

"I should go, Sister, there are some questions I must ask the Chancellor," he patiently explained. "I need his guidance. Letters just won't do, and with his help, I think I can finish my studies by the first of next year. Why don't I take Johnny with me? The climate might invigorate him." Lemuel paused and looked at the ground. "He could see his daddy too. Might do them both good."

Johnny had been acting lethargic for the past two months, a condition which Ellen blamed more than once on either the hot weather or his tiring of summer chores. She didn't know what she would do without Lemuel, she thought irritably. Frank, had begged to make the trip too; Ellen appeased him with the promise that he could go to Pine Grove as soon as Johnny came back. "I suppose," she remarked to Lemuel with some sarcasm, "that Manse has plenty of time to give attention to Johnny."

Ellen and Mary, and Mary's brother, Buck, pushed a little harder, and by early September she thought they had gotten along without Lemuel very nicely. In fact, Ellen reflected, the entire summer had yielded good crops and raised confidence in her ability to stand on her own two feet.

In the late afternoon of an early September day, Ellen sat on the vine–covered piazza holding a letter from Sarah and hoping for a cool breeze. The day had been hot and sticky since early morning, and more than once she had plunged her hands into the cool spring at the back of the house and splashed water on her face. She hardly had time to miss little Nellie or Johnny, but each time she received a letter from Pine Grove, she opened it hurriedly, hungry for reassurance about them. Now as she read, the war closed in about her and the full force of man's animal nature hit her with a stunning blow. Martin D. had been seriously wounded at Bull Run, and when the news came, Lemuel had left at once for Washington. At the beginning of September, D. had been brought home on a stretcher, his left arm incapacitated from wounds in the chest and shoulder blade. The Chancellor was concerned that when the wounds sloughed off the artery might be opened, and D. might be exhausted by loss of blood. Lemuel had been shocked to find Washington in a state of panic, Sarah wrote. Government clerks were drilling militia companies, and the Secretary of War, prepared for the worst, had papers ready for easy transportation in the event of evacuation.

Ellen finished reading the letter and listened to the chattering of birds in the trees and vines that surrounded the house. War was so far from her thoughts that a shiver of guilt ran through her. The tents of the Union Army had sprung up like mushrooms on the Fair Grounds, and the streets of Louisville were filled with men in uniform, but other than that the actual brutalities seemed not to exist. How small her own troubles were, she thought, compared to those of mothers and wives who waited anxiously every day for news of their loved ones. How small her troubles seemed even compared to D.'s, who might not be able to use his arm again. A pang hit her when she thought of her little brother lying wounded. How handsome he was, and what a pity that he was so heavily involved in this mess; Martin D., who had seen the Army as only a duty, hoped to be a great lawyer one day. In her letter Sarah had said that D. had been commended for gallant and meritorious service and had been promoted to the reserve rank of colonel. He was carrying on his ancestors' love of country, Ellen thought proudly. Putting one's own desires aside to serve one's country was the noblest effort there could be. Standing up abruptly, she vowed never to let her own troubles defeat her. She was living in peace, in a lovely home with her children, and in a country their ancestors had helped build and defend. With that foundation, surely their lives could be happy ones!

The air was still warm and heavy with the scent of grapes when Sarah came back to Bird's Nest, bringing little Nellie with her. Ellen hugged Nellie fiercely, laughing and crying at the same time. "Even when there are lots of children in a family," she remarked to Sarah, "there is such an emptiness when one is away."

Sarah had brought Dolly back also, and proudly Ellen showed them the preserved fruits, the conserves, jellies, jams, and vinegars she and Mary Fair had put up. Jars of tomatoes lined the pantry shelves, and she brought out the ledger book in which she had meticulously kept accounts of the produce she had sold. "It's not the best way to earn money," she conceded to Sarah, "but at least we spend very little on food. Perhaps I shouldn't pay such high wages to Mary and her brother, but I don't know what I would do without them. This year I learned I can do it; maybe next year I won't make so many mistakes, and I'll realize a better profit."

Much to Ellen's dismay, Sarah had left Johnny at Pine Grove. "He can come home with Lem. He's having a fine time," Sarah reassured Ellen, "and his listlessness has abated. He's quite active and happy."

"And Manse?" Ellen inquired with studied nonchalance.

"He's working on a book," Sarah answered shortly. "There's D., trying so gallantly to recover from wounds he received heroically defending the Union, and Mansfield is terrified of being drafted. He wrote Major General Dix, saying that as a citizen of Kentucky and a paroled prisoner of war, he was exempt from military service. He said he had removed his family to Kentucky in the summer of 1861 with the intention of making this his permanent home."

"Mansfield has yet to do anything he should do," Ellen said. "What did the Major answer?"

"He heard from the Judge Advocate," Sarah said, "and advised Mansfield that the particular details of his case would be considered if he was drafted." Then after a pause, Sarah added reluctantly, "I will say this much for him. He does dote on Johnny."

Ellen wanted to ask Sarah if Mansfield ever asked about her and just what if anything he said about his family, but she was afraid that in Mansfield's mind she had ceased to exist. She didn't ask, and Sarah didn't say.

The damp heat of the summer had given way to pleasantly warm days, and although the sun still rode hot in the sky, there was a hint of coolness in the air. The summer had been a success, she thought proudly, and now that the harvest was finished, she could enjoy the last treasures of the earth before the cold came. As she preserved the last of the grapes and tomatoes and took the remaining cabbages and squashes to the merchants, Ellen hummed senseless little tunes to herself and felt at peace. In the evenings, she and Sarah began sewing winter clothing for the children while Sarah filled Ellen's ears with Saratoga gossip.

On Ellen's twenty–ninth birthday, Sarah invited their Hardin relatives to Bird's Nest, and Dolly added to the festivities with a birthday
cake and ice cream.

Then in the middle of November, Sarah left for Pine Grove again,
reassured that Ellen was coping quite well and was reasonably happy.
Lemuel would be back at Bird's Nest with Johnny before Christmas,
and with the fruit cakes Dolly had made and the gifts Sarah had brought,
it promised to be a happy time.

In the weeks that followed Sarah's departure, Ellen found herself
looking forward to the winter, promising to steal a little time for herself
and read more. Then in early December, she received a telegram from
Saratoga that shattered her peace like glass breaking into splinters. On
December 3, Johnny had died.

Chapter 18

S he was alone. Incredibly alone and frightened. She stood in the hall, paralyzed and frightened, seeing ordinary shadows from the fireplace as menacing figures dancing on the wall. The house was utterly still, and the stillness soaked into her like a fine, chill rain.

"My, God!" Unbelievingly, she walked slowly to a chair, sat down, and dropped her head in her hands. She was too numb to feel sorrow or remorse. She was conscious only of her aloneness and of the clock ticking rhythmically in the stillness of the house.

When she heard the sound of Buck's wagon signaling that Frank was home from school, she hurried to the front door and, ignoring Frank, called out to Buck, "could you bring Mary right away? I need help!"

One look at Ellen's white face, the almost strangled voice in which she called to him, made Buck ask no questions. "I'll bring her soon as I can, Mrs. Walworth."

Ellen absent–mindedly patted Frank's head as he looked up at her solemnly.

"What's wrong, Mama?"

She clutched her hands to her side and said, "Nothing, Frank. Don't worry." She patted him again and went swiftly to the front door, knowing that if she stayed with him another minute her control would crack.

She stepped onto the porch and closed the door behind her, the December air cold upon her face. She leaned her head against the tangle of dead vines surrounding the porch and rubbed her aching throat. She had to tell Frank but couldn't, not yet, because she herself couldn't believe it was true. She didn't know how long she stood there, but it seemed an eternity before she heard the familiar sound of Buck's wagon.

"Mary, I need you to stay for a few days. The children will need help, and I can't ... " and in a voice choking with dry sobs she said, "Johnny died, and Frank mustn't know yet."

Going inside abruptly, she called for Frank who walked slowly and a little fearfully into the parlor. "Frankie, Johnny is very ill. I'm going upstairs, please come up if you need me."

Falling on her bed, the sobs began as the knowledge began to seep into her that she would never again hear Johnny's voice or see his face. Irritated with Lem for leaving and too preoccupied with her own problems, she had let Johnny go without a backward glance. Now her arms ached to hold him once again, to tell him how much she loved him. She had been sharp with him when he complained of feeling tired, and now she would never be able to tell him she was sorry.

Night passed into day and into night again as Ellen lay on her bed, racked by tears and sobs, the empty ache too heavy to bear. The sound of Johnny's feet running and his bubbling laughter cut through her, and she could feel his chubby arms about her neck. She wondered if Mansfield was pain stricken too, and then cried for herself and the promise of their marriage that was now split in pieces like kindling wood. How was she supposed to live through the hours ahead, through the long grief–stricken days without a husband to share her pain? Her body shook as she yearned for Mansfield, for his arms about her, needing Johnny's father to shelter memories and share grief. Perhaps in sharing, they could begin to heal.

She did not know how long she had lain there, wrestling with her sorrow, when Frank tiptoed into her room.

"Mama, Johnny isn't coming home, is he?"

"Oh, Frankie, oh no, he isn't." Pulling the child to her she held him tightly. "I love you, Frankie, so much, and you must be strong. You must be strong for Nellie and Clara and Manse."

Frank stood in her arms unmoving, bewildered. Then his childish sobs mingled with her own. "Why?" he cried. "What happened?"

It was possible, she thought, for one's heart to break. "We don't know yet," she said, holding him with her cheek on his head. "We'll have to wait for Uncle Lem to come home before we find out. Mama's coming downstairs, Frankie. You go on down now. I'll wash my face and be right there."

Everything was the same, but different. Never again, she thought, would she be parted from the children. They needed each other so desperately now.

Lemuel returned home, his face pinched and ashen. When Ellen saw him, she fell into his arms. "It's so hard to have him die, Lem," she cried, "how can we live without him? Frankie. Oh, Lem," she sobbed, "we have to help Frankie." She closed her eyes and buried her head on her brother's shoulder.

Later, she and Lemuel sat side by side on the sofa while he searched for words to comfort them both. "He's fine now, Sister, don't forget that. We're not certain what happened. His lethargy came and went, and then he developed a cough which got worse so fast. Dr. Allen was puzzled, he tried but just didn't know what to do. His funeral was very comforting, but Manse ... Manse is heartbroken too."

Ellen's fist flew to her mouth, and she looked at her brother wide–eyed. "Lem, Manse ... Manse dreamed Johnny died."

Lemuel pulled her to him. "Nothing could have stopped it, Sister, don't think it could."

Her pain was too great, and all the days ahead when the pain would grow greater piled up before her, up and up until she jumped to her feet before they toppled in on her.

"Wait, Sister," Lem said as Ellen started toward the stairs, "here's a letter Clarence wrote and asked me to give you."

"Thank you for coming home now, Lem," she said quietly as she took the letter, "I'll sleep better just knowing you're here with us and missing him too."

Once in her room, she opened Clarence's letter, his eloquence a soothing reminder to look to God in time of need. "When the spirit is hurt," he wrote, "it bleeds by the eyes, and sometimes, you know, the wound heals soonest where the blood runs freely."

Clarence's letter and Lemuel's presence closed in about her like loving arms, and she slept, only awakening now and then when she thought she heard Johnny's voice calling out to her in the darkness.

In the days to come, Ellen moved slowly through her chores, her tired mind forcing itself round and round the deeply worn circle of futile thoughts about the mess she was in. Her body and mind were tired, and she felt she was in a living nightmare from which she would never awaken. The children clung to Lemuel, frightened by their mother who was enclosed in her cold world of impenetrable grief, frightened that their brother wasn't coming home.

Sarah, unable to be with Ellen when she was most needed, sent a flood of letters beseeching her to be strong.

> "Johnny could only have been happy in contemplating nature and it would have been an awful responsibility for a mother to lead his mind from that to a higher and nobler worship of God. Perhaps your Heavenly Father saw that you might fail; sorrow is humiliating as well as mournful. It is not for the dead we must weep, O, think of your bleeding country, of the sad hearts of poor bereaved mothers who have sons dead upon the battlefield, mothers who were not permitted to hold the dying, bleeding forms of the beloved ones to their aching hearts. Take care of yourself this winter. Have Mary as much as you want her to assist about the work. I will pay for her myself as I have a thousand dollars in 'green backs,' and it is not much worthwhile to put it by."

A flash of anger brought tears to her eyes as she finished the letter. She would never have failed her son! And if there were mothers who couldn't hold their dying sons in their arms, well, she hadn't held Johnny either! But the anger helped, and it shocked her into a realization that she could still feel and care. She was still alive, and she had four other children she must not fail.

By the early spring of 1863, Ellen became resigned to her loss, pouring out her love upon Frank, Nellie, Clara, and little Manse.

Every afternoon when Frank came home from school, she sat in front of the fire with him listening to his day, hearing how well he had done with his lessons. Some days she made a party out of the afternoons, sharing milk and cookies with Frank and Nellie and Clara. Sitting together before the fire, the smoky warmth drawing them close, they could close out the often cold, damp winter days, their love a shield against the dreary weather and their mournful emptiness.

In the evenings, she started writing long letters to Mary Duncan again, unleashing the turmoil of her heart, and slowly her unbearable anguish began to subside.

She heard from Sarah that Mansfield had published another book, *Lulu: a Tale of the National Hotel Poisoning.* Sarah said little about it, except that it was structured around the spike case and the mysterious poisoning attempts on the life of James Buchanan.

She wondered if the Chancellor had softened his attitude toward Mansfield's literary gifts. She wondered if the book was being well received. Images from the celebration of his first book came to her mind, and tears filled her eyes when she remembered how she thought she would buy a new dress and have a celebration for every book Mansfield wrote. A rage of jealousy shot through her. The new author was carrying on with his life. She pictured him moving about Saratoga with their friends, ever the urbane gentleman, while she was buried here.

Spring came and with the lengthening days and the smell of damp earth awakening beneath the warm sun, fingers of happiness began to stir her deadened soul. She and Lem began planning the vegetable garden, and she looked forward to hard physical labor in the outdoor air.

In June, Sarah came back to Bird's Nest, and Ellen and the children fell on her like weakened prisoners just given a reprieve. Sarah brought Timmie, the young boy who helped the Chancellor at Pine Grove, so that Ellen could have an extra pair of hands to help with the gardening.

"Lem," Ellen asked one afternoon as they walked among freshly planted rows, "do you think we could get one of those photographers who are always hanging around the soldiers to come out and take our picture?" She stopped and looked out at the distant hills, her eyes misty with longing. "You don't know how I regret not having a picture of Johnny. If I could only see his face again.... " She held the back of her forearm against her eyes and swallowed hard. "Anyway, it could be a present for the Chancellor. He hasn't seen Frank or Clara for so long."

"I'll get one of them to come out, Sister, I promise." He stood up and stretched his back. "You want it real life–like? With you and me standing here in the dirt and you with that smudge across your face?" She smiled, picked up a handful of dirt and playfully threw it at him.

It was a golden day, the kind of day when the sun kisses the earth lightly with its warmth. The leaves were full on the trees and the garden was breathtaking in its first flush of beauty. Birds sang with high pitched trills and a light breeze made soft shhh's through the air. Everything was green, a virgin green almost blinding in the sun's brilliance.

Ellen, with the baby in her arms, the children following curiously, stepped out onto the porch when the photographer came. She was dressed in an organdy dress the color of lemons, white lace cuffs billowing out around the sleeves at her elbows, feeling as fresh and bright as the day.

"We'd like the picture made in the garden," she said a bit imperiously. "Frank, you run out back and show him where."

Calling to the rest of the family, they all trooped out back a little self–consciously, curiously watching as the photographer set up a small platform. The man studied them a moment, then like an artist arranging his canvas, directed Ellen and Frank onto the back of their horse, Lem into his buggy with Pet, and Timmie sat on the wagon with a load of hay. "This mustn't be stiff and formal," he said with authority, "not for a family. Then it's not interesting," he said, half to himself. "Now, you," he directed Sarah, "you hold the baby and sit by the tree with the little girls." Then, evidently pleased with himself, he stepped onto the platform he had constructed and called, "Ready?" Just then the platform rocked, the camera toppled, and as he tried to grab it, the photographer tripped and fell to the ground.

"Oh," Ellen cried as she slid from the horse and ran to him, "are you all right?"

"Fine, just fine," he assured her as he rose to his feet, his face red with embarrassment, "but I think I broke my instrument." As he examined the camera, Ellen turned back to the rest of the family trying to compose herself. Shaking with suppressed laughter, they could stand it no longer, and for the first time in a long while the air around Bird's Nest resounded with merriment.

Then, in the middle of June, Martin D, who had come to be known endearingly as D., came to stay with the rest of his family. Ellen had not seen him since his graduation from West Point, and now she was shocked by the appearance of this man who had taken the place of the fresh–faced boy. His left arm hung stiffly at his side, as he was able to lift it only slightly. But he looked bright and cheerful in spite of the faint lines of sorrow and weariness in his face.

For the first time in eleven years, Sarah, Ellen, Martin D., and Lemuel gathered around the dining table, a grown–up replica of the family they had once been long years ago in Jacksonville. They had all changed more than they knew, and through the hard shell that was slowly forming around each one, love still bound them. Now when Ellen needed them so desperately, they had come to her, and she basked in their love and her good fortune.

Chapter 19

The sun was almost directly overhead when Ellen, D., and Lem with Frank and Nellie in tow, waved good–bye to Sarah, Clara, and Manse.

When D. had first suggested going to Shelbyville to visit their Uncle Mark Hardin and his family, Ellen had protested with dismay. "I can't leave little Manse now, D., he's fussy and into everything. Of all the children, he's becoming the most difficult."

"Nonsense, Nelly," Sarah interrupted firmly. "You could use some time away. Take advantage of my being here when I can watch the children."

Ellen bit her lip. "Mama, you know I would worry myself sick away from them."

"Nelly, the very roots of your life have been damaged. You're young, you need company."

Finally, Ellen decided to go, stricken with anxiety at her decision. She packed with dread, fear closing around her. She was afraid to let even one child out of her sight, and guilt rode on her heels at the thought of leaving them.

She hugged Manse and Clara to her before she left, their wide–eyed trust wrapping itself around her heart. "I'll be back in a couple of days," she promised them. "You have fun with Grandma now, you hear?" She stared at them intently as the carriage pulled out, fearful of never seeing them again. But her spirits had been subdued too long, and as the carriage bounced down the road, eager anticipation pulled the sorrow and guilt from her and freedom took their place. At noontime they stopped by a creek, and happiness and fresh air made them eat hungrily of the fresh bread, smoked ham, and fruit she had packed. Ellen walked with Frank and Nellie to the bank of the creek. "If you're real careful," she told them, "I'll let you wash your face and hands in the water." Sliding down the bank, they leaned over the cool water and splashed it on their faces. "Can we put our feet in too, Mama?" Nellie cried.

"No, we—oh, why not?"

To the children's delight, Ellen joined them, the water as refreshing as a night's sleep. How good to be out in the world again, she thought. What joy to see Frank and Nellie's eager faces anticipating fun and adventure. They had been locked in the dark abyss of their own cares and sorrows for too long, and now, away from home, the world looked fresh and new and promising.

It was a flourishing time. D. and Lem took over most of the outside chores, and when Ellen worked in the vegetable garden with them, she did so with renewed energy. When thoughts of Johnny working in the garden with her the year before crept in, she pushed them away firmly, not wanting her own sorrow to be a reminder to Frank.

Before they had left Shelbyville, she had gaily cried out, "You all must come to Bird's Nest to see us this summer!" Now she decided to give a party, the first one she had given at Bird's Nest, and in her eyes there was a glitter and happiness was on her lips.

They would invite all their Hardin relatives, of course. And Lem could invite some of the people he had met in town. Then, too, she would ask Dr. Gray and his wife, Harriet, whom she had seen only once since the day Harriet had surprised her with a visit. And Sarah's good friend, Mrs. Boyle. The list grew longer every day until sheer economy of time, space, and money put a halt to it.

The afternoon of the party was sunny and pleasant with a blessedly cool breeze drifting over the garden and piazza. Ellen groomed herself with great care, choosing a green challis dress with white lace trim Sarah had brought her. Her sorrow for Johnny was still raw, but it lifted her spirits to be out of mourning clothes. She twisted her hair into a braid and wound it on top of her head so that her neck would be cool. When she was finished, she stared at her reflection. With surprise, she thought how young she looked. The eyes staring back from the glass should belong to someone with a light step, someone with the expectancy of youth; she felt so old she thought she must be staring at a stranger. Going downstairs, she surveyed her home with an independent pride. One didn't need a husband for social occasions, she told herself with assurance, as long as one had a mother and brothers on the premises. She had a home and garden she could be proud of. She had nothing to hide from.

It was good to have Bird's Nest filled with people. She did her best to put everyone at ease, to start conversations in those awkward moments when guests walk first through the door, suddenly uncertain of what is expected of them.

Amid the chatting and laughter there was a nervous undercurrent of seriousness. Brows knitted and eyes widened in fear when it was mentioned that the guerrillas were within twelve miles of Louisville. "Do you think, Colonel Hardin," boomed Dr. Gray, "that Grant will be obliged to raise the siege of Vicksburg soon? If so, Kentucky will be full of troops."

"And then you will never be home," pouted his wife. "It seems like the troops that are here now need you all the time as it is."

One by one they asked D. about the war, what it was like out there on the battlefield, what did he think would happen next? To each he responded politely, if noncommittally. "In war," he said politely, "positions change so rapidly that what I say right now would be wrong before it's out of my mouth."

As dusk began to descend, Ellen listened with satisfaction to the goodnights of her guests, all assuring her that they had had a wonderful time. "We're neglecting each other so badly because of this war," Harriet complained. "This has raised everyone's spirit."

"We all needed this, Harriet," Ellen agreed. "We've needed it for a long time."

By early June, Sarah and D. began to make preparations to leave. Sarah was anxious to get back to the Chancellor, and D. was hoping to return to active duty. "I was trained as a soldier," he explained, trying to calm his family's fears, "so I get restless languishing in peace and safety when I know I should be out on the battlefield." Lem agreed to accompany them back to Saratoga, so by mid–summer Ellen and the children were once again alone. But now it was a different aloneness, a solitude of peace, without the raw loneliness of previous months.

She stood in the garden one morning listening to the twittering of small birds, gazing at the shadings of green of the surrounding country and the Indiana hills in the distance. A euphoric calm came over her, as though she had traveled a great distance and had gratefully reached her destination. Whatever she had suffered from Mansfield had been expunged by this time of tranquil living with her family, a tranquility which took so strong a hold that she felt she could wait out the rest of her life here. And as the slow, long, hot days of summer drifted by, her eyes became bright, her laugh happy, and her steps buoyant.

Early in October, Ellen and Mary Fair were busy in the kitchen making grape butter when they heard the staccato sounds of horses' hooves slowing in front of the house. Hurrying to the front door, Ellen was surprised to see her mother's friend, Cora Boyle, who hurried up the steps with great importance. "Ellen, dear, have you heard?" she asked, her breath coming in short gasps, "We're being asked to leave our homes."

"Why?"

"General Nelson is asking everyone to leave in case they are unable to keep the Rebels out of Louisville."

Mrs. Boyle moved to a chair and sat down gratefully. "I thought of you, dear, out here alone with your children and thought it might be best for you to leave."

"Are you leaving?" Ellen asked wildly, wondering where on earth she would go.

"I'm not leaving for anything," Mrs. Boyle said firmly, "but I'm not a young woman alone with small children."

"Thank you for driving out here to warn me, Mrs. Boyle. After coming all this way, the least you can do is have a cup of coffee. I'll ask Mary for some." She hurried to the kitchen, her thoughts tumbling around each other in near panic.

"Mrs. Boyle," she asked as she returned, "how close are the Rebels? Do they really think Louisville is in danger, or is this just a precaution?"

"I don't know, dear, the city can be easily defended now. They have entrenchments all round, and large trees have been felled to throw on the road so that it will be almost impossible for an army to get along."

Despite her reassurances, Ellen noticed that Mrs. Boyle's hands shook as she held her coffee cup. "Well, dear, you and the children can always stay with us. The more people in a house, the safer it will be for all of us. Think about it," she urged Ellen as she stood to leave. "You know you are welcome."

Mrs. Boyle left, and Ellen wandered out to the garden where many of the rosebushes were still blooming. "I have so many plants yet to put in the hot house," she thought randomly. She thought of the grape butter she and Mary had hoped to finish today, the mountain of work she would have to do if she were to close the house.

She had lost so much she had loved, and now she was being told to leave even this house where she had taken refuge. Loss was the greatest fear in her life. Something was wrong with her, a frightening wrongness that pervaded everything like a dark, impenetrable fog, stealthily closing around her and everything and everyone she loved. "No!" she thought suddenly and firmly. "I won't leave. I have withstood separation from my husband and family, near poverty, and the death of two children. Why should I run from my own countrymen?" With a quick prayer to God, she returned to the house, determined not to give in to fear.

The next few days pulsated with a suspended waiting. But Bird's Nest remained safe, and Louisville was largely unscathed. Her relief was immense, but the anxious waiting had strained her nerves so that her actions were tense and taut, and now relief mingled with the threat of depression.

As December came nearer, Ellen relived again the memory of Johnny's death. A year, she thought, just one year. And as she listened to the soft rhythm of cold rain on the roof and watched water slide down the windows, loneliness once again wrapped itself around her like a cold, damp cloak.

It must not overtake me, the children have had enough sadness, she told herself. Perhaps if she worked hard enough for Christmas, if she concentrated on the happiness of her remaining children, it would pull her through. All over the country, she reminded herself, there are mothers struggling to put on happy faces.

She managed. They had a Christmas tree, decorated with ornaments they had all made, and there were stockings filled by Santa. On Christmas morning they drove to church, exclaiming over the spectacular red–orange sunrise in the cold sky. All day she struggled to keep her thoughts from Saratoga, and although there were no friends or family to help celebrate the day, Ellen and the children had a festive turkey dinner, punctuated by all the noise and merriment excited voices can produce. Later, after they were all in bed, Ellen gave in to the sadness she had been fighting all day. "But now," she thought victoriously as she drifted off to sleep, "now I'm too tired for it to matter."

A few days after Christmas she received a letter from Sarah. D had been wounded again, this time seriously, Sarah wrote in an uncharacteristically shaky hand, "and this time it had been necessary to amputate his arm."

"Dear, God," Ellen cried aloud when she read the letter, "is there no end to bad news?"

Since he had returned to active duty in the fall, Sarah wrote, D. was part of the force that repelled a Confederate attack at Bristoe Station, Virginia. He was also present when General Burnside ordered his troops to make a twilight push against the enemy along the Rappahanock River. Then on December 13, while inspecting the guard of the Orange and Alexandria Railroad at Catlett's Station, Virginia, Confederate guerrillas had penetrated the Union line in a lightning raid. A few days later the Chancellor received news that Martin D.'s arm, broken in the raid by a gun shot, would require amputation.

Ellen closed her eyes and leaned back in her chair. "I pray he thought of our father. How necessary it is to give service to one's country in thankfulness for one's freedoms. There are no words to measure bravery, only action. Because of our grandparents, our father, and now D., my children will inherit not only bravery, but freedom defended by the nobility of those who refuse to face fear." She absent–mindedly reached up to the dampness on her cheeks and felt her tears. "Still," she thought, "I hope the loss of his arm has freed him from any more battles."

Chapter 20

The depression that had hounded her since Christmas refused to leave. She moved through her days slowly, exhaustion in every lift of her feet, her arms heavy when she picked up a dish or a child. She sat down often during the day, sinking into the chair as though she would never get back on her feet, her eyes dull, staring into nothingness. Poverty faced her like a menacing enemy, bills mounting steadily regardless of how she tried to save. She had done as well as she could the previous summer, but now she had to admit that no matter how much produce she sold, no matter how many jars of preserves or pickles she made, she would never be able to make enough money to support her family. She would forever need to rely upon the Chancellor and her mother or be a drain to D. and Lem.

Covering her eyes with her hands, she wondered how she had come to this point in her life. In Jacksonville, she and Mary had been full of girlish laughter and pranks. She had looked forward to her future questioningly, pondering how best to fulfill her life, but then she had assumed her future would include a comfortable marriage, a lovely home, and children and stimulating friends. She had thought herself sophisticated and intelligent, and had assumed she would have the leisure to cultivate her mind. When she became the stepdaughter of the New York Chancellor, she had taken the position for granted. Now she was humiliated. No matter how often she told herself or the children that Mansfield was away from them because of the war, she had to admit to herself that the reason he was away in the first place was because their marriage had failed. No matter how comfortable Bird's Nest was, she felt she had been banished from civilization, from all contact with society. And there was simply no money. She had hoped to be able to support herself and the children by farming, but she couldn't; and when she was honest with herself, she had to admit she didn't really want to. Money had become the paramount issue in her life, so important that even after her most exhausting days she lay awake at night, thoughts of poverty mocking her in the stillness.

She felt like an old woman, dulled by repetitious routine. So much life lay outside the confines of Bird's Nest, but there was no way to touch it. Her life was a blank wall, and she had no idea how to climb it and no energy to try.

Lem remained her only lifeline to the outside world, that world of people and conversation and ideas. How she longed for ideas! In the evenings when Lem came home, she questioned him endlessly about his day, hungry for every small detail of it, clinging to his words in hopes that he'd had some encounter to relate which would add a spark to her day.

On a cold, wet January evening he came home later than usual, his face strained. To her questions he answered little, and when he did speak, it was in low, mumbling phrases. Ellen wanted to scream at him, she wanted to hear every little detail of his day, but they ate supper in near silence. All evening he kept to himself, seemingly trying to avoid her as she cleaned the kitchen and put the children to bed. A while later she went in to check on little Manse, only to have Clara climb out of bed and run downstairs barefooted. When Ellen came wearily down after her, Lem said, "Sister, when you have the time, come sit by the fire. I want to talk to you." Her nerves tightened in fear and foreboding and a cold block formed in her stomach. Clara ran past giggling and Ellen shouted, "Clara! Get back upstairs this minute, or I will have to spank you!" One noise from the children, happy or otherwise, would split her strained nerves like that of a crazy person. Clara, subdued by the current of tension in the house, crept back upstairs meekly.

"Sister," Lem said as she sat down in front of the fire, "I've got some news that might upset you a bit. I don't mean to desert you, but I've joined with Morgan."

A sense of overwhelming relief swept through her. At least no one was dead or dying. And then reality shot through her as she realized that this meant Lem was leaving. "Lem, no! You can't. Your law practice, this will just delay it, and you've worked so hard for it." If Lem left, she would be totally alone, and she couldn't stand it. "What will I do?"

"This war is going no place," Lemuel said, ignoring her question, "and I've not been involved at all. I don't feel right, working for a bright future for myself when so many men will never have a future."

The old familiar ache started, and she clutched her throat. She looked at Lemuel sharply. "Lem, why Morgan? Why the Confederates?"

"They're being slaughtered. It's just plain murder. North or South, it doesn't matter, but somehow this killing has got to be stopped. The Federal Government is prolonging this war, Sister, and the South needs men desperately."

An unasked question hung heavy in the air between them.

"Lem," she whispered, "what about D.?"

106

Lemuel said nothing for a moment and stood staring at the floor. "I know," he said finally. "Sister!" he cried with an imploring look in his eyes and a catch in his voice, "The South is being decimated! The plantations are gone, the farms are stripped, they have no means of support, the men are gone. They need help! They have tried to fight this war on sheer guts, and it's not working! Our own roots are right here in Kentucky, and by temperament and breeding, our ancestors were always Southerners. I'm not trying to undo what D. has done or become his enemy, I'm just trying to help this country, and the South has no more men!" He paused for a moment. "Morgan fought in the Mexican War, you know."

General John Hunt Morgan was a dashingly handsome Kentuckian who had taken the fight in the West into his own hands. Known as the "rebel raider," in 1863 he had gone on a rampage through Kentucky for more than three weeks destroying federal supply dumps, dodging or beating the federal calvary detachments that came to stop him, wrecking railroad lines, and beating up the environs of Lexington and Frankfort. A thorn in the side of the Union forces, his raids had been effective in disrupting federal communications in the West. Regardless of one's sympathies, Morgan was a renegade, and Ellen was shocked by Lem's choice.

During the dismal winter days when she was surrounded only by the children, it dawned on Ellen that she had no idea why this war was being fought. Since Fort Sumter had been fired upon, she had been so immersed in her own problems that she thought of the war only when she feared for D.'s safety, or when she heard from Sarah about the activities in Washington. Her father, this war, D.'s hideous wound, her country, all these fragmented thoughts produced patriotic stirrings within her. She wondered just why the country was covered in blood. Was all this murder and destruction atonement for the South's iniquities? Couldn't the President have handed down a decree demanding salaries for the slaves? Anything but this wanton bloodshed.

The winter passed slowly, and every night Ellen wondered where she would find the energy to face another day. Only Sarah's letters, bubbling with news from Saratoga or Washington, provided companionship.

Sarah was commuting back and forth between the two towns, torn between loyalty to her husband and excitement of being in the forefront of history. The letters contained so much news that Ellen's imagination ran on for days thinking of the people and social events all stimulated by the danger of war and the sense of history.

"There has been a sister of Mrs. Lincoln's here, a Mrs. White from Selma, Alabama." Sarah wrote, "Mrs. Lincoln refused to see her in any way, and Cousin John Stewart made her over to me to get a pass to go South the best way she could."

Ellen chuckled to herself as she pictured her mother's efficient smugness, doing something the President's wife refused to do. In another letter, Ellen read:

> "I had an invitation to visit the Army and accepted it, as I may never have another opportunity to see the ground now rendered famous forever in history and in story. I saw the field where Beauregard first pitched his tent. There in imagination I could see the battle of Bull Run where D. received that fearful wound."

As the weather began to turn warm and green began to blanket the earth, Ellen faced the spring with alarm, for this year there would be no one to help her in the garden with the exception of Buck, who came out only occasionally, and Mary, who was much better in the house than in the garden. Frank would help, of course, but Clara and Nellie were still too small to do more than get in the way, and they would have to help with little Manse. With a great sense of relief, Ellen received a letter from Sarah saying she had some time in May and would be able to visit. "God bless her," Ellen thought with overwhelming love, "she knows how much she is needed."

"Oh, Mama, it's so good to have you here again!" Ellen cried as she hugged Sarah. "The children have asked every day, 'when is Grandma coming?' " They've been right lonesome with nobody but me to be with."

"I'm sorry I couldn't come sooner, Nelly, but I am lobbying through all our influential friends in Washington to get a promotion for D. After all he has been through, a promotion would in some measure pay him for his sacrifice in this unhappy war. I'm going to stay here for only a month, and then I'm going right back to Washington."

Ellen clung to Sarah and peppered her with questions the way she had done with Lem.

"Mama, what was it like at Bull Run? Can the marks of battle be seen? At social events is the talk all of war, or is it all just empty talk? Did you spend time with the President too, or just Mrs. Lincoln? Does he speak of our father? Oh, Mama, I should so like to go to Washington!" Her eyes filled with tears. Almost as an afterthought Ellen whispered, "I would like to come back to Saratoga again, too."

Seeing how badly Ellen needed her and how lonely her daughter was, Sarah was debating whether or not to extend her stay at Bird's Nest when word came from Saratoga that D. had again been wounded. Sarah left immediately, and with her mother gone the loneliness came back, and though she felt less imprisoned being outside, the work oppressed her, and Ellen felt that each day a lonely mountain had to be climbed. There was just too much work for one person to do, never–ending work. Weeds sprang up faster than vegetables in the garden. There were produce to be canned and preserved, beds to be made, floors to be swept, food to be cooked, dishes to be washed, clothes to be mended, and children to be cared for. In the evenings, she dropped wearily into bed only to rise early the next morning, determined to get ahead of the work and falling behind by nightfall. The summer was an unending cycle of days which pushed her each morning into total exhaustion by evening.

One afternoon as Ellen worked in the kitchen with Mary stirring fruit and sugar over the stove, she heard the sound of horses' hooves and hurried to the front door in time to see Lemuel slowly slide down the side of a horse.

"Lem!" she cried running to him. "Oh, how happy I am to see you! What—" she looked at his leg, bandaged from the knee to his hip, and her hand flew to her mouth. "Oh, no! What happened? Are you here to stay?" The questions tumbled over each other as she took his arm and helped him up the front steps.

She made tea for him and sliced fresh bread and spread it with butter and some of the peach preserves she had been making. The children crowded around him noisily; Frank was especially proud to have a soldier, and a wounded one at that, in the house. "Oh, Lem, it is so good to have you home again!"

Between mouthfuls he told Ellen he had been wounded in the left shoulder. "A few inches lower and my heart might have been hit. When I fell from my horse, I broke my leg, but it's healing, if slowly. I just want to recuperate in peace and quiet for a while."

"What are the battles like? Is it bad out there?" Ellen asked curiously.

"I wasn't in any real battles, Sister, not like D. That's not what the war is like out here in the West. Our object was to cut the enemy's communications, to destroy their trains and supplies, to capture horses, mules, and arms. I guess we were successful, some." Lemuel paused, and Ellen was shocked to see tears in his eyes. "Morgan was killed. Just killed cold by federal soldiers. We were in Greenville, Tennessee, and the Federals surrounded our headquarters. They demanded that Morgan surrender, and all of a sudden he yelled, 'My, God!' we heard gunfire, and he fell." Lemuel passed a hand over his eyes. "I don't know what's wrong with this world."

"I'm glad you got out, Lem. I'm just real happy you're here safe. Mother can't take any more worries about her boys. If you and D. just stay put and out of battles, she can throw her cares away."

Ellen was overjoyed to have Lemuel home. Now there was adult company to talk with, someone with whom she could share her cares and concerns. Lemuel had been home only three weeks and was just beginning to look rested and cheerful when a letter from D. in Saratoga arrived at Bird's Nest.

"Lem!" Ellen cried running out to the garden where he stood in the sun. "Lem, D. is coming. He doesn't know you're here."

Lemuel looked at her for a moment, then replied. "Why that's just fine, Sister."

"But, Lem, if you're here he will have to arrest you! He won't want to, but he'll have to. D. is a professional soldier, he'll do what he has to do!"

"Well, let me think of something," he replied slowly.

Lemuel could be quite infuriating with his slow silences, Ellen thought. Days passed, a week went by, and he said nothing concerning D.'s arrival.

"Lem, you can't hide under a rosebush," Ellen said sarcastically. "Where do people go when they have to hide?"

Lem rubbed his chin for a moment. "Canada," he said shortly. "I have been thinking about it, but I don't want to leave. I don't want to run to Canada like a common deserter."

"You're not a deserter," Ellen cried abruptly. "You've been wounded, you can't fight, and you can't stay here."

"All right, Sister. I've about made up my mind anyway. I'll go to Canada."

Ellen stayed up most of the night packing a trunk with provisions for him to take. In the morning she dressed him in her brown traveling dress and a voluminous brown cloak. On his head he wore a large traveling hat, the brim pushed down over his face, a long veil reaching from the back of the hat to the middle of his back. "I don't know, Sister, I think I'd rather be arrested."

"Don't say that, Lem," Ellen commanded sharply, and then she giggled. "Oh, I do wish I could take a photograph of you for D. We'd show it to him after this awful war is over. He'll never believe how you look!"

She hugged him tightly to her before he left. "You never say much anyway, Lem, but make sure you don't talk any more than you have to now." The ludicrous sight of him dressed in her clothes tore at her heart. "Write to us, Lem, when you arrive safely." He would arrive safely, she thought—he had to. She would pray for his safety every day. This war couldn't last forever. By the grace of God, maybe it would soon be over, and people could go back to decent living and loving among families.

Indian summer came early and lingered. D. came with the news that he would soon marry Estelle Graham of Chicago, and his presence dispelled the bittersweet loneliness for these days of sunshine and chill air. The sun cast a golden glow over the leaves slowly drifting to the ground. Ellen was seized by a buoyant energy and happily picked the last of the apples and grapes. Then, in early November, a telegram came. The words she had been expecting but had dared not think about had arrived. Mansfield was coming to Bird's Nest.

Chapter 21

The house wore an air of expectancy, its every surface polished and shining. Ellen flew through her days, making and remaking each corner into perfection. She despaired of the garden, her pride and joy, standing brown and forlorn, only the outline of its summer grandeur visible.

For the first time in a long while she lingered before her dressing mirror, wondering how she would appear to Mansfield after an absence of more than two years. Every morning she spent more time than necessary arranging her hair. She chose her dresses carefully, just in case he should come early.

Frank was beside himself, playing pranks on Nellie and Clara, his eyes glittering and laughter trailing his every move. Every day he would ask, sometimes as many as a half–dozen times a day, "Is my father really coming? How soon will he be here?"

Nellie was excited, too, and she and Clara waited eagerly for this stranger whom they could not remember but whose visit as a father was greatly anticipated.

When at last the day came that they heard a carriage pull to a stop in front of the house, Ellen thought for one wild moment that her nerves might betray her, and she would be sick. Her heart beat wildly in her chest, and her hands were cold and clammy. As Frank ran down the steps yelling, "Father!" Ellen took a deep breath. The figure that bent over Frank and threw his arms about him with gusto was a little heavier than she remembered. Then he raised his eyes above Frank's head and looked at her standing there, Nellie and Clara peeking around her skirts. Slowly he walked up the front steps, and then he was in front of her. "Hello, Ellen," he said formally as he extended his hand.

"It's good to see you, Manse," and with surprise Ellen heard her own voice confirming that she was here, not at some faraway distance as she felt. "Well, come on in," she laughed self–consciously, "Let me show you Bird's Nest."

In the days that followed his arrival, they were like strangers, people who had once known each other but had forgotten just when or where.

Mansfield was an attentive father though, just like he had always been when he was with the children, and when he first picked up his namesake and little Manse cried, a visible pain stretched across his features.

"I've been away a little too long, haven't I?" he whispered in a half–choked voice, his eyes full of sadness.

112

"We'll get used to having you back," Ellen said with an attempt at lightheartedness, "that is, if you're planning on staying very long."

That evening they sat before the fire in an awkward silence, their attempts at formality melted by their mutual caring for the children.

"I don't know how long I shall stay, Ellen. I'm uncertain of just what to do next. But I do want to be here with you and the children as much as possible." Ellen said nothing, and the only sound in the room was the late November night creaking outside the house. "*Lulu* wasn't the success I had hoped for, but I do want to continue writing. It just depends on where I feel I can do my best work. Now that I've been here for a few days, I'm planning on spending some time at a desk, if that's all right with you." He passed a hand over his eyes. "Heaven knows, I've lost enough time doing everything but what I've wanted."

"We'll all make it as easy for you as we can, but you will have to be honest with us as to what you need. You're not a guest here, Manse, this is your home also."

His eyes met hers and held them and in their depths was no confrontation, only a softness. "You've done so well, Ellen. I'm proud of you. When I first met you I sensed a girl that was spunky, strong, and admirable. Now you're a woman, and you wear those qualities well." He paused for a moment, then said softly, "I know I can't expect you to believe this, but I've missed you. Not just you as a wife and mother, but as my best friend." He held out his hand to her, and she took it, both of them needing a firm grip to hold to, both needing a haven of security. She melted into his arms as if she had never been away from them. Despite the firmness with which she had held onto her emotions these past few days, she felt as if she grasped hope, as if the longing and loneliness she had almost gotten used to were things of the past which would never again be a part of her existence.

Their lives fell easily into domestic warmth, and they were happy. Mansfield spent as much time as he could with the children, even though he devoted a great part of the day to writing. He picked Frank up from school every afternoon and listened attentively as Frank outlined his day, detail by small detail. Frank was beginning to excel at his studies, flying through Latin and math. "I think we have a rather bright boy," Mansfield said with barely concealed pride.

"We must give him the very best education we can, Manse. Frankie may be the great lawyer your father has always wanted." As soon as she said it, she regretted the remark, but Mansfield let it pass. She didn't dare speak her hopes for Frank out loud, but he had the makings of a great man, she had been sure of that for quite a while. It was obvious he had a first rate mind, and with his family connections he could easily confront the world on its own terms and win. Perhaps Frank would be inspired by the essays Mansfield was writing about her ancestors and their accomplishments.

The year turned warm again, full of promise and new beginnings. Wild enthusiasm shook a weary nation when Lee surrendered the Army of Northern Virginia on Palm Sunday.

"This does mean the war is over, doesn't it, Manse? I guess it does," she reasoned, answering her own question. "If there isn't any more enemy, there can't be any more war." She laughed joyfully at her own simplicity. "If I were a man, I would do something great for my country, do something to eradicate its weaknesses and give some measure of thanks for its strengths."

A victory had been achieved. Just what kind of victory no one was certain, but for now it didn't matter. Now there was a future where men's lives would no longer be threatened by bullets or mastery over others. Now, as President Lincoln said, the Negro must have complete freedom, and the nation would be indivisible.

Less than a week later came the stunning, awful news that the President had been assassinated. "But why?" Ellen cried. "Why kill a leader who has just achieved victory?" Her father's friend, the man who had once promised to look after the Hardin boys should anything happen to their father, lay dead in his moment of triumph. Ellen felt as if loss had once again struck her personally.

The war was over. No longer in fear of arrest, Lemuel came home looking happy and rested and at least as young as his twenty–four years. Lem had always liked Mansfield, and if he couldn't understand his brother–in–law's moods or approve of his actions, he at least enjoyed his company. He and Mansfield spent hours in conversation together, Mansfield giving Lem the benefit of his knowledge about law, of what was good and bad, questioning the boredom and tedium he had found in a career which his father could only see as noble and exciting.

Still, Ellen could sense a restlessness in Mansfield, and she feared his inability to stay at his desk had to do with more than just the fine weather outside.

One afternoon when Ellen was out in the garden admiring the lilacs and tulips in full bloom, Mansfield came out and joined her. "It is a lovely place, Nellie," he said as his eyes roamed over the garden and out to the hills. "You got your home."

She looked at him in surprise. "It's not really been a home, Manse, more of a halfway place, I'm afraid. I just did the best I could. It's been awfully lonely out here."

114

"Would you be lonely now, Nellie, if I weren't here? If you knew I was wanting to be with you as much as I could?"

Her heart skipped a beat and a cold knot formed in the pit of her stomach.

"Of course not, Manse," she said too brightly. "I got used to that long ago."

"I've been thinking of going back to New York. To the city. I have another novel in mind, and I must try it, but to do that I shall need to be there." There was pain in his eyes but also a soft hint of excitement.

She sat down on a bench. "It's the children, Manse. I can't bear to see them missing you. Frankie—he'll be beside himself with disappointment."

"I know. Nelly, I don't want to leave, I really don't, but now—this could be a wonderful book, and I just don't think I can make it work here." He took her hands in his. "Look, money has been a problem for me as well as for you. I know how badly I've treated all of you, but I want to be able to make some money so I can support us all. I just need to try, Ellen," he said with pleading in his voice.

Bright tears welled in her eyes. "I was hoping you would stay, Manse. But if you need to go, there is nothing I can say or do."

"Why can't you and the children come to Saratoga this fall? By then I might be finished, and I could come back with all of you. You know, Nelly, it wouldn't be too bad if I could stay here all the time except when I was writing. I would like that."

She turned to him and smiled, wiping away the tears that slid down her cheeks. She put her hand to his hair and smoothed the curls. "There's no law that says we have to be together except when we most want to be, I guess. Do you promise that if you go, you'll be enough of a success that we can be together even longer?"

She was sustained through all the long, hot days of summer by her anticipation of being in Saratoga again. She could almost smell the pines, and on the hottest days at Bird's Nest she kept cool in her imagination by the feel of the sharp, scented air on her face.

One afternoon Lemuel came home with a friend and shyly introduced Annie Jacobs to Ellen. It had been years since she had had time for a friend, and now Annie filled that need, the first close friend Ellen had had since coming to Kentucky. With Annie, friendship took no time. She just appeared with Lem and helped Ellen wherever help was needed. As they worked in the garden or the kitchen, they talked and gossiped and laughed. Annie lifted the burden from the summer, and a happy lightheartedness gripped Ellen. Without being aware of it, she counted each day that flew by, every evening bringing her closer to fall, to Saratoga, and to Manse.

115

Chapter 22

Her heart pounded with excitement as Buck helped her put her valises and boxes into the carriage. She had a long and affectionate farewell with her mother, who had come to Bird's Nest to watch the children while Ellen and Clara traveled to Saratoga. "Have a nice rest, dear, and don't worry, we'll be fine," Sarah whispered. Ellen hugged her mother, grateful to her for staying with the children so she could get away. She held little Manse tightly to her for a moment, and then bent toward Frank, who stood looking at her reproachfully, angered because once more he had to stay at Bird's Nest instead of traveling to Saratoga. Nellie waved good–bye gaily, delighted at the prospect of living with her grandmother for a while. Ellen, taking Clara by the hand, moved quickly to the carriage.

Ellen was planning on staying in Saratoga through the Christmas and New Year's festivities, then spending time with Mansfield in New York City and returning to Bird's Nest in late January in time to help her mother with preparations for Lemuel and Annie's wedding.

Once she and Clara were seated on the train, Ellen stole a peak at the books she had brought along. Books! For the first time in years she would have time to read. The journey couldn't be long enough to fill her mind with all the words she so sorely missed.

The engineer tooted the soprano whistle, and the engine jerked to a start. Ellen leaned back against the cushions and smiled at her daughter. "We're going to have so much fun, Clara," she said gleefully, already relishing the free feeling within her. "Wait until you see Saratoga!"

Timmie was at the station to meet them, almost dwarfed by the heavy overcoat and black top hat he wore. It was a raw blustery day. She had forgotten how cold it could be.

As the carriage started down Broadway, she noticed that a slow change had stolen over Saratoga. The U.S. Hotel had burned and been torn down, as had Marvin House, leaving an immense gap in the town. A few new shops had opened, but most of them looked the same. Change had been kind though, and many of the homes still wore their familiar primness.

The carriage slowed to a stop in front of Pine Grove, and for an instant she felt again like the eighteen–year–old girl she had been the first time she had seen this house. The door opened, and the Chancellor came slowly out to the porch. Ellen paused for a moment, shocked to see an old man where once there had been a vigorous personage. He walked with a cane, slightly bent, but an inquisitive intelligence still sparkled in his lively eyes. He was plainly excited to see her and Clara, and he hugged each one of them tightly as if he couldn't quite believe they were there. Dolly came out, and Ellen was startled to see a change in her that she hadn't noticed in Louisville. Or was it herself who had grown older, who had changed the most?

In the next few days she felt like an intruder into a former younger life, sleeping again in the room of a restless young girl where dreams were so pure and trusting, whose ideals, untarnished by life, seemed so simple and high.

She accompanied her stepfather on morning walks; she played hostess when friends came to call. But it was a curious house she moved through, rooms empty of her mother, her brothers, her husband, and her own children. Pine Grove, once overflowing with family and friends and important people, now echoed silently in stillness. It seemed waiting for energy to fill it again, hopeful and silent. The courtroom, once the scene of robust arguments, now sheltered the Chancellor as he worked throughout the afternoons on the Hyde genealogy, the record of his mother's family.

On one of their morning walks Ellen gave vent to her feelings of nostalgia. "I feel strange here. All of us have changed so much. And you know what saddens me most?" she confided in the Chancellor. "The silence in your courtroom. The energy from that room is what fueled the rest of us."

"Most of the energy was already gone from that room, Nelly, by the time you came here to live." He smiled sadly. "I miss the law. I don't always agree with some of the decisions being made right now, and there are times I would like to have my say."

"I think you will have a Walworth to carry on your name in law." Ellen smiled proudly. "Frank is a very bright boy and an excellent student. He has the Hardin and Walworth mind all rolled into one."

"Nelly, I've been thinking of giving my library to Frank. I have always abhorred the idea of its being divided and going to strangers. I hope it will have sentimental value for him, but more than that, I hope those books will help him become a distinguished lawyer and so make his mark."

"I will be certain," Ellen said, "to make sure that Frank realizes your library was used by the greatest lawyer in the state of New York and that he cherishes it accordingly."

117

The Chancellor put his arm around her and squeezed her shoulder. "It's been a hard life for you, Nelly. I'm afraid I have to apologize for my son. He's no husband, or father either for that matter. To have to watch what he's done to his family ... " the old man stopped and stared at the distance ahead.

"He's trying," Ellen said quickly. "I'm quite certain of that. I'm afraid a young family is a great distraction for a man trying to write a book, so if it's easier for Mansfield to write when he's away from us, then that's the way it must be. I believe things will work themselves out." The Chancellor listened but said nothing and retreated into his own world.

Privately, Ellen didn't feel the conviction with which she spoke. She had been in Saratoga for three weeks and hadn't seen or spoken with Mansfield yet. She thought he would be at Pine Grove for Christmas and the New Year's festivities, but as the holiday rolled nearer, she tried not to hope, not to think.

She sat with Dolly in the kitchen one morning planning the dinner for Christmas day and the food for New Year's open house. "A goose for Christmas dinner, Dolly, and then for New Year's Day we'll slice a large ham, enough for everyone who will call, and maybe some venison. We'll need lots of those small biscuits you make, and plum cake, and at least two different pies." She frowned in concentration as she wrote the list. When Ellen looked up, Dolly was staring at her with hesitation, "Miz Ellen, I don't know 'bout havin' so much. I've got orders to cut back on groceries. Since the price of food has gone way up, we got to be careful. Besides, we don't have many folks callin' here now."

Ellen felt foolish and coiled within herself. It had never occurred to her that her family might be having money problems. She had come back here like a child, expecting to find refuge from her own problems. Now she recalled references her mother had made to the plight of the Walworth finances and the visible guilt before Sarah would ask the Chancellor for money. She would reassure Ellen, "I'll see if the Chancellor can lend me some money to help you, Nelly, but don't say anything about it to him. Give me the bills first, and then I'll see what can be done."

Since the war, inflation had become the national enemy, and many households were struggling to hold together their pride where there had once been an abundance of affluence. The Chancellor had to support two households, Ellen thought guiltily, and it was draining him. The shabby gentility that Pine Grove wore now, only partly due to lack of interest or care, was mainly a result of the lack of money.

Mansfield arrived two days before Christmas, his face wreathed in smiles and looking for all the world like Ellen was the greatest gift he could possibly receive.

"I kept expecting to get here sooner, Nelly, but I just finished the book. Now we can truly have a merry Christmas."

Later that night when they were alone, Ellen asked about the book. "Did you bring it, Manse?" Could I read it?"

He kissed her delightedly on the cheek. "Prop yourself up in bed, Mrs. Walworth, and I will read it to you."

He brought out a sheaf of papers. "It's called *Stormcliff*," he said rather self–consciously as he seated himself in the brocade chair. As he began reading, she watched him intently, this husband whom she saw so little, this charming, urbane gentleman who often harbored so much darkness within himself. Ellen closed her eyes and listened as the flowery prose brought recognizable scenes of herself and Mansfield to mind. "She flew to his society," he read, "as the bird flies to the fountain. At the clear spring of his genius she quaffed delicious freshness and purity of thought; then, like that bird, she raised her lips and heart to Heaven, and trilled forth louder and clearer notes of the song." He read on, but Ellen heard very little. Indignity flared within her. Calling himself a genius! Referring to her as needing his purity of thought! Mrs. Morris certainly hadn't been taken by his purity of thought! The blood began pounding in her temples, and she dug her nails into the palm of her hand to keep from shouting at him.

Her anger kept her awake that night. Did Mansfield really see their relationship as one in which only she needed him? Couldn't he understand that marriage was a partnership? These past few weeks in Saratoga she had been able to rest, to read, to feel young again, and to hope their relationship had passed the worst point. Now she wasn't certain that Mansfield could see anything at all to their marriage. As she turned onto her side and burrowed her head into the pillow with a vengeance, she thought spitefully, "the book isn't even very good. It's exceedingly romantic and slightly ridiculous. He could have written something just as good at Bird's Nest."

The house was decorated with pine boughs and filled with Christmas smells of ginger and wax candles, yet the gaiety of the holiday was missing. Clarence came home late on Christmas Eve to join Ellen, Clara, Mansfield, and the Chancellor, but it seemed to Ellen they were all working too hard to mimic holiday cheer. Clara was the center of attention, entertaining the adults with her playfulness. But Ellen's heart ached as she thought about the continuing struggles of her family.

When Ellen and Mansfield left for New York City on the third day of January, Ellen promised Clara that she would be back for her in two weeks. It was blissful to be alone with her husband again. There was no worry about maintaining a household, about sewing clothes or packing lunches or planning dinners. She read, brushed her hair with scented oil, creamed her hands and face, and slowly relaxed into the life of a young matron with no encumbrances.

"Remember, Manse? When I first came to Saratoga and had to come to the city with our folks, but you couldn't come? I couldn't see how I was going to have any fun here without you."

"It will be even better now, Nelly."

Mansfield had a large, sunny room in the Grant Hotel, and they took their meals in a small restaurant nearby. They roamed the city, poking into corners and alleyways, marvelling at the shops. Ellen felt intensely alive listening to the constant murmur of traffic and watching people hurry to some important destination. And she was feeling alive with Mansfield's love.

In spite of all the humiliation she had suffered, in spite of the loneliness and the rejection, she found she still loved Mansfield. Yet there was a constraining barrier between them, a barrier built of unasked questions and unsolicited reproaches. She wondered if Mansfield felt it as she did, if he missed the easy rapport that love needs to flourish. As she lay next to him at night, or walked by his side during the day, or sat in front of the fire with him, she searched her mind for directions out of this jungle of constraint but could find no answers. "Time will take care of it," she thought. "Given enough time, we will drift back together, needing each other more than ever. He needs me and the children as much as we need him."

"Manse?" she questioned one afternoon as they came in from walking, their cheeks red and their eyes bright and sparkling from the cold, "Why couldn't we all move here? We could have a small place, and you could have a separate room to work in, maybe even in another building, apart from where we would live. Oh, Manse, it's so alive here!"

He said nothing for a moment as he removed his gloves and overcoat. Then as he bent down to light the fire in the grate, he said, "It wouldn't do, Nelly. We just can't afford to live here."

"Think, Manse," she pleaded excitedly, "how it would help Frankie. He's so bright, and exposure to the city—why, he needs other minds like his if he is to become a great lawyer!"

"Nelly, be practical. The purchase of Bird's Nest was split three ways between you, D., and Lem. So it costs you practically nothing to have a roof over your head. You grow your own vegetables and fruit, and the rest of the food you buy cheaply from farmers. All that would cost twice as much here."

"And is it fair to the children, Manse, to be separated like we are? Or to you and me, for that matter?" She was quiet for a moment, the silence broken only by the sounds outside of city commerce on an ordinary afternoon. "Do you get lonely here, Manse, or is there another Mrs. Morris nearby?" He looked at her sharply, all expression gone from his eyes. "I'm sorry," she apologized, "I swore to myself I would never bring that up. But while I've been in the country, lonely, away from other people, trying to support the children and myself, I can't help wondering what you're doing in the city, who you are talking with, who you want to be with. Oh, Manse, don't you understand?"

He said nothing, but stared into the fire, elbows on his knees, his hands supporting his chin.

"Now I've ruined our time together," she thought. "I've only driven him further away." Angry with herself and perilously close to tears, she picked up a book and settled into a chair in the far corner of the room. "If I could only be quiet and not push him," she reprimanded herself, "our marriage would work itself out, and he would want to be with us. Instead, I continually ruin our chances." She stared at the book, love beating its wings against the empty silence of hopelessness.

Chapter 23

Mansfield returned to Louisville with her and stayed until February for Lemuel's wedding to Annie Jacobs. Then a few days after the wedding, he was off again to New York City to begin work on another novel.

She knew now that hers would never be a conventional marriage and to try to make it one was foolish. She might not like the arrangement they had, but she had to accept it or go continually mad with disappointment. The thought that bothered her most, that flitted unbidden across her consciousness when she was sewing, or cleaning the kitchen, or lying in bed on sleepless nights, was whether she and Mansfield would eventually have a marriage at all. How could she be a wife when she never knew when her husband would turn up, when she could count on support, financially or otherwise, from him?

After their marriage, Lemuel and Annie came to live at Bird's Nest, and companionship that had been denied Ellen for so long was now fulfilled in Annie's presence. Annie and Lem, so obviously in love, filled their home with happiness, and if Ellen felt a painfully missing link in her life as she watched the happiness in theirs, they at least provided a family life she could share. They soon fell into a pleasant routine with Lemuel going to his office every day while she and Annie shared the household chores and care of the children. In the evenings after dinner they sat around the dining table and shared letters and news of the day. As the burdens of overwork and loneliness fell from her, Ellen reflected how much their love had brought laughter into everyone's lives.

In May Mansfield returned to Louisville to celebrate the completion of his fourth novel. *Hotspur* was a melodrama set in upstate New York, and the plot centered on a heroine "whose tender heart carries around with it the terrible secrets of a murder." The early reviews were favorable, the best acclaim Mansfield had heard yet, with one reviewer proclaiming the author as "a dawning genius."

Was Mansfield fulfilling his destiny, Ellen wondered? Maybe her function in his life was to make it as easy as possible for him to write, and if he could only write when he was separated from them, then she shouldn't complain.

In early June Mansfield left again, just before Sarah and Dolly arrived to help with the summer chores. She had hoped he would stay through the summer and help them so he could see what they all went through to earn enough money to survive. But pride kept her from asking him to stay, and even though anger at his leaving caused her breath to come short and a hollow to form in her throat, she could not risk a breach with what little marriage they had. She watched her words and acts with scrupulous care to make sure she wouldn't cause him that anxiety which could lead to a violent argument and leave–taking.

The summer was stifling hot, and although Ellen drove herself as hard as she could, the work was always ahead of her. Annie was pregnant, and while they all rejoiced in her and Lem's happiness, she could be of little help to them. Sarah, who had stayed after Lem's wedding, was bothered by the heat to the point of illness, and headaches and a constantly upset stomach forced her to rest frequently.

At the beginning of July Ellen's wisdom teeth became infected, and Dr. Chineworth extracted them. Then nausea overcame her, too. Between the pain of the infection and extraction, the heat, and the nausea which refused to leave, Ellen wrestled with the garden and was short with the servants who seemed to be unable to do anything without her. If this was the summer she had hoped to double her output, she had to concede defeat. Sarah tried to be philosophical. "Nelly, as bad as it seems, our only problem is abundance. All we need do is walk out and see the fruit growing; it gives such a feeling of plenty and reliance on the abundant kindness of our heavenly Father. We have not money in our pockets or the banks, but we have a beautiful world filled with blessings, both temporal and spiritual, more than such sinful, unthankful beings deserve. There is such a feeling of humble dependence upon our creator whose Almighty power has provided all these good things for us."

Ellen looked at her mother whose face and bearing reflected the troubles of her family. She took a deep breath and sat down in a chair. "How right you are, Mama. I've been thinking I could do it all myself and fighting the abundance instead of looking at it with thankfulness. Other than going to Mass on Sunday, I think about the Lord so little and the work so much!"

Exhaustion overtook her, and the nausea continued. She tried to help Dolly preserve peaches, but the smell of the vinegar and spices only made the nausea worse. Then, toward the end of July, Ellen realized that the ailment which was bothering her was not the same stomach ailment which afflicted Sarah. She was pregnant again.

Sarah was furious. She trembled violently and stalked about the house tackling chores with a vengeance. Her dislike for Mansfield was growing into a barely concealed hatred. He had aged his father, and Sarah was convinced Mansfield was primarily responsible for the Chancellor's ill health. He had drained their finances by not supporting himself or his family, and he had ruined her daughter's life.

Only Ellen's obvious distress melted her temper. "Nelly, why not go to Saratoga for a month? Mansfield must be told, for whatever good that will do. It will be a good deal cooler there, and you can rest. Besides, you will provide the Chancellor with company, too, he's so lonely, and his sugar has made him quite ill. Dolly and I will stay here and take care of the gardens and the children. We'll assign Annie to be the messenger. She can write to you every other day and tell you whether Dolly and I make good servants or not."

"Oh, Mama," Ellen said throwing her arms about Sarah, "I am so sorry to be such a burden, but I couldn't survive without you."

Saratoga was blessedly cool after the torpid heat of Louisville, and she breathed deeply that pine scent which seemed to permeate the air.

There was an air of melancholy around Pine Grove, the very trees looked sad and drooping. The Chancellor was no longer master of the house but more like a tenant.

His legs bothered him, and when they went for walks, he leaned not only upon his cane but upon her arm as well. They all had to support each other, she reflected bitterly, both morally and physically.

She had written to Mansfield telling him she would be in Saratoga and had some news for him. He came soon after her arrival, and when she told him she was pregnant again, his face lighted with delight. "Nelly, that is just wonderful." Taking her into his arms, he pressed her to him ardently.

"I am happy you think so, Manse," she replied as she extricated herself, "I'm finding it difficult to be quite as thrilled. You see, raising children is a difficult, time–consuming task, and very lonely when one attempts it alone."

"Nelly, maybe we can work something out. Right now I am working on the biographies of the chancellors of New York State, with particular emphasis upon Chancellor Robert Livingston. Father has wanted me to do this for a long time and has arranged access to the papers I need. For that I have to stay in New York, but maybe after that I can arrange to be with you more." He stroked his mustache and looked at her, then lowered his voice to a near whisper. "You know, Nelly, there is something else to consider. Father is old, he is in poor health, and he won't live much longer. When he dies, there will undoubtedly be more money for us. Then we can hope for a more permanent living arrangement."

Infuriated by his lack of love and concern for his father and disgusted by his greed, Ellen lost her restraint. "Mansfield! That is quite the most vile thing I have ever heard you say!"

"It may sound vile, but I am only being realistic."

"Since when has reality encroached upon your mind? I tremble when I think that our children might inherit your character. I hope to God they have been blessed with only Clarence's traits!" She stalked out of the room, barely able to suppress her rage. The only thing keeping her from slamming the door and stomping down the stairs was the Chancellor, patiently waiting for her to join him on a walk.

She took his arm tenderly, sorry for this old man now stripped of his power by age and disease, sorry for them all. They took their time, Ellen unwilling to return to Mansfield any sooner than she had to. When they did return, she saw that he had been drinking.

"So, are you trying to butter him up?" Mansfield asked sarcastically as the Chancellor returned to the old courtroom to work on his genealogy for a while before supper.

"Mansfield, just what is your reason for writing the biography of Robert Livingston? For the first time in your life you want to please Father. Why?"

Mansfield laughed. "Maybe the same reason you're at his beck and call all day."

"That's not the kind of person I am," Ellen replied coldly. "I came here for a rest and to see you. Louisville is unbearably hot."

"Nelly, I told you. We will inherit some money before too long."

She looked at her husband with amazement and disgust. "I don't want that kind of money, Mansfield. What's wrong with working for it? You could earn as much as Father, maybe more. After all, you're not only a lawyer but a writer as well, and I still think you'd make a very good politician."

He poured another drink, then laughed. "Work, Nelly? What do you know about work?"

She stepped close to him, trembling with rage. "See my hands?" she cried, thrusting them at him. "One look at them and anyone could tell your wife is a field hand. Your family will survive this winter only on what we earn during the summer and what my family is willing to give me. Not only am I a field hand but a beggar as well. I can't afford to sit in the city and dream. I see a family daily who has needs and only me to supply them!" He slapped her face, a hard, stinging blow, then threw her against the bed, her head striking the bedpost as she fell.

She was no better than those poor unfortunate women everyone whispered about and banished from society, she reflected, as the train lurched and bumped its way south. She shared the common bonds of rejection and loneliness with those women who fell in love and were abandoned when they became pregnant. The only difference was her children had their father's name. They had his name, but she hoped to God they had not inherited the capricious darkness that inhabited his soul.

125

Chapter 24

R enewal and hope pushed aside the damp cold of February as Reubena Hyde's cries were first heard at Bird's Nest on February 20, 1867. Just the previous month John J. had been born to Lemuel and Annie, and now the house was alive as never before; babies' cries mingled with children's noisy activities and laughter. Nellie, Clara, and Manse were beside themselves. They played "having a baby" every day, and dolls were strewn everywhere with instructions to all not to disturb the "people." One afternoon before Ellen picked Ruby up to feed her, she checked on Nellie and Clara, who were quietly playing in the parlor. Nellie was sitting solemnly in a chair with a pillow over her stomach, and Clara was cradling her doll and singing to it. Only Frank, at age fourteen, found himself too grown up to allow more than a passing curiosity in the newcomers. As the oldest child, he was becoming the authoritative member of the family. With Nellie's help, he had taken on the project of raising chickens, but his interest in the task soon vanished into instructions for Nellie. She kept struggling to please him and do as he told her, but eggs and chickens were beginning to appear less and less on the family table as rats kept getting out of control and thinning out the birds.

Frank had recently received a new saddle horse from D., and now he reveled in unaccustomed freedom. Twice a week he rode into Louisville to recite Latin and took advantage of all the time he could to roam the countryside as far as possible.

Both John J. and Reubena were blessedly good. Annie's delight in motherhood was all–encompassing, and if Ellen had not been delighted at the prospect of another child, Ruby soon dispelled all her doubts and burdens. As the months passed, the baby began to display a remarkable likeness to Johnny. She had his slender structure, the same wide blue eyes and blonde hair. She was a fairy baby come to live in their midst and was accorded the stature of princess by the family.

May arrived, beginning again the endless cycle of hope that this could be the most productive summer yet, that with more work from them all and cooperation from the weather, they would be able to turn a profit.

Sarah and Dolly arrived for the summer. Dolly had been ill most of the winter, and an alarmed Sarah had brought her along more out of concern for her maid's welfare than for any help she could be. From Saratoga, they had traveled first to Detroit to see D., and by the time they arrived, Dolly was completely prostrated and spitting up blood. D. immediately called for a doctor who dispensed enough medicine to give Dolly strength to continue on to Louisville. When they arrived at Bird's Nest, Dolly had to be helped into bed, and Ellen anxiously called Dr. Chineworth. He gave Dolly medicine, diagnosing her condition as disease of the heart and lungs. She could do nothing more than hold little Ruby, the baby's strength and innocent happiness seeping into Dolly's soul as well.

Sarah was thrilled with John J., her first husband's namesake, and with Ruby as well. Even though she had despaired of her daughter's pregnancy, she was now completely delighted by this new granddaughter. "I was upset," she told Ellen one afternoon, "that Manse did not come at once to see his new child, but now that he is coming this summer and bringing the Chancellor, I feel better."

Expectations were running high for the Chancellor's first visit to Bird's Nest, and Ellen was taking special pains to have the garden look perfect for him. "He can sit in the sun, Mama, and just admire the flowers and read Lem's law books. If that doesn't restore him, nothing can." But as the promise of June faded into the heat of July, Mansfield, first for one reason, then another, didn't come.

Ellen felt disappointment in a husband who showed no interest in seeing his newest child and who refused to bring their father to join the family. Together with the oppressive heat, endless work, bills that could not be paid, and not enough sleep, everything began to grow like an invisible tunnel around Ellen. She developed neuralgia in her jaw, and the pain caused her to be short–tempered with everyone. She wanted nothing more than to be alone, but those thoughts only brought guilt and despair, which added to the burdens she carried.

Late one July night, clad only in her chemise and a skirt that she pulled up above her knees, she sat on the piazza hoping for a cool breeze. She closed her eyes and tried to blot out everything but the sounds of summer and the cloying scent of roses. But her feelings were too ponderous within her, and all she could see when she closed her eyes was the image of herself, heavy and exhausted, her skin turning coarse, her hair without shine. Her hands were calloused and her nails split; she felt used, like a workhorse existing only for the plow, working to fulfill others' needs and expectations. She, Ellen Hardin Walworth, stepdaughter of the Chancellor of New York State, daughter of a U.S. Congressman, granddaughter of a U.S. Senator, was a plain country woman, poor and desolate. What was it she had expected from life? There had always been a vague sense of importance within her, a sense

127

of contributing her presence to the world, at least to the small space of time she inhabited. She had hoped to do this through the church and her marriage. If she had become a nun, at least she would be working for the greater glory of God, but now she was just working endlessly to support a family, and there was never enough. If her marriage were better, if she had a husband who would support them, she would have time to dispense comfort, to bring joy and laughter to her family, to do those thousand little things that make a home more than just a structure with a roof to keep out the heavy weather. She listened to the crickets singing and heard a bullfrog croak his lonely song on the night air, and thought fiercely how she would love to be in town, how badly she wanted to be part of a community. Whatever her expectations had been, whatever she had hoped to gain from life, she had not intended to find isolation and rejection.

She put her head down on her arms and let the tears come. She heard the screen door open and Annie call softly. "Nelly? Are you all right?" When she didn't answer, Annie came and sat beside her. "It's hard for you, Nelly, I know," Annie whispered.

"I can't help it, I can't go on," Ellen sobbed. "We haven't any money, and I hate farming. I never thought my life would be so beggarly."

Annie threw her arms about her sister–in–law, but what could one say to a woman who believed she had reached the bottom? Annie, reveling in her good fortune of loving Lem and bearing him a son, could only watch Ellen's misery, but in her own happiness could not really comprehend it.

A few days later after dinner, Lemuel approached the subject he and Annie had been discussing since John's birth.

"Sister, I have a business proposal for you. I don't want to upset you, and if you don't like what I have to say, please tell me." He paused for a moment and studied Ellen's face. "How about if I buy your share of Bird's Nest from you?"

Ellen looked at him implacably.

"Of course, you can live here as long as you want," he went on, "forever if you like. Now, I expect property values to go up out here before long. The streetcar line will soon come out this far, and already people are beginning to inquire about land in this area. If you want to hold on to your share and sell it to me later, or not sell it at all, then that's fine."

"Lem, you know I can't afford investments. I just need money. And you and Annie should have something to show for all you've lent me. I'll sell you my share for whatever you say."

"I'm going to ask D. if he will sell me his share, too. Annie and I will make our home here in Louisville, but D. and Estelle probably won't do more than just visit here. Unless he wants it for an investment now, he might as well get it off his hands and get some cash for it."

Ellen went to bed that night feeling that at last a very heavy door had opened a tiny crack. In the days to come, selling her share of Bird's Nest brought a sense of freedom. Perhaps she and the children could go elsewhere where there was an opportunity for her to make some money; she had certainly found out she could work! She began to reason her situation out in her head. She had five children, no husband to speak of, and no money. She wanted to be in the mainstream of life, not isolated in nature. She felt she was intelligent and capable, but just what she could do or how she would do it, she didn't know. She thought of the teachers she had loved and admired at the Female Academy in Jacksonville and thought perhaps she could teach. Or perhaps she could be an amanuensis. For the rest of the summer she waited vainly for Mansfield, worked in the garden and orchards, drove to town to arrange the sale of vegetables and fruit, nursed little Ruby, and enjoyed a rare moment of leisure with Annie, Lem, and Sarah. All the while, the thought took root in her consciousness and grew. Somehow, she and the children could go somewhere where there was opportunity for them all, where Frank could get the education he was so suited for, maybe even New York City.

Welcome coolness descended upon Louisville, and Sarah left for Pine Grove, leaving Dolly behind to convalesce and to help Ellen as much as she could. Ellen began storing the cabbages and apples and finished preserving the last of the grapes. But the work felt lighter, and the disappointment and desolation she had lived with for so long slowly began to take a back seat to hope. Sometimes it takes only the germ of an idea to produce hope when there isn't any and fashion courage to reach for a vision.

Then, on Thanksgiving Day Reuben Hyde Walworth died at the age of seventy–nine. Ellen received the news with shocked disbelief. Although she had seen how he was failing, how frail he was, there had always been in him the remembrance of vigor. Somehow, he had always seemed above mortality.

Ellen left with Lem and Annie for Pine Grove at once, taking little John and Reubena with them and leaving Frank and Dolly in charge of the other children at Bird's Nest. Sorrow engulfed Ellen as she thought of the young man pushing a plow, planting a dream far beyond the fields he worked in, and of the old man he had become.

Reuben's still form lay in the black–draped library among his well–loved books. "He died in Clarence's arms," Sarah told her quietly. "Together they recited the Lord's Prayer and Psalms from the Book of David. They were saying, 'In the shadow of death, I will fear no evil for Thou art with me,' when his breath just failed him."

"We had the best example of a human being for a father anyone could hope for," Clarence stated. "If dignity means a grandeur of soul arising from a high sense of honor, he had his full share."

Mansfield arrived showing little grief for his father, but seemed completely captivated upon seeing his newest child for the first time. "She is a jewel, Nelly. I predict she will enrich every life she touches." D. and Estelle arrived, as did Reuben's daughters, Ann Eliza Backus, Mary Elizabeth Jenkins, and Sarah Davison. The great and near–great came, the Chancellor's neighbors in Saratoga, and the people whom he had befriended wherever he went. It was almost as it had been those first years in Saratoga, Ellen thought, as people descended upon Pine Grove. Guests had to be greeted, fed, conversed with, and for a day or two the Chancellor's spirit still filled the house.

Mansfield suffered less than the rest, Ellen noticed, as she watched him greet the guests with perfect graciousness, solicitous of all who had thought highly enough of his father to pay their respects. "If only the Chancellor had encouraged his good qualities," she mused, "perhaps he would be different." And yet, the Chancellor had tried, he had given Mansfield every opportunity he could. Mansfield's soul just recoiled from all that forcefulness, she decided. With the family, Mansfield was at his jovial best and worked hard to keep up their spirits. Ellen knew though what the others might be suspecting, that part of the reason for his solicitousness had to do with the fact that now he would have some money.

A few days after the funeral, the family gathered in the parlor to hear the will which the Chancellor had written just a few months before his death. A strange mixture of disbelief, sorrow, and expectancy registered on their faces. Sarah, having shouldered the burdens of her family these past few years, seemed totally broken by this new grief. The Chancellor, even in old age and bad health, had been her anchor, and now she could take no more. The black dress she wore only accented her pallor and the fatigue in her eyes and face.

Jonathan Backus, the Chancellor's son–in–law, had been appointed executor of the will, as had Clarence, and now Jonathan shuffled papers, cleared his throat for silence, and prepared to read the complex document which reflected a lifetime's legal experience.

To Sarah, the Chancellor had willed all his property in trust. Despite earlier financial worries, he left over $50,000 in stocks and cash, in addition to Pine Grove and other real estate. Ellen, D., and Lem were to act as trustees for their mother's estate. The use of these funds was at Sarah's discretion, as it was also her right to will the capital of the trust fund as she wished. "It would be in the interest, as well as the duty, of all to treat her with kindness and respect during her life," Jonathan read. If Sarah did not make a will of her own, then after her death the remainder of the estate was to be divided into five equal shares for the Chancellor's children. The share of the three surviving Walworth daughters were to be held in trust for them by their husbands or male children. Clarence was to inherit his share outright, with the proviso he would later pass his legacy to other Walworths. Mansfield's share was to be held in trust for him by Clarence, and he would have to share his inheritance with his wife and children. Legacies and mementos such as the Chancellor's church pew, office spring exercising chair, stereoscope, and painting of George Washington's birthplace, were carefully doled out to family members. A decorative portfolio that had belonged to Mansfield's mother, Maria, was left to him. Clarence was instructed to personally write the Chancellor's biography or pay someone to do it. If Mansfield was selected, then he was to receive the profits.

After the will was read, the family went to the dining room for dinner, talking softly about anything except what they had just heard. Mansfield's mood had become icily impersonal. As the family talked around the table, lingering as though to stretch this last day shared with their father, Mansfield sat as a stranger would, taking no part in the conversation. His jaw was tight, and he ate little, and as the voices went on about him, he sat silently, clenching and unclenching his fists. Now and then Clarence stole a glance at his younger brother as though wondering what could or should be said to him.

As soon as the family left, Ellen retired to her room, too exhausted by tension to stand company any longer. Mansfield came up, a wild look replacing the guarded one that had been in his eyes all day. He stood before her, his hands hanging helplessly at his sides. "So, Ellen, your trips back here paid off after all."

"No, Manse," she replied wearily, "you know that's not the reason I came. We're both so tired, let's be as reasonable as possible."

"All my life I have been as reasonable as possible and look what has happened." His voice shook, and he began to pace up and down the length of the room. "I am to be treated like a woman, like my sisters, having to depend upon another man for my security. My father never

131

knew he had a son, except for Clarence. He disliked me from the moment of my birth!" Mansfield ran his hands through his hair, then covered his face and threw his head back. A strangled sound came from his throat. "You," and he seemed to spit the word at Ellen, "your mother inherited everything, and you were appointed a trustee for her. My father trusted a woman with his money, a woman not even of his own flesh and blood, more than he trusted his own son." Hate filled his eyes and his voice. "Do you know why he had to ask Clarence to find someone to write his biography? Because he knew no one would do it unless he paid them!"

Ellen was incapable of placating his rage. She knew that no matter what she said or did, it would only tip the scales of his balance precariously. She sat in exhaustion and fear, her eyes closed, afraid of a movement or a sound that could erupt in violence. Mansfield raved on through the night, and as the objects in the room became more discernable in the ash light of dawn, he got out his valise and began to throw his belongings into it. "I'm leaving, Ellen," he shouted. "You obviously won't need me anymore. If you find it fit to include your husband in your life, you know where to find me."

132

Ellen awakened while it was still dark, in that indistinguishable time between night and morning, and the image of Frank's face wreathed in an excited smile floated into her consciousness. Last night just as she drifted off to sleep, she made the decision which had been playing around the edges of her mind since Mansfield had left. "I won't return to Louisville. I'll stay right here where I can be of help to Mother. First thing in the morning I will write to Dolly and instruct her to bring the children here." She smiled into the darkness. "At long last, Frankie will have his turn to come back to his childhood home." She lay there day-dreaming until she heard the early morning carriages clattering down Broadway and muffled noises coming from Pine Grove's kitchen. She shivered in the chill room as she quickly got out of bed and splashed cold water over her face, more to add to her freshness than to hasten her awakening. She wrapped a dressing gown around herself and rang for coffee, then sat down at her desk and began a letter to Dolly.

She finished the letter and looked out the window at the park across the street. Her mind reeled backwards recalling the afternoons she had spent there with Mansfield. For an instant, the room was filled with his youthful presence, then she rose abruptly and went to her wardrobe. Mansfield isn't here, she told herself firmly, and won't be here. She pulled a brown wool dress off a hook. Whatever role Mansfield was to play in her life, she must accept the fact that it would be an absent role. It was her actions and decisions she and her children must depend upon if they were to survive. As she buttoned her dress, she frowned. Survival. She had only the money from the sale of Bird's Nest and the portion of her inheritance to rely upon, as well as whatever money Mansfield was forced to send them. She had five children to clothe, feed, and educate, and she would not drain her mother's finances. She sat down on the edge of her bed and studied the toes of her dark brown shoes. She didn't know what she wanted—yes, she did, but she couldn't have it. She must decide what was most important for her family, and then do it. Perhaps if she paid a visit to Clarence, he would have some ideas as to how she could manage. One thing was certain. She would most definitely find a way to educate Frank. He was too intelligent, his ancestry too brilliant, to be slighted on his education. She brushed her hair and tied it loosely in back with a white ribbon and went downstairs to breakfast with Sarah.

They sat next to each other, Sarah in the Chancellor's chair, Ellen next to her. The dining room seemed ridiculously large for the two of them and chillingly empty. Her stepfather's absence had created a vacuum of silence, and with a shiver Ellen thought how happy they would all be when the children arrived to fill the emptiness. She could not remember Pine Grove being so wholly quiet.

Sarah's unsmiling face was still sad. Her dark brown hair heavily streaked with gray was pulled down tightly from a center part, adding uncharacteristic severity to the sadness.

"Mother, I've reached a decision. I am not going back to Louisville this winter. I can't leave you now, and I'm certain Lem and Annie would be much happier alone. You have been such support to me ever since I moved to Louisville, and now it is my turn to support you. I've written to Dolly and instructed her to bring the children here as soon as possible." Ellen took a sip of coffee. "We won't drain you, Mother. If we can live here, it will help, but somehow I am going to find a way to support us. I just need a little time to figure something out. Tomorrow I am going to Albany to talk the matter over with Clarence. Perhaps he will have some sensible suggestions."

Sarah looked at Ellen with a curious but level look. "Nelly, I lay awake for a long time last night considering your situation. Perhaps I could get you an appointment in Washington."

Ellen looked at her mother blankly. "Washington?"

"More than a year ago when I was in Washington," Sarah said, "Senator McCulloch promised me he would give an appointment to a Kentucky lady. I have a friend who owes her appointment in the Treasury Department to the influence of Mrs. McCulloch, and she is able to support not only herself but her mother as well. I'll write to Senator McCulloch today if you agree."

"Of course," Ellen said with astonishment. "Do you think I could find a place for all the children? Frank could go to school there." Thoughts tumbled over themselves in her mind; Washington was far more than she had expected.

"I have enough friends in Washington City," Sarah continued, "that you wouldn't be just a working woman with no outside life. You will be among cultivated people and part of society there."

"But what—what could I do?"

"You could be an amanuensis, which is probably what you would do anywhere. You are intelligent, and you could learn office efficiency quickly."

With a little laugh Ellen said, "Isn't it strange? I, who so hoped my husband would do it, I shall be serving my country. Maybe not as heroically as my father, but serving nonetheless."

"We'll see what we can do," Sarah promised.

While they waited for a reply, Ellen traveled to Washington and enrolled Frank in Georgetown College. He would have his education, and Ellen had no doubt he would fulfill the opportunity with brilliance.

It was February before Sarah had a reply from the Chief Clerk of the Department of the Treasury. Ellen's hands shook as she tore open the letter, and with a sinking heart read the reply. She had been turned down for the position. "He promised to give an appointment to a Kentucky lady," Sarah exclaimed, "and I wager they have no one working there from Kentucky!" She frowned and reread the letter. "Nelly, I am going to write to Senator Yates, as well as to Senator McCulloch again, and remind them of the sacrifices your family has made for their country. With your background they should be proud to have you employed there."

A short time later Sarah handed Ellen the letter.

> "My dear Sir:
> A letter has been received from the Chief Clerk of the Department of the Treasury, unfavorable to the appointment of my daughter, Mrs. E. H. Walworth, in the Department.
> I hope you will pardon the liberty I take in writing to remind you of the promise you made me (when I called upon you more than a year ago) to give an appointment to 'Kentucky.' You might have been jesting, but I was in earnest. I trust you will yet remember her claims as a 'Kentucky Lady' when a vacancy occurs in the Department.
> I honor your benevolence to the weaker sex that you have retained them in the Department over which you preside, and Mrs. McCulloch also for her gentle influence in favor of her sex.
>
> I am respectfully yours,
> Mrs. R. H. Walworth"

Ellen read the letter and looked at her mother. "But what good will it do? They have already made up their minds."

"In Washington City, persistence counts. Your father gave his life for his country, and D. was severely wounded in his service. They owe you something."

Two weeks later Ellen followed her mother's letter with one of her own:

"I find myself in circumstances that make it necessary for me to contribute to the support of my family. I am induced to make application to your Department for a clerkship, feeling that the services rendered the Government by my father, Col. John J. Hardin, and my brother, Gen. Martin D. Hardin, entitle me to at least make the request. You will perhaps remember too that some time ago you promised my mother, Mrs. Chancellor Walworth, that you would give an appointment to a lady from Kentucky. It was not for me she made that application, but I thought it might be an inducement for you to consider my case as that appointment was not urged further, and I too am a resident of Kentucky. I know you are much harassed with these applications, but I hope you may consider my case kindly.

Respectfully yours,
E. H. Walworth"

It was the middle of March when she received a reply. She had an appointment as a clerk in the Treasury Department for $900 a year. She was to start immediately.

Chapter 26

There was no time to contemplate the future or to be frightened. Uncertainty and the excitement of the unknown reached out and carried her to the edge of predictability. She couldn't sleep, she couldn't eat, and she was in a state of constant turmoil. Now she had a source of income. It might only be a clerk's job, but it was a golden opportunity for a woman approaching middle age with no discernible future.

With Sarah's help, Ellen found an apartment at 55 Lafayette Street in Georgetown. They moved into the apartment feeling excited, but strange, as though they now had to share their lives with someone unbeknownst to them.

"We're going to trip all over ourselves," Nellie proclaimed with a giggle. "Even Dolly, as thin as she is, couldn't fit into the kitchen."

"Nonsense," Ellen grunted as she moved a chair into place. "You are spoiled. Bird's Nest was large, and you have all the space you need at Pine Grove. Still," she said, as much to herself as to the children, "this is really quite a spacious place for the city. Besides, you are going to be in school, and I am going to be working, and in the evenings the housekeeper will go to her own home!" She hugged Nellie to herself and laughed.

She dressed carefully in a gray lightweight wool dress which buttoned up to her throat and had only a hint of crisp white lace peeking from the neckline. The skirt was flared and there was only a slight bustle in back. Ellen smoothed her hands over the skirt and then anxiously looked at her reflection in the dressing mirror. Her hair was pulled back from her face too severely she thought, and with the end of a comb she loosened it around her face. She put her fingers up to her bangs and tried to rearrange them into a softer line. "Well, there's nothing more I can do." She picked up her handbag with cold hands, closed her eyes, and took a deep breath. Mrs. Mead, the housekeeper, was waiting in the hall. "You look just fine, Mrs. Walworth. We'll be just fine here, don't worry."

There was a subdued air of intensity about the office. She had expected a desk but was shown to a long table in a large room where all the clerks sat in rapt concentration, their hands seemingly flying with the importance of their tasks. With the exception of two other women sitting at her end of the table, all the other clerks were men. They looked up and stood as she approached. Nodding her head, Ellen murmured, "Please sit down," and slid into her seat quickly, trying to appear dignified and self–possessed. Her duties, as her supervisor had explained, were to open mail, answer letters, and file correspondence. She picked up a letter, and as she did, her shaking hands dropped the letter opener, startling the other clerks. Ellen started to murmur an apology, but the woman seated next to her looked at her in a mirthful, but conspiratorial glance. "Just don't stab yourself on your very first day." Ellen smiled, then relaxed.

In the days to come, she felt like she was treading in an eternal circle. She had never had to pay attention to details before, and now a punctual routine ruled her days. But instead of the despair and boredom that had characterized her life until now, a sense of importance occupied her. She mastered the work swiftly, feeling that this was what she had always sought, this was the mental stimulation she had longed for.

She had been in the city for only a few short weeks when she received an invitation to dinner at Mr. and Mrs. Chiles' residence, friends of her mother's. Sarah and Mrs. Chiles were working on the Washington Monument project, and Sarah had let it be known that her daughter was working in Washington.

"It must be interesting," Mrs. Chiles said, "to have a job. Do you enjoy the work?"

"Oh, yes," Ellen replied quickly. "It was a little strange at first, but now I'm completely at home."

Mrs. Chiles' daughter was the only other single woman at the table, but quite a few years younger than Ellen. Ellen steeled herself for the question she feared would be asked about why she was in the city alone, but although she could feel the question in the eyes of the guests, no one was rude enough to ask outright. Soon other invitations began to be issued asking her to another dinner or to attend the theatre. Sarah's friends became hers, and they seemed genuinely pleased to have a working woman in their company. Ellen reveled in the company of these cultivated people whose interests and boundaries lay far outside the confines of the city they lived in. Conversations might start with a discussion about fashion or what was currently playing at the theatre, but invariably the discussions would end in the muddy quagmire of passionate politics. Many nights, after an evening out, she would lie awake for hours, too stimulated by the evening's conversation to fall asleep.

One evening, lying in bed, she wondered what she would answer if someone had the effrontery to ask her about her marital status. She had no answer, even for herself. Mansfield had moved to Albany to live with Clarence, at Clarence's invitation. The news had startled her when she heard it, but dispassionately she hoped it would help Mansfield.

She had no time now nor inclination to think about him, and for that she was grateful. For the first time in years she was not ignoring life, she was living it. She had cast aside desperation and let her mind propel her forward. From the isolation of Bird's Nest, life had taken an exciting, dizzying turn, and careened her into work she enjoyed and a social life she had sorely missed. There was a sense of freedom that had never existed for her before, and she felt intensely alive. She was thinking for herself and discovering that there is no real meaning to existence until one has begun to think for oneself.

As she was dressing for work one morning, she looked in the mirror and was startled to see a youthful woman with a bright sparkle in her eyes looking back at her. "Why, I look younger than I did last year," she murmured to her reflection. Younger, but with a new sense of dignity that was reflected in the way she held her head.

Washington in the summer was a strange land of solitude. The excitement of the city was subdued and entertaining ground to a standstill. She decided to send the children home to Saratoga where the cool air was more healthful. Now that they were older, they wouldn't be such a handful for Sarah to watch. In fact, she thought proudly, they had all grown more self–sufficient.

By fall, Sarah was adamant that the children should stay in Saratoga so Ellen would not have the extra expense of a housekeeper. The days darkened earlier, and a melancholy depression settled upon her. As Christmas approached, the briskness and joy she had experienced months earlier could not be recalled.

She walked back to her apartment one rainy December afternoon, feeling empty as she watched figures under dark umbrellas pulling themselves tightly into warm cloaks and hurrying to what she imagined were happy homes. There was a letter from Dolly waiting for her, bemoaning the fact that they would miss her at Christmas. "Plum cakes are made," she read, "and a ham is hanging and ready for dinner. I am making sure that the children are dressed warmly when they leave the house in the mornings, and we have a gift for each one. Don't worry about us. We will miss you and be thinking about you." A few days later, Frank stopped by with the news that he would be spending Christmas with a classmate from Georgetown. Pleased that her son was making friends and doing well at school, Ellen did not say anything to him about her depression and assured him that she would be fine. After Frank left, she sat quietly in the dark room. She had never intended to be alone like this, without her children, and tears of self–pity rolled down her cheeks as the image formed in her mind of children and a home with a loving husband by her side. Even though she was invited out to dinner on Christmas day, a hollowness persisted inside her until well after the New Year. Then in April, with a fresh warmth stealing over the city, Ellen was informed that due to a change in administration, her position was being dissolved.

She stayed in her apartment, afraid to go out, doing nothing but staring into a blank space she knew she must shape. Perhaps, she thought, God has closed this door to remind me that my family is my most important value and that I belong with them. Then on the heels of that comforting thought came the contradiction that they needed her first to survive, and then the blank space would widen and the questions with no answers would assail her again. What do they do now? Where do they turn? How do they face the days ahead? Sitting there, suffering mutely, scarcely able to breathe, her heart beating hard against her chest, she let the gray beginnings of loneliness wash over her. When she could finally stand the overwhelming despair of defeat no longer, she began to make plans to return to Pine Grove.

Chapter 27

Saratoga now seemed more opulent than ever. Ostentatious and raffish, a careless attitude was in the air, and questionable people flocked to the village hoping to get rich overnight on the amusements John Morrissey provided.

A troubleshooter for Tammany Hall and a notoriously prosperous gaming–house proprietor, John Morrissey had come to Saratoga in mid–summer of 1861 trailing an assortment of dealers, bouncers, and gambling house paraphernalia. The stalwart citizens of Saratoga had gasped in whispered tones of a "gambling hell" and assured themselves he would make no money at all in their town. But the scattering of vacationers who still came to the Springs were war–weary with a craving for amusement of any kind, particularly risqué amusements with the promise of sudden riches.

To quell the townspeople's fears Morrissey had donated generously to their charities, and then, in 1863, he brazenly introduced a racetrack. Starting August 3, he announced, there would be a program of four days of racing with two races each day. Only two years later, the handsome Irishman had turned his eye toward fashionable Congress Spring and bought thirty acres of land adjoining the estate of Dr. John Clarke for the purpose of building a Club House.

John Morrissey may have shocked the stalwart citizens of Saratoga, but he had provided an income for them by attracting a new surge of vacationers. By 1869 the hotels were full and a few of the homes in town were taking in summer boarders.

Despite the rowdiness of her family, Ellen thought Pine Grove desperately quiet, echoing with memories of vigorously intelligent and important visitors flocking to it when it was young and vital and bursting with energy. With its extra bedrooms it would be perfect for vacationers. Sarah had recently been appointed a vice president of the Washington National Monument Society and was in Washington and New York City much of the time. To Ellen's hurried inquiries, she agreed that her room could be let out also. Dolly and the Irish girl, Kate, could certainly cook for a few extra people, Ellen decided. Why, when the Chancellor was alive, they never knew how many people might turn up at a moment's notice. She could rent the rooms for ten to fifteen dollars a week, and for the rooms with balconies she would charge more. Transient guests would be charged two dollars a day prior to July 1, and thereafter two dollars and fifty cents. She had advertisements printed emphasizing the fact that: "This house has been frequented for years by a select class of guests, and no effort will be spared to maintain its established character through the approaching summer season." Theirs was a dignified home, and only the best families would be welcomed.

She was sitting near the parlor window one afternoon in May of 1869 when she saw Mansfield come bounding up the steps, his face wreathed in smiles. Before she could recover from her astonishment, he proudly thrust a book at her, *Warwick* stamped in letters across the front. Ellen looked up at him. Not yet forty, he was dressed with meticulous care, every inch a distinguished gentleman. "You look wonderful, Manse," she said rather shyly. Then, after an awkward pause, she gave a self–conscious laugh. "You must excuse me, I'm completely taken by surprise."

"I don't exactly blame you, Nelly," he said as he removed his Panama hat. He stopped and looked at her, and his eyes were kind and soft. "Even after all our trouble, you are still the first one I think of when I have some success. And that," he said pointing to the book Ellen held in her hands, "that isn't just success. It's going to be a great victory."

With *Warwick*, he had vanquished his father's ghost. Constant Earle, the hero of the novel, was a struggling writer in a desperate financial condition. He had been born into a prominent, affluent family, but his father had inexplicably disinherited him. Not even coarse clothing could make Constant look beggarly; instead, he looked "pitiably beautiful." He had been a lazy dilettante in the past, but now he labored diligently to achieve success as an author. Mansfield wrote that it was "manifestly unnatural" for a parent to disinherit his child no matter "how erring, how depraved, how disobedient" he might be. The novel ended with the restoration of Constant's inheritance after the discovery of his brother's forgery of their father's will.

Mansfield was right. The novel was his victory. It attracted the attention of all classes, especially the cultivated. All summer the novel's readers could be seen everywhere at the resort—in parks, parlors, and on hotel piazzas. It collected favorable notices from numerous publications, including the *New York Tribune*, *New Orleans Times*, and the *Public Opinion of London*. The *New York Citizen* called Mansfield one of America's best satirists and stated that Mark Twain could not "for a moment be compared with Mansfield Tracy Walworth." Wherever he went, he was constantly pointed out as "one of the lions of the Spring."

It was an idyllic time, the happiest time they had spent together since the summer they were married. One night in July Ellen awakened to find Mansfield leaning over her on one arm. He kissed her awake and then settled down against her with his arms about her, his mouth to her ear. "I just solved a problem, Nelly. I figured out how to save the hero from falling into the bottomless pit after he gets to the end of his rope."

Mansfield spent the mornings writing, and Ellen attended to household duties. Afternoons they joined the public in walks about town or sat in the shade of the backyard with their family, and occasionally there was a game of tennis or croquet. They renewed forgotten acquaintances, and evenings they attended concerts, plays, or had dinner in the homes of friends.

As the weather grew chilly and the last straggling visitors left town, Ellen noted with dismay that Mansfield seemed to become increasingly restless. His moods grew dark, and he withdrew into himself, often not coming out of his room for a full day. One evening as Ellen was tallying up the figures from the summer's boarders, Mansfield looked at her with a sneer on his face. "Quite a business woman, aren't you, Mrs. Walworth? I think it's a disgrace the way you have turned our home into a hotel." She looked at him in astonishment, a cold knot forming in her stomach, and her hands turning to ice.

"Here am I, a famous author," he said mockingly, "and I have just spent the summer with boarders in my home!"

"Mansfield, please, don't. I only saw it as a way for me to add to our support. I didn't know you would publish a great book, I didn't know you would be coming back to live with us. I just knew we needed some money!"

"It wasn't a very good idea, Nelly. It has been humiliating to see my home turned into a haven for gamblers. Where is your sense of dignity?"

She rose abruptly and stood before him, her eyes blazing, her hands on her hips, her voice rising to an unnatural pitch.

"Dignity? Do you know how I felt having to beg for a position in Washington because we had to have some income? Do you know how I felt knowing people wondered where my husband was?" Her eyes filled with tears. "Do you know how I felt having to fill this dignified old home with strangers because I needed money? For that matter, Manse, do you realize how hard it is for me to have any semblance of dignity when you have berated me, struck me, humiliated me, and refused to live with us or support us? You're a writer—go think about that word, 'dignity'!"

Unbidden tears of anger and frustration rolled down her cheeks, and she turned to the window, her back to the room. "Manse," she pleaded as she wiped her eyes, "let's be happy like we have been this summer. That first summer I came here, you were the only human being who could make me laugh." She turned to him. "You still make me happy, Manse, and all I want in this world is to be your wife and raise our family together." She bent down toward him, put her arms about his neck, and kissed the top of his head. "Please, Manse, let's be happy."

Happiness is a condition of well–being and contentment, and Ellen was at a loss to explain either its appearance or disappearance. In her mind, she turned endlessly toward the late summer days, wondering what she had said or done that had displeased her husband, that had burst the bubble of success that encased him.

She took extra pains with her appearance, cautioned the children against being too noisy, and vowed to be as cheerful as she possibly could.

"It's time for me to get back to the city," Mansfield announced abruptly one evening during supper. "I can't continue a career in Saratoga."

"Why, Daddy?" Young Manse asked innocently between mouthfuls. "Why don't you want to be with us?"

"The apartment I took there last year is big enough for everyone," Sarah stated. "Would you consider moving in with me, Manse? Ellen and the children also, of course. We can share the rent, and financially it will be easier for all of us." Sarah spoke brightly, but her eyes were serious and studied as she watched Mansfield's face. Ellen held herself very carefully, knowing that any mention of money was apt to throw Mansfield into an uncontrollable rage. She had hoped that *Warwick* would appease the anger he still felt over being denied his inheritance, but now that the recognition had lessened, she could feel the anger which still infused itself into his soul.

Mansfield stared at his plate, then lifted his head and smiled at Sarah. "Why not?"

Despite her excitement at being in the city, despite the fact that they were together, Ellen fought a daily battle against the fear it wouldn't last.

Sarah tried, but she couldn't conceal her dislike for Mansfield. While she had offered her apartment out of kindness, Mansfield evidently thought of it as just one more instance of the family treating him like a child. The anger he could not vent against his father was turned on Sarah, so that now, in accepting her kindness, they had also accepted unspoken hostilities. Mansfield reminded Ellen daily that if he had received his proper inheritance, they would be living under their own roof and not dependent upon her mother for support.

The children, uprooted once again, were growing rowdy and undisciplined. Clara picked incessantly on little Manse, whom they now called Tracy, and his whining and sniffling were more than his father could bear. Mansfield hardly spoke to his namesake, paying attention to him only when he was forced to, and Clara and Nellie were left to the care and concern of Sarah and Ellen. Only Reubena rated Mansfield's attention, and often he referred to her as "my dream child."

In mid–January Ellen came down with a cold which sent her to bed with chills and fever. Sarah mothered her, piling quilts on her to bring out the fever and rubbing her chest with mustard plasters. Ellen lay in bed in the mornings, listening to Sarah getting the children ready for school, relaxed in the knowledge that she could let go, all she had to do was rest and get well.

She was still feverish when Mansfield entered her room one evening looking harried and dishevelled. He ran his hand through his hair, then sat down beside her and kissed her. He said nothing, but his kisses grew insistent, and his hands fumbled at her nightgown. "Oh, Manse, no," Ellen whispered. "I don't feel well, I still feel so weak." He ignored her. "Manse, no!" He sat up then and looked at her bitterly. "I have no rights at all in this house," he whispered hoarsely. "I can't write with the place full of kids, and if there is a lull, it is filled with your mother's friends. I can't have my wife, because she is always resting." He stood up and looked down at her. "Are you resting from counting your money, Ellen?"

Ellen closed her eyes and sighed. "Manse, why don't I take the children and visit D. and Estelle for a while in Buffalo? It would give both you and Mother a rest.

"Are you going to run off and tell your hero brother what an awful husband and life you have? You bitch, you'd do just that wouldn't you?"

She looked into wild eyes she didn't recognize and cowered in the bed.

"I'm your husband, and I'm not supposed to touch you!" He slammed his fists into the pillow at either side of her head, and she flinched. "I hate you, you bitch, and all your little bastards!"

"Manse! Please! What is wrong with you?"

"I'm going to take what's mine, Ellen, and everything I want I'll get!" His hands were pressing on her throat until she could hardly breathe, and his teeth sunk into her arm until he drew blood. He took his hands off her throat, and she screamed and struggled to sit upright, but he pushed her down again and clawed at her nightgown. She screamed again and tried to get her hands on his throat, but he slapped her and clamped his hand over her mouth and nose so that for one wild moment she thought she would suffocate.

"Mansfield!" It was a shocked, desperate cry as Sarah entered the room, ran to him, and tried to pull him away from Ellen. He jerked his arm from his wife and whirled and hit Sarah with such force that she staggered back against the bedside chair. Mansfield stepped back then, breathing heavily, and looked at them. "You are both bitches," he said when he had recovered his breath. Then he laughed a short, sarcastic laugh, turned and left the room.

God had forsaken her and life held no meaning, only terror. She wondered if Mansfield was insane, or if she was. Was she really the embodiment of some evil, drawing only evil to her? She lay in bed in a trance, afraid to move, knowing that movement of any kind, any utterance, would result in wounded–animal howls from her. As long as she lay still, she couldn't feel, and wouldn't think. There was no refuge from hate, and she had no weapons with which to fight.

She moved through the long winter numbly, and other than household sounds or street noises muffled against the closed windows, it was a silent life they had together. She and Sarah conversed, planned their days, and occasionally laughed, but when Mansfield was around, there was a careful tension in the air. Ellen knew there were times when he came home slightly drunk, knew that he occasionally hid bottles of liquor in their room, but she said nothing about it to Sarah or to him. She protected the children from her fears as much as she could and smothered them with love. It was not only a strained life, but also a hollow one, and fear often turned to anger, and then to despair, so that she felt like a cat mentally chasing its tail. When she thought about her situation, she felt trapped, not knowing where to turn or what to turn to. She prayed and tried not to think, but despite her best efforts, she felt like a prisoner being slowly but inexorably led to the edge of a cliff.

As spring came, she was adamant about returning to Pine Grove again to get the house ready for summer boarders. After the stifling winter, feeling suffocated in the silence of her marriage, she craved the clean, cool, pine–scented air of Saratoga.

Clarence came back to Pine Grove in mid–September as the last summer guests were leaving. "It's that glow I come back for," he remarked one afternoon. "Just before the green fades from the trees, the world seems to glow up here; then it turns to that brilliant scarlet. I wouldn't miss it for the world. If we ever question the abundance of God, this time of year in Saratoga would make us remember." It was good to have him here. He was calming and loving and stimulating and directed her gaze away from her troubles. One afternoon she asked if they could have a talk. "A rather long talk, I'm afraid. I need some advice. Perhaps we could go to the courtroom. So many successful decisions have been reached there that it might be the best place. Besides, we could be undisturbed there." She prepared tea for them both, and as hers grew cold, she talked to Clarence about Mansfield, about her fears for his sanity, about her despair. "I no longer know what to do. Of course, I haven't seen him all summer, maybe I'll never see him again. Sometimes I'm afraid he will kill me, and sometimes I'm afraid he won't.

Clarence was silent for a moment and sat with his hands clasped in front of his mouth, lips pursed, and studied the carpet. "Nelly, my heart breaks for you and the children. I have fears for Manse, too. That he is erratic and irresponsible is obvious, but it seems like there is more, some undercurrent which I can't identify." He leaned his head back against the chair. "He is a good writer, but he should take a job, one that would enable him to support you and the children. Maybe that would lessen his hate for Father also."

"Manse wouldn't take a job," she said bitterly. "He considers himself a great writer, and I know he thinks honest work quite beneath him."

Clarence rose and walked to the window. "There is a position in Albany I've only heard about recently. He could use his skills as a lawyer, which might make him unhappy, but it is a very good position. At least if he made enough money to support a wife and family, it would increase his self–respect, and that might very well prevent these outbursts." He was silent for a moment, and the only noises that filled the old room were the soft stirrings of the pines surrounding the house. "Have you thought," Clarence asked after a moment, "that out of concern for your own safety, you might have to leave Manse?"

"You forget, I've left twice already." She wrung her hands and spoke agitatedly. "I tried to farm, and I worked in Washington." Self–pity and hopelessness engulfed her. "I have failed at everything I have ever done in life. If I leave him, I would be going against the Church, I would have even failed in God's sight! There just isn't anything left!"

It was a perfect October day, mild and still. The sunlight was warm, bathing the world in the vividness Clarence had described. Ellen was standing in the yard putting pine needle mulch around the roses when the back door opened and Mansfield came out. "Oh!" she exclaimed with a start. "You startled me."

"It's almost your birthday, isn't it?" he said as he stood smiling at her. "Thirty–six years old, Nelly. Unbelievable isn't it? I thought I would come home and help you celebrate."

"Why, thank you."

They were like two polite strangers, she thought despairingly, and how ridiculous it was, how pitiful. There was no longer excitement when Mansfield appeared, or disappointment when he left. The children were used to their father appearing at odd times and disappearing again just as inexplicably.

147

She had been thinking about the position in Albany for the past three weeks, and the more she thought about it, the more she felt that it was the only chance she and Mansfield had for a normal life. She had wondered and prayed about how to best approach him on the subject. Perhaps, she thought more than once, perhaps he is as sick of this way of living as I am, maybe he would be more receptive to the idea than I think he would.

He was in her room reading one night as she was getting ready for bed, and as she stood in front of her dressing mirror, brushing her long hair, she said very casually, "Manse?" When he put down his book and looked at her, she said, "I have an idea. You may not like it, but please listen, and please don't think me wrong for suggesting it." She took a deep breath and ran the hairbrush through her hair again. "There is a position opening in Albany which is eminently suitable for you." It seemed to her a dark shadow passed over his face, and she shut her eyes for a moment. "I thought maybe you could apply for it, and we could move there. Your novels are very good, Manse, but they have little earning potential. This would be support for all of us, but, Manse, please, if you don't want to support us, you could use it for yourself, and I could work something out for the children and myself."

"Support myself?" He stood in the middle of the room, very still. "You mean that you and the children would live on your inheritance from my father while I support myself?"

She put the brush down. "Why not support all of us, Manse? You are much too wonderful a person to let your family flounder like this." It sounded all wrong, even to her.

"You are a bitch, Ellen." His voice rose. "A shrew and a bitch." he yelled.

"Manse, no! I didn't mean to upset you." She began crying, and he came to her and grabbed her hair so that her head was pulled back, and she could only look at the ceiling. "Don't, Manse," she pleaded, "if you keep doing things like this, I'll have to leave and go live with D. or Clarence."

"Go live with Clarence then, you bitch. He has my money, he can have my wife." He stood over her, holding her head back, and looked down at her. He lowered his voice so that it sounded like a soft growl. "You don't understand, Ellen, you don't understand who I am. I am Mansfield Tracy Walworth, and I could kill you!" She felt his fist with a great blow on her cheek, and then he began beating her arm. He grabbed her by both shoulders and dragged her to the bed. She heard a great crack as he threw her against the bedstead; then she was engulfed in darkness, a blessed darkness that blotted out fear and hurt.

Chapter 28

Ellen felt like a sleepwalker moving within the circle of a nightmare as they moved back to New York City.

Her arm was stiff and swollen, and if she tried to move more than her hand or forearm, she had to bite her lip to keep from gasping with pain. When she looked at her arm, she shuddered. It was black, a dark, frightening ugly midnight color with only a tinge of blue. It burned constantly, and when she touched even the clothing that covered her arm, she could feel the heat from her skin.

Because she was afraid of him, because she herself couldn't confront the fact, she didn't tell Mansfield she was pregnant. His rages were becoming frequent and more intense. At the slightest provocation, and often for no reason, he would kick a piece of furniture, or even seize a chair and fling it across the room, often breaking it. He abused her verbally, but he could no longer wear down her resistance, because there was none.

Sarah had discretely gone to Washington when thcy moved back to the city, and now Ellen felt there was no one to whom she could turn for comfort or support.

Frank came up from Georgetown for the holiday, full of youth and good cheer, but after a few days with them he fell silent and moody, acting cheery only when the other children were around.

One evening she and Frank sat alone in the living room. While Ellen worked on some embroidery, Frank looked at her intently. "Mother, you're holding your arm strangely. Is something wrong with it?" Silently, Ellen pulled her arm from the dressing gown she wore and watched as the blood drained from Frank's face. "This cannot be," he whispered as he stared wide–eyed at her arm. "This must not be."

"Frank, I'm sorry," she apologized as she hastily covered her arm again. "I shouldn't have shown you. It actually looks much worse than it is."

"Father did that?"

She winced at his open acknowledgment of Mansfield's abuse. "Yes," she said softly. "I shouldn't have let you see it. I know I enrage your father sometimes, but I never mean to. I never know what it is I've done wrong." She leaned her head back against the chair and closed her eyes. "There are some marriages that should never take place." She looked at her first born son and an overwhelming tenderness for him

149

poured through her. "Whatever has gone wrong between your father and me must not overshadow the fact that our marriage produced you. You are very, very dear, Frankie."

Ellen had enrolled Nellie and Clara in Kenwood, the Convent of the Sacred Heart in Albany. She was relieved to have them out of the house and away from the escalating conflicts. She missed them, and on cold nights when she wondered if they were sniffling out of homesickness, she comforted herself with the thought of Clarence close by. Only Tracy and Reubena were still at home on a daily basis, and she prayed to God they were too young to be marked by the tensions in their home.

It was only a few days after the New Year while she was methodically folding clothes one afternoon, that she heard a light knock on the door. She opened it, and squealed with delight when she saw D. standing there. She threw her arms about him. "It must still be Christmas. This is the best gift I could receive." She led him into the living room, helped him take off his coat, and indicated a chair. "Sit down and let me believe my eyes. What are you doing here?"

"I'm here with hopes of obtaining a release from the Army. Estelle is terrified that I will be sent to some remote outpost in the Western states." He stretched his legs out in front of him. "We're both ready to settle down in Chicago. I'm ready to try the law career I was sidetracked from before the war."

Ellen looked at him lovingly. Just barely in his mid–thirties, he looked tired. There were deep lines around his mouth and a set of resignation in his eyes. "We both missed our youth," Ellen mused. "D. lost his in cannonball fire, and I in the war of my marriage." She felt she had been old for a long, long time.

Her days took on a strange edge. She went through them dutifully, automatically, speaking to the children in a monotone, trying not to think about the new life she carried within her, trying not to think beyond a meal to be planned or a shirt to be mended. Now and then she would pause at the windows, watching people hurrying down the streets, intent on their own lives. She was strangely suspended in time, living on a canvas of monochrome color, only the movement of strangers giving texture to her days. Monotony was mixed in the food she ate and the air she breathed. At night, when she went to her room and locked the door, not even the release of another day could stir relief within her. She would lay in bed rigidly, every bone and muscle in her body aching, her eyes wide and staring, her suspension reverberating hollowly within the room, encompassing her, poisoning her.

150

She could not understand Mansfield and no longer wanted to. On the few occasions they were out together in public, he was such a gentleman that she was certain it was she who was at fault in their marriage. They were invited to Mrs. Astor's for dinner: Mansfield the celebrated author who had dedicated a book to Mrs. Astor, she the dutiful wife. Mrs. Astor fawned over his genius, playfully but harmlessly flirted with him, and Mansfield conversed with wit and intelligence, his manners gracious, his voice well modulated. At such times she would know with certainty that it was she who was wrong, that whatever had gone wrong between them was all her fault. Then they would go home, and the thought of being alone with him would fill her with terror, so that she would lay in her bed sleepless, listening for footsteps in the hallway outside her door.

Late one evening they sat silently in the living room, Ellen holding a book she was attempting to read.

"I have an idea for a new book," Mansfield said into the stillness. "It will be based on our marriage. Our marriage would make a fine story, would it not?"

"I really don't care," she said quietly.

"You would care if I made money from it, wouldn't you?" His voice was soft and mocking, and she felt the familiar stirring of fear. She put the book down and looked at him.

"I would be very interested in the book. I would be interested in reading just how you perceive our marriage."

"My hero," he said, "is married to a shrewish wife who harps incessantly about money. She is fretful and sarcastic, qualities which irritate him, and he stays away from her as much as possible." Mansfield stood in front of her with an elegant grace, negated only by the hideous look on his face. "He would gladly pass his evenings with her if she would devote herself to entertain him." He lowered his voice to a menacing whisper and put his face close to hers. "But she sneered at his literary plans, at their lack of earning potential. Therefore, Ellen," and his voice began to rise as she sat very still in the chair, "the woman who might have become his ideal, becomes his terror." He spit in her face. "Take that Hardin. What do I care for you?" He spit at her again.

"Mansfield, quit. You treat me as if I were a beastly, disgusting animal."

"You are," he yelled. He raised his closed fist above her head. "I'll blow your damned brains out, Ellen." She stood up abruptly, her book dropping to the floor, and started to run to her room. He caught her and, with his fist, struck a blow to the side of her head so that for a moment she saw only blackness. She put her arm to her head to ward off any

151

more blows, and as she did, he raised his leg and kicked her in the stomach with his boot.

"Mansfield!" she screamed. "Don't! I'm pregnant!"

He backed off, a sneering look of disgust on his fine features. "Then you must go lie down, Mrs. Walworth, you bitch. That's what you always do. Pretend you are ill."

Trembling, she walked down the hallway to her room, shut the door and locked it. As quietly as she could, she began grabbing at clothing and stuffing it into her valise. When she was finished, she sat down on the edge of her bed to wait until she was sure he was asleep, her heart pounding with fear, wondering if in his fury he could break down her door.

It was two o'clock in the morning before she dared to put on her cloak and tiptoe to Tracy's room. "Tracy, wake up," she whispered urgently as she leaned over him. She shook him slightly and propped him upright. "Don't make any noise, and listen to me," she commanded. "I'm going to put your coat on you, and then we'll get Ruby and go to Uncle D.'s hotel. I'll explain everything to you later." He fumbled with his coat buttons, and she handed him his slippers. "We must be very quiet," she cautioned as she led him into the hall. She didn't bother to awaken Ruby. She picked her up and wrapped blankets tightly around her. She indicated the valises to Tracy, who, without a word, picked them up and struggled to the door.

The icy January wind made them gasp for breath and stung their eyes until they watered. "Keep your coat up tight around your throat, Tracy, and hurry." She hugged Ruby to her tightly as she carefully stepped around the icy spots. Somehow, they arrived at D.'s hotel and made their way to his room without being questioned. She knocked on the door desperately, and for one wild moment feared he had left for Chicago without telling her. Then the door opened and D., sleepy and surprised, took Ruby from her and without a word shut the door behind her and hurriedly locked it.

"He'll kill me, D.," she said frantically. "He'll kill us all, I know he will. I have escaped," she sobbed, "from unbearable misery." She related the events of the night to her brother. "It's not the first time. It just keeps getting worse."

"I'm going to get Cousin John," D. told her as he began to grab his clothes. "As soon as he arrives, Ellen, we'll begin to draw up a divorce decree. You mustn't be around Manse again."

When D. returned with Judge John Barbour, they hastily spread papers on the table and began asking terse questions and giving suggestions to one another. It had only been daylight for a few hours when Ellen's suit for divorce was filed.

To the Chancellor, divorce had been the ultimate defeat, the giving up of a godly gift. He could not understand incompatible couples. "They can become good husbands and wives from the necessity of remaining good husbands and wives," he often said. "Necessity is a powerful master in teaching the duties it imposes." Her duty had become self–defense and survival, and Ellen had no time for remorse. Like an animal trapped behind bars she had broken down a door and run for her freedom.

Two days later at four o'clock in the morning, a loud pounding on the door awakened them. D. opened the door a crack and faced Mansfield pointing a pistol at him. "I want my wife and children," he yelled.

"Wait a moment, Manse," D. cautioned in a quiet voice, "let me get my dressing robe."

D. closed the door and locked it while Mansfield stood outside pounding on it and shouting.

"Nelly, you and the children hide," D. whispered, "he has a pistol."

"Be careful, D.," Ellen pleaded. "He's a maniac."

"With all the noise he's making, the police are bound to come up."

Her heart pounding, Ellen said a quick prayer as D. closed the door behind him. When the yelling ceased, Ellen realized she was holding her breath, afraid of hearing a gunshot.

What was only a quarter of an hour seemed forever before D. came back in, unharmed. "I told him you were going back to Pine Grove, that he hasn't lost you or the children completely. A policeman came up and arrested him, thank God." D. brushed his hand through his hair in relief and exasperation. "I think you should go to Clarence, Sister. He has plenty of room, you can be with the girls, and you will be safe there."

For the next two months she stayed with Clarence in Albany. She was tired, her future uncertain, yet she felt relieved. Every day she visited Kenwood and saw Clara and Nellie. They were happy and thriving and, at twelve and thirteen, took the news of the divorce with surprising calm. There on the spacious snow–covered lawns of Kenwood, and in the sheltered peacefulness of its halls, Ellen relived her own school days at the Jacksonville Academy. "I don't think I was ever so happy as I was when I was with my friends laughing just being carefree and young," she told the girls. "But we were stimulated too, and as anxious to learn the classics and mathematics as we were to go riding or have taffy pulls after school. It was the only really glorious time of my life." And the only time I felt I was accomplishing anything, she thought. What a sad commentary on my life.

She sat in church on a cold Sunday morning and listened to Clarence say Mass, wondering when she should return to Pine Grove and inwardly shuddering at the emptiness that awaited her. Just she, Tracy, and Reubena alone in the big house, with Sarah coming only for short visits. With Nellie and Clara in Kenwood. Kenwood! The thought came to her like a thunderclap, the obvious solution to her problem which had been awaiting her all along. In her excitement she almost ran back to the rectory, but she said nothing until they were seated at the dinner table. As the roasted chicken was being passed, she broke into Clarence's murmurings about the food. "I have decided to open a school."

"Yes?" Clarence's eyes were upon her, amused and amazed.

"Pine Grove's drawing room and courtroom will make perfect classrooms." She looked at Clarence with excited satisfaction. "Will you help me find the instructors? We will have only the highest quality instruction, and we will teach all the subjects that are taught at Kenwood."

Clarence helped himself to another piece of chicken. "And when would you open?"

"Why, this fall."

"Not so fast, Nelly. It is a reasonable idea, but you are expecting a baby in June, and you and the children are far from settled. Perhaps it would make more sense to wait until next year."

"No." She was resolute. "Father Walworth, one does not simply wait for a baby to be born and do nothing else. Not after all the children I have had. Besides, since I thought of it in Church, might it not mean that it is God's will? If I love God and the Church, then I must accept with grace any task set before me."

She began drawing up plans. "This will give dignity to my existence, I won't have to be the wronged wife tainted by divorce." With her fist she lightly pounded the table. "I shall return, and I will succeed."

Chapter 29

A decree of limited divorce became final in April. The children were awarded to Ellen, and Mansfield was restrained from exercising any control or authority over them or any property belonging to them which they might inherit. He was allowed to visit the children once a month if Ellen agreed, and as long as a member of the family was present. He was ordered to pay $100 per year for each child until they were of age, and to Ellen he was ordered to pay $500 per year for the rest of her life.

The baby was born in early June, on Corpus Christie day. "A perfect day," Clarence assured them, beaming at the tiny girl. "She will be a devout, holy Christian." "We should name her after a saint," Ellen said softly, "a happy saint who brought joy to others."

"I say we should name her Sarah," Clarence said, looking at his stepmother, "for the most selfless one among us."

Sarah laughed. "Thank you, Father Walworth, but we all know a saint I'm not."

"Well, we have until July to think about it," Ellen said, "for I won't have her named or christened until the girls are home from Kenwood, and Dolly is back to bake a cake like she has for the other children."

Dolly had been in New York City working for another family. Economically, Sarah could no longer afford her. They had only lived part–time at Pine Grove the last few years, Sarah rationalized, and since there were no longer so many little children, they were able to get along with only Katy's help in the kitchen. Still, letters flowed back and forth as a homesick Dolly wrote to ask about her family and about her baby, Reubena. Sarah's letters constantly reminded Dolly to remain true to the family, hinting to her that true affection never fails but lives through time and eternity.

"If only Dolly were here, she could help us with the baby," Ellen sighed one evening.

Sarah Margaret was frail, and cried all the time. She spit her food up as soon as she was nursed and didn't seem to be gaining weight. It took both Sarah and Ellen to care for her, and Ellen was exhausted. In addition, she was alarmed at Sarah's noticeable frailty. Her mother moved slowly and walked with stooped shoulders. She was still active in the Washington National Monument Society, which was dedicated to erecting a monument to the country's first President, but her eyes were tired, and she spoke haltingly in a frail tone.

In spite of their exhaustion, Sarah began receiving callers soon after the baby's birth. "This home shall be open to friends again," she stated. "We have had our troubles and lost some of our fortunes, but we don't intend to close ourselves away."

"I suppose they will come just to make certain we still have our legs and arms," Ellen remarked. "Let them peer all they want, they will soon get used to us."

"People will think nothing of your troubles if you hold your head high and go about your business," Sarah said. "Everybody has problems. They are just curious to see how we handle ours."

"I certainly don't intend to pretend I haven't had troubles," Ellen declared. "I am a divorced woman, and I do have to support my family, but I intend to purport myself with dignity."

Still, it wasn't that easy. The careful sideways glances and the not-so-guarded scrutinies were hard to bear. Ellen was painfully aware that in Saratoga, Mansfield was seen by many as a successful author, the son of a notable father. And after so many years of neglect, of abuse, she was uncertain if she could earn a living or not. If the face she turned toward the world was one of poise and self-confidence, in the dark of her own bedroom she often fought panic. Yet she didn't have the luxury to fear failure, she reminded herself, she had to succeed.

Ellen had just finished interviewing a prospective teacher one hot July afternoon when Frank brought a letter to her. "I believe it's from Father," he said with a slight frown of apprehension on his face. She had not heard from Mansfield since the divorce, nor had he attempted to contact the children. Surprised, she tore the letter open and scanned its contents. Then she started at the beginning again, letting the words sink in slowly:

> "I go down in five minutes to see if my lawyer has received and filed the agreement signed. But my superhuman second sight tells me that you have prevaricated, and that Chancellor Walworth's second son must be a murderer and a suicide. I have done all I could to avert it. You are pushing on your doom. By the eternal, Ellen Hardin, the purpose of three years of abandoning me and grasping that property shall be thwarted in your blood and mine. All the intensity of hate in my life is centered on you. Listen for the crack of the pistol!"

Silently, Ellen handed the letter to Frank. "He doesn't believe I have nothing to give him," she sighed.

"But he knows he has to support you, doesn't he?"

"Maybe he doesn't believe it. He never has supported us. I don't think his anger will ever be placated, Frank. Your grandfather treated me like a natural daughter in his will, while he mistrusted your father."

"If I had enough money," Frank mused, "I would not only help you, I would give some to Father, too, so he wouldn't harass us."

"We'll just ignore it, Frank. That's the best thing we can do."

Two weeks later when another letter arrived, Ellen knew that it would be impossible to ignore Mansfield. She opened the letter and gasped when three live bullets fell out along with a powdery substance.

"I am crazy for just a few dollars to push my book *Delaplaine* into success," he wrote. With horror she read that he would not hesitate to kill her mother and his sons for $950. He thought *Delaplaine* would not sell if he did not have $200 worth of advertisements printed for the novel. Pride of authorship was all Mansfield had left, and he felt that Ellen was remorselessly knocking "from under a despairing wretch the last plant on which I can succeed. You robbed me of everything sweet in life and of peace. But let go, my sweet darling, precious money. Too late I have learned that money is the hope of life—I would gladly murder for it and die—you have miscalculated Mansfield Tracy Walworth."

Saratoga's summer gaiety could be heard in the music coming from Congress Park. Sounds of horses' hooves clip–clopped down Broadway, carriages rattling behind them. Outside Pine Grove someone laughed, a high musical laugh, the sound of carefree joy. Ellen slowly picked up one of the bullets and looked at it. She sat very still for a moment, then started shaking. Despite the heat, she felt cold and rose abruptly to shut the window. She reached for a shawl that had been carelessly thrown over the back of the love seat and wrapped it tightly around her. She closed her eyes for a moment and tried to calm herself. She needed to think, and she took deep breaths as desperation clawed at her. She glanced at the letter again. It was the raving of a lunatic, a madman, but madmen often carry out their threats, and she had no doubt Mansfield meant to carry them out. "I shall summon Clarence," she thought as she had so many times in the past. "I won't say a word to anyone, and when he comes, we will calmly decide what course of action to take." Until then, she decided, she wouldn't worry. She had too much to do and think about with the baby to care for and the school due to open in October and—the school! If anyone heard about these letters, they would be afraid to enroll their children. "Damn you, Mansfield Wal-

157

worth," she suddenly thought, "how dare you interrupt the life I'm trying to build!" Angrily she went back to her desk in the courtroom. There were desks, books, infinite supplies to be ordered, and advertisements to be written and printed. In another hour it would be time for Sarah Margaret's feeding. Deliberately, with great thought, she began to write:

> "The Walworth Academy will open October 1. Teachers of experience and highest culture will assist Mrs. Walworth in the inculcation of correct moral principles, gentlemanly habits, and refined manners."

Clarence came as soon as he could, bearing a letter Mansfield had written to his sister, Eliza:

> "I have conceived the great secret of my existence. I was not born as men are, but was let down from heaven in a basket. All who have preceded me are impostors. I am the true Messiah. It will cause a great commotion on the earth when I am summoned, for I shall be a soldier–king and have in Heaven the home of my Father—God. You, of course, are not morally my sister, but during our terrestrial intercourse you have manifested such kindness for me that I shall make you one of the queens of the earth. Keep this secret until I am announced by the sound of ten thousand trumpets, then fall down and worship me, for I am Mansfield Tracy Walworth, the eternal and true son of God."

Ellen finished the letter, scanned it once again, then slowly looked at Clarence, "Dear, God," she whispered, "what can we do?"

"There is no way we can prevent him writing letters, and he has committed no crime so he can't be put away." Clarence winced. "I am beginning to fear though, that he should be put away. Nelly, if Mansfield tries to visit you or the children, make certain that I am here, or maybe even Judge Barbour. Have you shown any of these letters to Frank?"

"Yes."

Clarence rubbed his forehead. "You shouldn't. Don't let him see any more of them, and don't tell him about them. The less troubled the children are, the better. And for heaven's sake, don't tell Mother. It will just complicate the entire matter."

On the first of October, Pine Grove became The Walworth Academy. Many people of Saratoga still viewed the old mansion as an intellectual haven and were proud to have their children educated there. Ellen was satisfied and grateful and more than a little proud as quite a number of scholars filled the old drawing room. In her school, subjects would be taught as diligently and intelligently as in any other school in the East, and she would make certain the children would also learn a love of study just for the sake of knowledge.

Then in early January, Sarah Margaret died. Ellen could feel nothing.

"God took her in her innocence," Clarence commented ruefully, "and undoubtedly she has in this way escaped a great deal of trouble."

The day after the burial, Ellen was again back in the drawing room, supervising classes. Suddenly a child laughed, a gleeful irrepressible laugh, and the pain in her heart felt as though she had been stabbed with a knife. She turned and fled upstairs. Once in her room, she sank into her rocking chair. She thought of Mansfield kicking her in the stomach the year before, and sheer hate for him enveloped her. She squeezed her eyes shut as anger against herself engulfed her, anger that she had stayed with him, that she had not left him sooner. She stayed there the rest of the day and into the night, rocking and staring at the floor. Now and then a sob would well up inside her, and she would hold her breath and gasp and choke as though she might drown in her tears. As the light from a new day began to streak across the dark sky, she dozed. Now and then she roused herself, and in the half haze of consciousness she knew trouble would always be with her. It would be a part of her days as much as the night and the dawn, but for whatever reason, she couldn't quit. She had to go on.

All through the year Mansfield's ravings continued in one letter after the other.

> "Sign this paper, and I will trouble no further. The devil says to me, you fool, she wants to beggar you; she wants two–thirds since her father died; she has kicked you out like a dog; she does not care a groat whether you succeed or not; she means to torment you about that property, because she is a thief and a traitress. Now sign this paper, and I will try to bring this tortured brain once more down to literary work. My lawyer says she will never sign anything that you want her to because she gloats in torturing you. You, Ellen Hardin. It is in me to succeed at books if you leave me alone and take the

apprehension of lawsuits from me. Sign this paper or a tortured author will kill you. Why did you make me give up my children to you and make no fight for them? Because I thought the trust property would be left to me, and I could succeed as an author. My lawyer says that you say I am a fool; that you hate; that you say you will do nothing that I want you to do just to keep me uneasy, and that your brain cannot bend to literary work; you know that if I succeed, your affidavits must be perjuries before the world. Now, sign this paper, or I will murder you. I do not believe in any God, but I believe there is a devil, and that devil is you. Why, in the name of common sense, after you robbed me of the sweetness of life, do you not leave me in undisturbed possession of the property, so that I can stay in New York and work? In the name of God, when I gave you my children for money, am I not allowed to live in peace, when I would sell my soul for it? Oh, money is as sweet to the Hardin's as anybody else; but there is not one of them who has courage to murder for money as I have, and I will it I am not left in peace with this two–thirds; for when that goest, my last plant of ambition will be taken from under me, and I will murder."

Ellen threw herself into supervision of the school and made plans for its expansion. She set aside two hours every day for her own reading and study. When summer came, she again sent out advertisements for boarders.

Still, the letters continued.

"Listen to these terrible words. They will show you how keenly and fiercely I feel the humiliation of Reuben H. Walworth's will, and what a Scot, the descendent of King Malcolm, will do when all is taken from him. Reuben H. Walworth hated me from my cradle. He always hated anyone who was high spirited and would speak out their thoughts. He always liked cringing hypocrites, like Eliza Backus and Clarence Walworth. Although he saw my ambitious spirit, he hated it because it would not toady to his favorite Yankees. Hence from my cradle he persecuted me and headed me off in every pursuit or speculation. I could not please him in anything, because I would not whine to him about his favorites. He has stung me into madness and broken up my family by placing me in the humiliating position of being under a trustee, and that trustee my brother, who has neither ambition or heart. From his grave he glares at me and says: 'Ha! You were always proud and high spirited, but by my will I have put in your side a thorn for life. You have no dignity under it, and it will sting you to your grave. The only ones of my name who have any dignity under my will are your sons, Frank and Tracy, who will bear my name to posterity.' Now, Ellen Hardin, knowing I am helpless under that will, if you will persist in trying year by year to see how much of that trust property you can get out of me by threats of law, by personal blandishments to my trustees, or by any other means; if you doubt and will not see that I ought to have something for my entire life, whether intended to me or not, then mark what will be the finale of my vengeance upon that dead scoundrel dog who has made me so pitiable before men and before you. I will—so help me the demons who wait upon the persecuted and the proud spirited and the revengeful—I will, when stripped by you of my property plunge my dagger into Frank and Tracy's heart, and cut off the Walworth name forever. God damn him, he has elevated them and degraded me, and you gloat over it. With cold, calm purpose you contemplate my eventual beggary and humiliation. I will kill your boys and defeat the damned scoundrel in his grave and cut off his damned name forever. Now you just persecute me about that property and keep this thorn alive in my heart, by the eternal God I will kill your boys as well as you. The dead villain shan't rob me of my wife, children, and revenge. If I can't have anything, I'll have revenge. I have lost nearly everything which makes life tolerable."

161

Chapter 30

Finally, the letters stopped coming. Ellen told herself that Mansfield had been advised to give up and was abiding by that advice, but it was an uneasy relief.

She was too busy running the school and caring for her family to give much thought to Mansfield, and for that she was grateful. She had only very tentative and vague plans for the future, but she could foresee expansion of the school. No students had dropped out, and she had heard no complaints from parents. She was proud. In one year she had accomplished enormous changes. With a sense of great relief, she felt that she was afraid of nothing. The days now had a rhythm of discipline that imbued her with purpose and dignity.

Now that she had a housekeeper in the person of Winnefred Roche, she was able to devote most of her energy to the school. She rose early and had breakfast with her family while they exchanged plans for the day. When the students were assembled, she opened the school day with a prayer. She held meetings with the teachers twice a week, going over each pupil's progress and difficulties and asking advice. She knew each child by name, as well as each one's parents, and what kind of home they had. She was proud, too, that she was able to build a social life for herself. Old friends were seeking her out, and she was thankful for those who invited her for dinner or to their musical evenings even though she was alone.

Clara had returned to Kenwood, but Nellie had offered to stay home and help Ellen with the school. Eager and energetic, drawing upon her experiences at Kenwood, Nellie was able to give Ellen helpful and invaluable advice.

Tracy, at eleven, was benefiting from the atmosphere too, but he stayed aloof around most of the students and even among the family was quiet and sullen.

Reubena, at five, was a beautiful child, with white blond curls framing an oval porcelain–like face. Everything about her, her movements, her laugh, proclaimed lightness, so that she often reminded Ellen of a high musical note struck in joy.

Frank was becoming an enigma. He had refused to return to Georgetown and was studying law in the office of Joseph Hill. He had quit speaking of Corinne Bramlette, the daughter of Kentucky's War Governor whom he had met in Saratoga the previous summer. He had given every indication then of being a young man in love. She assumed Frank still wrote letters to her since she had seen a letter from Corinne addressed to Frank, but when she brought up Corinne's name, his reply was noncommittal. He spent many afternoons playing whist with Benjamin Amsdell, the gun manufacturer, and often played billiards and went driving with Dr. Charles Grant. He saw Charles Pond often and his cousin Walworth Barbour. But the eager demeanor of youth had vanished from him, and he was withdrawn and moody. He moved through every day, Ellen thought, seemingly preoccupied. He rarely spoke with her or the rest of the family except at mealtimes, and then it was usually she who precipitated the conversation. When she occasionally sent him on an errand, he would often come back not having done it and not remembering what it was he had been sent after. On a few occasions Ellen had been awakened by screams from his room and had gone to quiet him, but he would say nothing as to what thoughts or dreams might have caused the outbursts. Mrs. Roche reported to her that a few times she had found bloodstains on Frank's pillowcase.

One afternoon as she cleared away the lunch dishes, Mrs. Roche remarked, "Frank seems very nervous, Mrs. Walworth, is he all right? Do you know that he gets up at night and checks all the doors and unlocks them, opens them and then locks them again?"

"Perhaps I will put him in charge of closing the house at night," Ellen murmured.

He was, she thought tenderly, concerned for their safety, but it cut her to the core to watch him wrestle with his burden. "With no more letters coming from Mansfield, Frank's unease will soon dissipate," she told herself.

One evening at supper, Frank barely touched his food and said nothing. Tracy and Reubena were excused before coffee was poured, and Frank kept glancing uneasily at Nellie. Finally, he looked at Ellen and said pointedly, "Mother, I would like to speak with you for a few minutes as soon as Nellie has finished her coffee."

"Why don't you just ask me to leave?" Nellie said peevishly. "You don't have to treat me like I'm one of the pupils." She pushed her chair back abruptly and flounced out of the room. Frank poured himself another cup of coffee and sat staring into it for a moment. Finally, he raised his eyes to Ellen's. "I saw Father today."

"You did?" she asked in astonishment. "Where?"

"On Broadway, here in Saratoga. He didn't say why he was here. In fact, he barely spoke to me. If I hadn't gone up to him, I doubt if he

163

would have said anything to me at all." Frank's mouth twisted into an expression of bitterness.

"What did you say to him, Frankie? You know, I never have prevented him from seeing his children."

"I know, Mother," Frank said quietly. "I asked him if he had come to see his family. He just looked at me for a moment and then laughed." Frank sat up and straightened his shoulders. "I told him," he said in an authoritative voice, "that there were bounds beyond which I would not allow any man to go, and that if he sent my mother any more of such letters, I would shoot him."

Ellen's eyes widened. "Frank! You mustn't threaten him, it will only anger him further."

"You needn't worry, Mother." Frank said reassuringly, "I carry a loaded pistol with me at all times, and I am prepared to defend my family."

Ellen sat back against her chair and looked at her son. "What has he done to us?" she whispered weakly. "We cannot continue to live in fear of him." She sat up. "At least those awful, threatening letters have stopped, and we must hope that his mind is occupied with other things."

Frank stared down at the table.

"You, Frank, must put your mind to the study of law. We will not live in fear." Ellen put her napkin down and rose from the table. "We shall go right ahead and make a good life for ourselves."

By the end of May, Ellen could look back on a winter of satisfaction for the first time since Frank was a baby. With zest and energy she began making lists of tasks to be completed so that the school could again become a boarding home for the summer.

Sarah was in Chicago visiting with D. and Estelle and was planning on traveling from there to Louisville to see Lem and Annie.

Clarence had invited Frank to accompany him to Europe for the summer. Ellen was hopeful that the trip would take Frank out of himself and carry him further away from all that was bothering him.

On the last day of May, she and Nellie, with Tracy and Reubena, clipped boughs of lilacs, picked bunches of daffodils, and carried pots of geraniums to the cemetery to lay on the Chancellor's grave. "We must come back when the roses are blooming," she told Nellie.

"He cared deeply for his roses; he must have some from the bushes he so lovingly tended."

On Saturday evening at supper, Ellen pursed her lips and looked at Frank. "You must find out your uncle's itinerary. Then you will have to read all you can about the cities and towns you will be visiting." Frank

164

had initially been excited about the trip to Europe, but in the past few days Ellen had been perplexed by his silence. "No book can ever give you the historical perspective you will have by seeing it first hand, but it will prepare you."

Frank seemed not to have heard her.

"Frank?" she asked at length, "What do you think?"

"I may not go," he answered dully.

"But you must! It's a wonderful opportunity!"

He said nothing, but got up from the table. She heard him in the hall, but restrained herself from asking where he was going as she heard the front door close. She would have to ask Clarence to intervene and persuade Frank to go. He was too intensely preoccupied for a boy of nineteen, and getting away for a while would be the best thing for him.

On Monday morning, she awakened later than usual, rose, and dressed hurriedly. There was only one more week of school left, then boarders would start arriving, and she still had so much to do. When she got to the breakfast table, Nellie was already there with Tracy and Reubena. "Where's Frank?" she asked, as Mrs. Roche appeared with a tray holding boiled eggs and toast.

"He left early this morning, Mrs. Walworth. He said if he didn't return by tea–time today, he would be back tomorrow."

"Tomorrow?" Ellen was stupefied. It was unlike Frank to leave and not tell her where he was going.

"Did he say anything to you, Nellie?"

"No, Mama."

She put her cup down. "Excuse me a moment." She rose from the table. "Go ahead, you can all be excused from the table," she said over her shoulder as she hurried to Frank's room.

His bed was unmade, and she frowned as she noticed a reddish brown stain on his pillowcase. A bureau drawer was half–opened, and papers were scattered on its top. She caught her breath as she picked up a page and noticed Mansfield's handwriting:

> "Prepare yourself for the inevitable. I am over my wasting fever and shall be out of my room in a few days. I am going to call upon my children; my heart is aching for their caresses. Make the interview easy and pleasant as possible. I cannot stay from them much longer. I will see them—peaceably if I can or with a tragedy if I must. Their little faces haunt me, as they are mine. Popish cruelty

165

must bend to the demand of a father's breast, or the Walworth name goes out in blood. Keep Frank Walworth out of my way. You have taught him to hate me, and his presence or obstruction in any way will only excite fatal exasperation. I want to see my little girl and come away peaceably. Beware that you do not in any way arouse the frenzy which you have known to exist since you left me. There is a reasonable way to deal with me. I shall have my rights under that decree, with no further legal delay or expense. I have conceded promptly every right under that decree, and now I am going to see my children, and you shall not bring them up to hate their loving father. Eliza Backus has written to me that you will do it if you can, from your associations with them, and then I shall shoot you and myself on those doorsteps, for I have nothing further to live for. I am a broken–hearted desperado. I admit it. Save this letter for lawyers and courts if you please. God is my lawyer; not the remorseless brutal God that you and Eliza Backus and Clarence Walworth worship, but that God who has planted love in my heart for my little girls, and that says to the tiger bereft of its young, "Kill!" You are an infamous wretch to keep me from the little hands and hearts that love me. Your only excuse was my poverty and misfortune. When Frank refused to speak to me in the streets of Saratoga, I said to myself, "She is teaching them all to hate a tender–hearted father." Then all is lost and the tragedy must come. When I know from the conduct of my little girls that you have taught them to hate me, that moment two pistol shots will ring about your house—one slaying you, the other myself. I know that you have no personal fear, no more than I have, but we both must die when that discovery comes that you have estranged my young children from me. It is possible you have not done so, and you shall have your life. If my little girls do not love me, then life is valueless, and I shall die with a feeling of luxury and rest to come; but you will have to attend me to the spirit land. The God of justice demands it. Therefore, I say to you, do right under that decree, then all may be well; but now my heart is agonized for my little children. If you had common sense, you would know how to appreciate the danger."

Ellen leaned her forehead on the top of the bureau. The letters had not stopped coming after all. Frank's absence was suddenly tangibly ominous. She must get a telegram to Clarence at once. She quickly pinned a loose strand of hair under the bun at the back of her head and ran down the front stairs. She walked fast, half running to the telegraph office, her breath coming in short, desperate gasps. Ellen was only vaguely aware of the sunshine and the soft air of late spring, only dimly conscious of the smiles of people she passed in the street. She had better alert John Barbour too, she thought, they must find Frank.

Tuesday afternoon she was in the classroom reading some papers when Mrs. Roche came to the door. "Excuse me, Mrs. Walworth, you have some visitors."

Ellen hurried to the front hall and was surprised to see Wilma French and Dorothea Ritchie standing there, their faces strained and uncertain.

"Dear, Ellen," Wilma said as she stepped forward and extended her hands. "We have come with bad news, I'm afraid. Mansfield has died." There was a pause, and Wilma looked about her uncertainly. "He was shot, Ellen. Frank killed him."

Chapter 31

C larence met her at the depot in Albany, the sad, blank look on his
face a mirror of her own numbness. They boarded a steamer for the
trip down the Hudson River to the City, and when they were settled,
Clarence said, "I got a telegram from Frank. It read, 'I have shot Father.
Take care of Mother.'" His voice sounded flat, almost hard.

Ellen stared into empty air over the railing of the steamer. "He
thought he did the only thing possible, I know he did. Those awful letters were still coming, those letters threatening to kill Frank, Tracy, and
me. Frank hid them from me and kept the fear to himself. He just
couldn't take it anymore." She bit her lower lip to keep it from trembling. "Where is he?" she asked tentatively.

"He's incarcerated in the Tombs. That's the jail," he said to Ellen's
inquisitive look. "He turned himself in." Clarence reached into his
pocket and handed a piece of paper to Ellen. "I received a letter from
him on Monday, just before I got your telegram."

"I am of the opinion," she read, "that it would be neither safe nor
wise to leave her unprotected against Father's acts. In fact, I do not
think her situation is by any means safe as it is. I enclose a letter from
Father to her, which I received yesterday. I am going down to New
York in the morning to see him, and, I may add, without informing
Mother, for she would feel very uneasy. My trip will determine any
questions in regard to my going to Europe or anywhere else. I will be
heartily sorry if I shall have caused you any trouble or expense."

"Frank," Ellen whispered, clutching the paper.

It was ten–thirty at night before they reached New York City, but
John Barbour was at the dock to meet them and drive them to the
Tombs. She was ushered into the private office of Warden Johnson and
was shown a seat. It was an austere, officious room, smelling faintly of
cigars. Ellen shuddered at its coldness. "Mrs. Walworth, you may see
the prisoner now." She followed the warden into a counsel room where
Frank was standing against the door. For a moment she looked at him,
his gray prison clothes a contradiction to the relaxed, smiling face of
the youth wearing them. She uttered an involuntary cry and then took
him into her arms, smoothing his hair, kissing his cheek. She held him
to her tightly. "My Frank," she whispered. "Oh, my Frank." She felt his
shoulders shudder with a sob, and she wanted to rock him as she had
when he was a child and give him assurance of her love and his safety.
Then he kissed her on the cheek, and they sat down by the table. For a

168

second or two neither spoke. Frank looked into her face, then put his hand on her head and smoothed her hair. "Dear, Mama, I know you will not forget me. I love you more than my life."

She took his hands in hers. "What happened, Frank, how did it happen?"

"He was going to kill us all, Mama, I knew it from the day I met him on the street." He laid his head on her hands, then straightened up and looked into her eyes. "I came to the city and registered at the Sturtevant House. I didn't want to tell you, I knew you would be upset and try to stop me. But, I knew I had to get to him." Frank agitatedly ran his hand through his hair in a gesture so reminiscent of Mansfield that she caught her breath. "After I registered, I went to Father's residence and asked if he was at home. The servant who opened the door told me he was out walking. I wrote him a note then. 'I want to try to settle some family matters,' I said, 'call at the Sturtevant House in an hour or two. If I am not there, I will leave word at the office.' I stayed at the hotel all evening and stayed up all night, and he didn't come. At six–fifteen in the morning a bellboy brought a card from Father saying he wished to see me. He came to the room and sat down in a chair. I said, 'You must promise me not to make any more of the threats against my mother and to cease writing insulting letters to her.' He sneered, then said, 'Yes, I suppose I'll promise.' I had my pistol in my hand. I said, 'You have lied to my mother and myself so often that I can hardly believe you now.' He insulted you and me most grossly." Ellen laid her head upon her hands and bit her lip as a familiar surge of hatred against Mansfield engulfed her. "I stepped forward," Frank continued, "and he put his hand in his pockets as if to draw a pistol. Then I shot him. He then came toward me, and I fired three shots at him. When I fired the last shot, he had me by the collar." Frank sighed heavily and half–sprawled back against the chair, relieved to have told it all. "I have no regrets, Mother," he said quietly, "except for the anxiety this causes you and the family."

Ellen laid her hand against Frank's cheek again. "Do you have everything you need?"

Frank smiled wryly. "A cot, a blanket, a stool, and two candles. It's amazing what little I need."

"You know there will probably be a trial, Frank."

"Of course."

"We haven't any money, but thanks to your grandfather, we do have friends and access to the best counsel in New York State."

"I won't be convicted, Mother, not when they examine Father's acts. And I did turn the gun over to the police and turn myself in. Don't worry. I won't be mistaken for a criminal."

169

In the morning she and Clarence drove to the undertaker's where Reverend James Ludlow of the First Presbyterian Church was to offer a short prayer. For a moment, as they drove up Carmine Street, Ellen couldn't comprehend what had happened, why police officers were holding back curious onlookers and keeping them from blocking the pathway to the building and obstructing traffic. Clarence took her arm to help her from the carriage. "It's in all the papers," he said grimly, clenching his jaw. "They don't realize what has happened. All they know is a son shot his father."

There was a cloying quietness inside the building as they were led to Mansfield's coffin. His face looked puffy, and Ellen felt nothing as she gazed upon a countenance perfectly still, not sneering or grimacing, no look of hatred or malice, no smiles, no twinkling eyes, no trace of the youth she had loved or the man she had feared. A bouquet of roses lay upon his body. "Who ordered them?" she whispered to Clarence, but stopped when she saw a tear run down the naked grief of his cheek. Reverend Ludlow came in and offered his condolences, said a few short prayers, and then left for the return trip to Saratoga and Mansfield's funeral.

In Saratoga, news of the shooting spread like wildfire, and people milled about the telegraph office waiting for more news or brazenly stood in front of Pine Grove vying for a look at the family who had brought infamous fame to a village never grown used to its own infamy.

"No," Ellen whispered horrified as the carriage pulled up in front of their home and people stood aside to let them pass.

"Pay them no attention, Nelly," Clarence said softly as they hurried up the front steps. Inside the house, the relatives were already assembled. Ellen briefly hugged Clara, Nellie, and Tracy to her, and then picked up Reubena. Mansfield's sisters were there, their faces masks of disbelief and apologetic grief. Mary Elizabeth, her cheeks wet with tears, embraced Ellen. Eliza Backus and Sarah Davison each kissed her on the cheek as their husbands stood awkwardly aside. Ellen looked blankly at her mother, then she was in Sarah's arms and sobbing. "Frank, oh, Frankie," she cried over and over.

A crowd of onlookers stood at the depot on Friday afternoon, staring as the funeral procession drove up, watching silently as the pine box containing the coffin was lowered out of the train and into a hearse. Then they started the slow drive to Greenridge Cemetery. The burial plot was on a hill, shaded by a large, old pine tree. The faces around the graveside were composed, eyes dry, not a murmur or sob was heard. Ellen tightly held Tracy's hand as the Reverend Dr. Camp of the Epis-

170

copal Church and the Reverend Mr. Newman of the Presbyterian Church began to intone prayers. On top of the coffin, someone had placed a wreath of white tuberoses, the green leaves of the flowers catching a glint now and then of the late spring sun. Ellen stood poised and calm, feeling nothing, able to stand apart and observe herself going through the motions of paying last respects to a husband she had long ago ceased to respect. In the horrendous depravity of the man he had become, she had forgotten the youth who could make her laugh, as though that existed in a long–ago dream, a figment of her imagination. And now this was the other side of the dream, this black dress and veil she wore, mourning not for a husband but for the child forced to bear responsibility for a father's depravity.

She shuttered the windows and closed her ears to the headlines that were screaming at her in silence. If her nights seemed endless, the days were unbearably long. She stood at the window, her back to the parlour and to the presence of John Barbour, who had come to tell her what the counsel was planning for Frank. The world outside Pine Grove was washed clean from the morning's rain, and water still dripped from the oaks in the park across the street. A ray from the sun caught a drop of water on the tip of a pine branch, and for an instant, light was fractured on the surface of that single drop into all the colors of the rainbow.

"There is a weight on my heart that feels like a piece of lead," she remarked. "I have put Frank into God's hands. It's all I can do."

"Ellen," John said quietly, "we are going to have to enter a plea of insanity for Frank."

Her hand flew to her mouth as she turned and looked at him in wide–eyed horror. "No!"

"We must. It's the surest way to keep him from being convicted."

"Convicted?" she repeated dully. "John, how in the name of sanity could Frank be convicted? Not when all the evidence, Mansfield's letters—" her voice trailed off in silent realization. She moved to the sideboard and with shaking hands poured herself a glass of water.

"We are going to have to use as evidence Frank's bouts of epilepsy."

"But it wasn't really epilepsy, just a few episodes in Kentucky and then now, this year, when he was under such strain. John!" she cried, her voice rising high with pleading, "he was such a good student at Georgetown. Everyone knows Frank is brilliant."

"The papers are full of the horrors of this parricide," John announced wearily. "People are already debating the question of whether or not Frank should be hanged. Nelly, we know what happened and why it happened. Now we have to convince a jury."

171

The courtroom smelled of fear. Dressed in a black silk dress with black satin ribbons tumbling down the front of the skirt, a black veil hiding her face, Ellen felt perspiration drip down her back in tiny droplets. The occasional breeze blowing through the open windows only seemed to intensify the smell of dust, furniture wax, and closely packed bodies. She, Clarence, and Tracy sat at the counsel table where Frank would sit, and she could feel the sustaining presence of D. and Sarah behind her. Lemuel, Dolly, Eliza Backus and her husband Clarence, Sarah and John Davison, and Mary Elizabeth Jenkins all formed a protective family shield against evil and gossip.

Frank was led in, and Ellen felt her heart swell with pride as she watched him walk confidently, his bearing erect, giving a slight nod and smile of recognition to his family. He sat down, inclined his head toward her and whispered, "Good morning, Mama." Frank's counsel, Charles O'Conor, William Beach, ex–District Attorney Garvin, and Henry E. Davies, sat reassuringly next to them. Charles O'Conor had a wide reputation as the best attorney in the state. He had been a good friend of the Chancellor's and was a candidate for lieutenant governor when Reuben had been nominated for governor on the Democratic ticket in 1848. He also had been attorney general for one year in President Franklin Pierce's administration.

Ellen's eyes traveled over the jurors, men from every walk of life, a merchant, a mechanic, a dairy farmer. Only one member of the jury disturbed her and that was Charles Milbank, whose brother had been a member of the jury that had indicted Frank.

Benjamin Phelps, the energetic young lawyer for the prosecution, was a newcomer, having been in the office of District Attorney for only a few months. He had been successful, though, in prosecuting William M. Tweed for official peculation, as well as for prosecuting Edward S. Stokes, a wealthy New Yorker who had shot a man named Fisk.

Daniel G. Rollins, the Assistant District Attorney, stood and in a monotone voice began presenting the case for the prosecution, minutely detailing the circumstances of the shooting. Ellen inwardly cringed as she glanced at Frank, then at the jury, as Mr. Rollins' voice filled the room. "Parricide," he intoned with great emphasis on the word, "is a crime so revolting to nature that many nations have considered it impossible."

Eliza Simms, the proprietor of the rooming house in which Mansfield had lived, was the first witness called. She looked nervous, but eager to comply, as she bit her lower lip and leaned forward in the chair. For a moment Ellen felt a stab of pity for her, for all of them whose lives were now on parade in this courtroom.

The colored doorman at the Sturtevant House followed Eliza Simms to the stand.

"Did you at any time on that morning hear the noise of the pistol shot?"

"I did."

"What time was it?"

"Very nearly half past six."

"What happened? What did you hear and see?"

"I saw nothing. I heard a knock at the door."

Ellen sat erect, and her hand, which clutched a handkerchief, began to ache. The testimonies droned on, each reiterating the events of the shooting at the Sturtevant House.

Dr. Russell Childs, the physician who had been called when Mansfield was shot, testified. He spared none of the grisly details he had found, and Ellen wondered wildly if she should subject Tracy to such a carnival as this.

It was half past three in the afternoon before William Beach stood and opened the case for the prisoner. He began to enumerate Mansfield's wrongs, the letters, the beatings, the long absences from home. "If this boy shot down his father in deliberation and cold blood, I have no apology for him, but if that father had maddened him, had driven his reason from its throne by his brutality, then I have something to claim from your hearts and consciences. Mansfield Tracy Walworth was either a madman or the very devil. This demonic fiend," he thundered, and suddenly Frank buried his face in his hands, and his shoulders heaved with sobs.

One day rolled into the next in a stifling cavalcade of voices, of tension, of maintaining dignity while the prosecution paraded Ellen's family life before the world. One by one the family was called to testify as to Frank's character. "Do you know he was in the habit of carrying a pistol during the past three years?" The District Attorney asked. Each of them was asked the same question and each replied with the same negative answer.

"The Reverend Clarence Walworth, please." Clarence took his seat in the witness chair, his collar commanding a respect in the District Attorney's voice that had been missing in his examination of the other witnesses. He told of the planned trip to Europe and his invitation to

173

Frank. He relayed that on June 3 he had received a telegram from Frank stating that he had shot his father three times.

Thomas Dennis, the telegraph operator, was called to identify the telegram he wrote at the direction and in the presence of Frank.

"Mrs. Mansfield Tracy Walworth." The name pierced the silence in the stilled courtroom, and for a moment Ellen felt suspended in a strange dream. She was aware of sudden stirrings and whispers among the spectators as she walked to the stand. "I am the mother of Frank Hardin Walworth," she said in a firm voice, "and was married to Mansfield Tracy Walworth in St. Peter's Church, Saratoga Springs, in 1852 on July 29. I resided at the Chancellor's house, which my mother now owns, and lived there until the summer of 1861." She gave the names and dates of her children's births and then began to recite the sad litany of her marriage, the years alone, the separations, her children's deaths. "I had a country place about three miles from Louisville by means of which I supported my family, was eighteen months a government clerk, during which time my husband was with his brother at Albany. We discussed the question of a future residence but came to no understanding about it; I went to my mother's house in Fifty–Second Street, New York City, Mr. Walworth being with me, and we remained there until the final separation on January 26, 1871. I then went with my children to Judge Barbour and since that time have not seen the deceased." She was not asked to tell of the beatings, the humiliations, the internal struggles produced by an absent and neglectful husband and father.

A recess was called, and in a private room off the main courtroom, out of sight of ardent spectators, Ellen swayed slightly with relief, then steadied herself. Someone handed her a glass of water, but her hands shook so hard she almost dropped the glass. She could take only a few sips of the liquid before her throat constricted and she felt she would choke. She dampened her handkerchief with a few drops of the water and patted her perspiring face.

When the trial resumed and she was on the witness stand once again, she identified a document which contained the stipulation modifying the divorce decree and signed by her. "I supported myself and my children entirely by my own exertions," she replied in answer to William Beach's questions, "with the exception of about $350 I received from the Walworth estate."

Charles O'Conor stood and walked toward the stand, his manner dignified and somber, his head downcast. He was almost bald, but had a full beard, and his long rather hawkish nose supported a pair of glasses which he peered over when he looked at Ellen. Gently, he showed her a packet of letters for identification, then opened one. Ellen watched the spectators lean forward eagerly in their seats, and for a moment she hated each and every one. She gripped her hands tightly together as Charles O'Conor began to read. "Prepare yourself for the inevitable. Keep Frank Walworth out of my way. I am a broken-hearted desperado." Ellen tried not to listen to the ridiculous and humiliating words. After Mr. O'Conor finished reading the letter, there was a shocked silence, followed by snickering and some loud guffaws from the back of the room. Frank bent forward in his chair, his face in his hands. District Attorney Phelps began arguing as to the admissability of the letters as evidence. Finally, Ellen was dismissed from the stand, and the court adjourned for the day.

"But why should there be any argument as to the letters being evidence?" she asked D. later over an untouched supper. "After all, they were what caused us to live in fear. When a man sends his wife a letter containing bullets and gunpowder and threatens to kill her and her children, I should think that would be evidence in a court of law!"

D. put his arm about her shoulders, trying to give her confidence. "You are worrying needlessly, Nelly. Frank has the best counsel in the state of New York, quite possibly in the whole country. This might take a while, so you will have to try to relax."

Ellen had no doubt that Frank would be acquitted. The letters alone were proof of what she and the children had suffered at the hands of Mansfield, and she knew that as much as she hated to see Mansfield's depravity shown to the world, Frank's counsel would not let them go unnoticed. But until Frank's acquittal, she had to walk through the crowds of staring men and women every morning, eager to see a "murderer" so malicious that he could kill his own father. How sad, she thought, that there was nothing else in their lives to provide interest or entertainment, that they had to rely upon the desperate actions of a nineteen-year-old boy for sensationalism.

Tracy was becoming the darling of the proceedings, his childish smiles at the bystanders a symbol of uncorrupted innocence.

Every morning Ellen entered the courtroom on the arm of Clarence, walking erect, clutching Tracy's hand, anxious to get through the day's proceedings. When Frank was led in, they would converse, each trying to give the other encouragement, until the Court Crier called attention to the opening with the cry, "Hats off!"

On Friday morning there was another argument over the admissibility of the letters as evidence until Judge Davis intervened and said only the threatening portion of the letter should be presented. "If there is a doubt," he said, "the doubt is to be given to the prisoner."

Mr. Beach took exception to the ruling so far as it excluded any portion of the letter. District Attorney Phelps consented to have the letter read in full, and again the courtroom fell into an expectant hush.

"Hence from my cradle he persecuted me and headed me off in every pursuit and speculation. I will plunge my dagger into Frank and Tracy's heart and cut off the Walworth name forever. Keep this thorn alive in my heart, and I will kill them and you too."

Ellen sat very still, scarcely daring to breathe as the letter was being read. "Now the jury will understand," she thought, "what prompted Frank to this desperate act."

Ellen heard her name called once again, and she rose and walked to the stand.

"After the decree of divorce," Charles O'Conor asked her, "when did you first learn that Mr. Walworth had any wish to visit or see his children?"

"In the fall of 1872, I think in November."

"Did you oppose in any degree his being allowed to see his children?"

"I did not. I was willing that they might be seen in the presence of their uncle, Reverend Clarence Walworth, upon a week's notice to my attorney."

Her venerable attorney stood in front of her and remained motionless and silent until he had the full attention of the courtroom. "Mrs. Walworth," he asked lowering his voice to a deeply concerned tone, "were any acts of personal violence committed upon you by your husband while you resided in Fifty–Second Street in 1871?"

"Objection!" Mr. Phelps cried.

Charles O'Conor peered over his glasses at his opponent. "We intend to prove that such acts were perpetrated and young Frank came into the room at the time. We intend to prove that it had a very great effect upon him for a long time."

"Do you intend to allege that he was insane when this murder was committed?" the Court asked.

"We intend to allege that his mind was so affected that he was not sound at the time of the interview with his father."

Mr. O'Conor again turned to Ellen.

"I had been subjected to personal violence," she said in answer to his questions, "which compelled me to scream; my scream brought in Frank. Once I saw him most violently affected, as I knew next day when I saw the letter he had already read. I was called up by one of the children saying, 'Frank is sick.' I went up and found him with his body rigid and this pallor of which I have spoken. There was a noticeable failure of his memory."

176

The defense produced four packages of letters written by Mansfield. "Do you recognize these?"

"They are in my late husband's handwriting."

"Mrs. Walworth, how would you describe the condition of your husband's mind?"

"Objection!"

Charles O'Conor turned toward his opponent with a scowl on his face. "An important element in estimating the condition of the prisoner's mind," he said, "is the condition of the parent's mind, and these letters, not one, but many, could hardly have proceeded from any but an insane mind. It is with a wish to show a hereditary strain of insanity that these letters should be admissible." He turned back to Ellen.

"What were the peculiar acts of violence on the part of the deceased in reference to yourself?"

"Objection!"

Mr. O'Conor picked up an object wrapped in a white cloth. Unwrapping it carefully, he showed a pistol to Ellen.

"I know this pistol," she said. "It was presented to the Chancellor by the inventor. He gave it to Mansfield soon after, and he had it ever since."

Mr. Phelps rose and stood in front of her.

"I saw Frank's pistol in his possession two weeks before he left Saratoga," she said in answer to his question.

"When did you last see Mansfield?"

"From the time I left New York in January 1871, I never saw Mr. Walworth again."

The letters were produced once again, opened and read. Ellen sat still, clutching her handkerchief, as her husband's blasphemous, maniacal ravings were read to the court.

At half past five, the court was adjourned for the weekend.

Once in her hotel room, Ellen sat in a chair and laid her head back on the brocaded cushion, blind–eyed and sick at heart. Anxiety and humiliation took control of her mind, and her raw nerves felt like live insects crawling over her skin.

She picked up the *New York Times* and scanned it until her eyes picked up the resort news from Saratoga. "The supply of millionaires is ample," she read. "America's top financial barons, William D. Astor, Jay Gould, A. T. Stewart, Commodore and William H. Vanderbilt, are already in summer residence. The Grand Union Hotel is preparing for the first grand ball of the new season. Visitors out for a drive often gaze wistfully at a large but unpretending old–fashioned house, the shutters of which are always closed, and about which there appears to be no sign of life. It is the Walworth Mansion." She let the paper fall from her hands to the floor.

177

Sunday she spent with her family, all of them straining to fill the void of worry with small talk, none of them succeeding.

"Do you think it's going well for Frank?" Ellen asked of no one in particular.

"It seems so, Sister," Lem drawled in his easy way.

She ran her fingers over the table by her chair. "I'm not at all sure it is. Have you noticed how much Benjamin Phelps is enjoying himself?"

D. looked at her carefully and said nothing.

"He is so full of energy, so confident," she said. "By comparison, Charles O'Conor is aged and reticent."

"It's the facts that count, Nelly, not the way the breeze is blowing." D. spoke sharply, and she turned to him, her eyes filled with tears of anxiety.

"Tell me honestly what you think."

D. sighed. "The only problem is that damnable law of second–degree murder. Counsel has to jump that hurdle."

"And if he is convicted on the second–degree charge, then what?" she asked.

"An honest answer is that we don't know," D. answered evenly. "The law only went into effect four days before the murder."

"Don't call it murder!" Ellen cried. "It's bad enough he has to be depicted as insane!"

"Nelly, it was murder. There's no sense in pretending otherwise, and this is the first case tried in New York State under this law."

On Monday morning the nightmare started over again.

"State as well as you can the nature and character of his appearance when he was enraged."

"He was always extremely pale and had the look of a wild beast," Ellen answered. "I cannot imagine any other like it."

"On any of these occasions of this peculiar conduct, did you receive any such violence as the use of his teeth upon you?"

"Yes, in my finger; he bit my finger severely."

"Have you seen any letters later than August?"

"I don't think I have."

The defense turned their questioning toward the plea for insanity. One after another, witnesses took the stand, testifying as to Frank's impeccable character but alluding to his sometimes erratic behavior. Mr. Hill, the lawyer Frank studied with, testified that he suddenly wouldn't converse as usual and made no progress in his studies. Mrs. Roche and Dolly told about his screams in the night, the occasional bloodstains on his pillow. Frank's friend, Dr. Charles Grant, was called to the stand.

178

"During the years you have known Frank, have you noticed any change in him?" he was asked.

"I noticed a decided change in him six or seven months ago. He was in the habit of coming to my office once or twice a week to play billiards. He came to my office, and we went upstairs; I told him it was his turn to play. He made no remark, and I said, 'Frank, it is your turn to play.' He spoke in a sharp, unnatural voice and said he was ready. He sprang up from his seat and struck the balls with great force. The stroke counted, but instead of playing the ball again, he struck one of the red balls so hard that it dropped on the floor, and almost instantly he dropped into the chair. His face twitched violently; he was breathing very heavily, and he was snoring. I sat by his side and said, 'Frank, what ails you?' He made no reply but made an effort to open his eyes. After three or four seconds, he put on his coat. I asked him where he was going; he said he was going home; he said he had to be home at six o'clock, and at the same time he began to take off his coat."

"Will you please state in a general way what these things indicate?"

"To my mind they indicate epilepsy."

"How does the condition called epilepsy affect the mind?"

"It produces unconsciousness and irresponsibility."

"What is called epileptic mania?"

"Yes."

When the court adjourned for the day, Ellen was too drained to speak. Back in her hotel room, she glanced at the *New York Times*, which was avidly covering every moment of the trial. "There is a difference in the outlooks of the Spa tourists and residents. The visitors think Walworth is guilty of 'a fearful murder' but should not be hanged. Many townspeople seem to hold the Walworths in affectionate respect and feel the murder was not terrible, considering the provocation. But Saratogians feel that no matter how sad the case is, Frank Walworth ought to be hanged." Ellen felt sick, betrayed. She folded her arms across her stomach and bent double while cold beads of perspiration formed on her face. Her Frank, her beloved son, stood alone with fingers pointing toward him accusing him of being an insane murderer. She had to think back to when he came home from Georgetown, a happy and carefree student. Frank only changed after he saw her arm where Mansfield had struck her. Anger, too deep to be controlled but with no outlet, welled up in her, and she sobbed helplessly in anguish.

On Tuesday the court convened with the testimony of Dr. John B. Gray.

"I have been a physician with the New York Lunatic Asylum for twenty–five years. I am familiar with the epileptic condition; it is a dis-

179

ease of the brain and spinal cord manifested by periods of unconsciousness and spasm; its causes are various: constitution or heredity, falls and blows, mental or physical shock, long–continued distress, and general disturbances to the circulation."

Mr. Phelps detailed the statement Frank made after the shooting and asked whether the recollection of the events by the prisoner would affect the doctor's judgement as to the prisoner's epileptic condition. Dr. Gray answered that there was hardly sufficient data to decide whether he had that morning an epileptic seizure.

Mr. Phelps called Mansfield's friend, Francis Street of the *New York Weekly*, to the stand.

"He was very quiet and gentlemanly. I never saw any violence or eccentricity. I never saw on him any sign of liquor."

Augustus Walters, a friend from Saratoga, testified. "Mansfield Tracy Walworth was the most agreeable man I ever met. His face reflected good fellowship. I was at their home in Saratoga when Mr. and Mrs. Walworth sat outside laughing in the afternoon sunshine. It was a scene of tranquility and merriment."

John Lary, a restaurant keeper, testified that for two or three years Mr. Walworth got his meals there. He always spoke with pride of his father. Never swore. He was generally cheerful.

Henry Ackerman, a barber, testified that he had known Mr. Walworth for four years. When he was sick, Mr. Walworth came and inquired for him and brought him grapes and other fruit. "He never got angry," Mr. Ackerman said, "he was never profane. Still, there was something in his countenance which overshadowed the man with mystery. Perhaps it was on this account that he showed on certain occasions slight traces of dissipation. I do not say from drink—it may have been from secret troubles or continued writing and reading."

Dr. Ralph L. Parsons, a physician in the New York City Lunatic Asylum, testified: "Epilepsy is characterized by loss of consciousness. It is usually a convulsive affliction and is sometimes connected with a change of mental condition. It frequently exists without such mental disturbances as to be considered insanity."

Mr. Phelps stood in front of Dr. Parsons and folded his hands in front of his chest. Then he raised his right hand and began making cutting motions through the air as he enumerated the facts of Frank's life. "The separation of the prisoner's mother and father, his care of his mother." Mr. Phelps' voice shouted out each occurrence as his hand punctuated the air, "his receipt of his father's letters, the last letter received, the offer to go to Europe." He paused, then asked, "From these occurrences, what is your opinion as to the condition of the prisoner's mind and whether he was conscious of the character of the act he was doing?"

"I see no reason," Dr. Parsons replied, "to believe that he was laboring under an attack of epileptic mania."

Mr. Phelps turned the questioning back to the defense, and William Beach rose.

In answer to his question, Dr. Parsons said, "From the evidence as given, I should not conclude that the act was epileptic or one of epileptic mania."

Dr. Abner Otis Kellogg was called. "I am at present with the Hudson River State Lunatic Hospital at Poughkeepsie. There is no evidence to convince me at the immediate time of the homicide he was in an epileptic condition."

Dr. Meredith Clymer testified and said there was nothing in the evidence that would induce him to believe that he was in an epileptic condition at the time.

Ellen sat transfixed. Not one of these men, these doctors, had testified that Frank's alleged epilepsy had impaired his reasoning at the time of the shooting. A ripple of fear ran through her. That was the entire reason for introducing the epileptic evidence, the pleas for insanity. "Why did they go through all this nonsense?" she wondered in panic. "Mansfield was the insane one, why not prove that, why should Frank have to take the brunt of a hateful father's actions?"

Wednesday morning Ellen sat next to Frank and put her hand on his as the District Attorney commenced his summing up for the Commonwealth. She could feel Frank's tension through her own as they listened to the state of New York depict him as a common murderer. Frank sat with his head bent earnestly forward, his eyes on Mr. Phelps, and his lips slightly apart. At the District Attorney's description of the scene in the room of the Sturtevant House, he turned inquiringly toward the jurors.

At the conclusion of Mr. Phelps address, Charles O'Conor rose. "Do not forget that he came to New York City," he said pointing toward Frank, "as an act of conciliation, not calculated vengeance. He was hoping as only youth can hope. There was honest innocence in all he intended doing. His calmness after the shooting did not reflect an assassin's deliberation but simple cooperation with the police." Charles O'Conor leaned forward and grasped the handrail that separated the jurors from the rest of the courtroom. "Does the remorseless law require Frank's life? Is there a human being on earth who would not say, 'My boy, would that I might give my life for yours?' Does the law require," he asked, his voice rising to a thundering pitch, "that this poor boy at the knees of his mother, should be seized and dragged forth to be hanged?" There was a pause, then he began speaking in a voice with rapid punctuation. "Under the evidence the prisoner cannot be found guilty unless there was in his mind a deliberate and premeditated purpose to kill, not a mere intent. If, at the time of the shooting, he was in a state of overwhelming terror, then he must be acquitted."

Benjamin Phelps rose and confidently began his charge to the jury. "Only Frank's motive should be considered," he said. He turned toward Frank, then back toward the jury. "This good, gentle boy," he said in a voice heavy with sarcasm, "brought no money, no baggage with him to New York, only a pistol. Did this look very conciliatory?" he demanded. "Did this look as though he had come to persuade his father to a settlement, except at the mouth of a pistol? There has been no evidence of even one violent word from the father, and may I remind you that this was a son who was cool, in total control of himself, immediately after murdering his father. Mansfield Tracy Walworth is not being tried, and I appeal to your sense of justice, not sympathy."

Judge Davis commenced his charge to the jury by describing the character of the indictment against the prisoner. "It was claimed that motive, the impulsion to crime, was shown in this case, in that the father's bad and violent conduct toward the prisoner and all his family was so bad as to lead to the contemplation of a crime like this. If the jury can see that such a state of circumstances existed as that the idea of relieving himself by an act of crime was presented, the jury may find there was a motive. The prosecution claimed that through the bad conduct of the deceased, his persistent threats and letters, a state of mind arose in the prisoner looking to the relieving of himself by the death of the deceased."

Judge Davis again enumerated the steps leading to the crime. "The public should be careful to remember," he said, "what they are very prone to forget, and that is that in the eye of the law, all men are under the protection of the law. The genius of the law protects every person, however humble he may be. It is a wild and foolish notion that a man may be called to have his grave laid open to show up his character and his pursuits in life, for the purpose of creating a public sentiment that he was so bad a man he ought to die. It is proper and just for you to discard from the consideration of this case the notion that Walworth was not fit to live. The Judge who is to determine this does not sit in the Court nor in this jury box."

182

In the small room off the courtroom where they sat, Ellen grasped D.'s arm. "The Judge told the jury what to think. He wants Frank convicted!" Panic enveloped her once again like a smothering blanket, and she fought for control of her breath. "How could this happen when we have the best counsel that could be assembled?"

D. shot her a hard look. "Nothing has happened." Then he sighed. "Phelps is young. He wants to make a name for himself, and this is his utmost challenge."

"How long will this take?" she asked in a tremulous voice.

"It's hard to say. We'll stay here until we get further word as to the length of their deliberation. In the meantime, why don't we go out for a bite of supper?"

"Supper!" Ellen almost screamed. "Do you expect to go out and eat supper like a family on holiday while a group of strangers are deciding my son's life?" She clutched her head for an instant with both hands, then dropped them.

Weeks of shock and worry gave way to tears, and Ellen sobbed. "I know they are going to convict him! The Judge is against him; how could they not understand how we suffered because of Mansfield?"

The evening light outside still had a golden hue to it when Judge Davis came back into court at a quarter past eight. Ellen stiffened almost imperceptibly, wildly searching the Judge's face for some sign. The Sheriff's officers came in with Frank, his face white but his head erect. Ellen thought her heart would break. She and Clarence followed Frank into the courtroom while Tracy threaded his way among them, smiling and waving to the spectators, then clambered over Frank's knee and sat down beside him.

The jurors sat down, and Assistant District Attorney Rollins appeared in his place. Charles O'Conor came in and took position at his desk.

"How say you, gentlemen of the jury?" asked the Clerk of the Court. "Have you agreed upon a verdict?"

"We have," replied the faint voice of the foreman.

An intense suppression of breathing was noticeable. Ellen put her hand to her breast and leaned her head intently toward the jury. She dared not breathe while hope, fear, and anguish chased one another and fought for control of her emotions.

"Gentlemen of the jury, stand in your places."

The jury rose.

"Prisoner, stand up."

Frank rose and turned his face rigidly toward the twelve men who held his life in their hands.

"Gentlemen of the jury, look upon the prisoner. Prisoner, look upon the jury. How say you, gentlemen of the jury? Do you find the prisoner, Frank Hardin Walworth, guilty or not guilty of the crime charged against him?"

"Guilty in the second degree."

"Of what—of murder?"

"Yes."

In formal tones, the clerk asked again, "How say you then? You find the prisoner guilty of murder in the second degree and not guilty of murder in the first degree?"

The foreman nodded his head affirmatively.

The clerk nodded at the jury, and they sat down.

Frank sat with his legs sprawled out in front of him and loosened his necktie. His jaw was slack. Ellen's shoulders drooped in relief, and she turned to Frank and smiled weakly. He nodded his head toward hers and passed a hand over his face.

Charles O'Conor approached Ellen. "Mrs. Walworth," he whispered, "I am going to ask that sentencing be deferred until counsel can file a bill of exceptions." Ellen nodded in agreement, although she couldn't comprehend what he meant. All she knew was that it was finally over, and Frank would live.

She was like a marionette manipulated by strings. She could move only woodenly, one section of her body jerking at a time. There were two days to fill before the sentencing. Two days of pure hell, lightened only by the knowledge that Frank would live.

"D., what is your opinion, what do you think the sentencing will be?" She asked the question a dozen times, hoping to be reassured, but only frustrated to tears when D.'s steady gaze met hers, and he answered slowly and softly, "I just don't know."

"We will be able to appeal, won't we?" she would ask hopefully. "A man just can't be allowed to terrorize his family without their fighting back to protect themselves! Even if they decide Frank has to go to prison for a short while, I know we will be able to have the decision overturned. Maybe he won't even have to go."

D. said nothing.

The night before the sentencing, she fell into a quagmire of nightmares. She found herself in a prison, with cold, damp air closing about her. Mutely, begging attention with her eyes, she pleaded for help, but everyone turned their faces from her. Finally, a voice said, "Follow me," and she walked down a long row of cells, each gate loudly and chillingly clanging shut as she passed. Ellen awoke in a sweat to face the day of sentencing.

On Saturday morning, July 5, District Attorney Phelps slowly rose in his seat and addressed the Court. "The trial of Frank Hardin Walworth for the murder of Mansfield Tracy Walworth has terminated in a verdict by an impartial jury of murder in the second degree. It is my duty to move in accordance with the verdict pronounced against him. I now do so."

"Walworth, arise," said the Clerk.

Frank stood.

"What have you to say why judgment of the Court should not now be pronounced against you according to law?"

Frank brought his left hand up to his face, straightened himself back, and shifted his weight from one foot to the other. He opened his mouth as if to speak and then closed it.

Judge Davis filled the uncomfortable silence. "Walworth, I have never been called upon in my life to perform a more painful duty than the one which devolves upon me now. You have been convicted of the crime of murder in the second degree. The duty I am to perform is rendered doubly painful by the fact that you belong to a family honored and distinguished both in the civil and military annals of your country. Your grandfather on the one hand was for a long time the chief equity judge at this great state, and he left a record for purity and integrity and for all the private virtues that advance and elevate man second to none who have adorned so high a station. And, on the other hand, a grandfather on the mother's side fell nobly fighting for his country on the field of battle and left a record of which all his descendants may be proud.

Your father did nothing to forfeit his life, even to the laws of his country, and least of all had he done anything to forfeit his life at the hand of his own and eldest son. I shudder when I think of it, and I think you ought to devote your whole life to a repentance such as God only can accept for so horrible a crime.

The sentence of the Court is that you be imprisoned in the state prison at Sing Sing for the rest of your natural life."

Chapter 33

Ellen lay in bed, overwhelmed by impossible misery. The drawn draperies closed out the light, but sleep was out of the question. When she did close her eyes, the austerity of the gray impregnable fortress that was Sing Sing rose in her mind. The image of Frank sitting in a solitary cell floated before her eyes, and she sat bolt upright and held her head in her hands. Mansfield's last novel, *Beverly*, had opened with a scene set at Sing Sing. In the opening chapter a prisoner was tortured by being strung up by his thumbs. "Today, similar cruelties are frequent at Sing Sing," he had written.

There was a knock at her door. "Nelly, I have called for the doctor," Sarah said quietly as she moved across the room. "You need to rest, and I know you can't." She placed a thin, dry hand on her daughter's forehead, and Ellen closed her eyes. "He'll be here any moment," Sarah said so quietly it was almost a whisper. Ellen wanted to protest, she didn't want her agony observed by anyone, but she was too numb to speak.

"How long has it been since you slept?" Dr. Allen asked when he entered the room with bustling efficiency.

She didn't remember, and she couldn't think. She could only stare at him hollow-eyed.

"You've had a traumatic experience," he said. "When you try to sleep, anxiety probably overcomes you. I'm going to mix you a rather heavy dose of laudanum. When you awaken, just alert your mother so she doesn't worry. Until then," he said as he turned to Sarah, "let her sleep as much as she can."

When she awakened, Ellen had no idea how long she had slept or even what day it was. Then, as the thoughts came flooding back, she felt the sharp knife-edge of remembering all she had wanted to escape. She rang for Sarah, who came up with a tray of tea and toast. When she started to open the shutters, Ellen said groggily, "No, Mama, I still need to lie here. I can't bear to look out yet." Ellen felt guilty as she looked at Sarah's face, worn with sorrow and anxiety, knowing that she, too, was suffering for her grandson. "Mama, I have to think what to do about our situation. There must be something." She sipped the tea.

"Nelly, you have other children who are not only worried about their brother, but about you too." She paused a moment. "There might not be anything you can do for Frank but pray. You must not exclude the rest of your family for the sake of one. Here's a letter," Sarah said, reaching into her pocket, "from Mrs. Lincoln. I thought you would like to read it." With a frail hand that trembled noticeably, she handed the letter to Ellen. "Nelly, please come downstairs as soon as you can, or at least ring and let us know how you are."

When Sarah had gone, Ellen opened the black–bordered envelope and unfolded the pages, those also bordered in black.

      St. Catherine's
      Ontario, Canada

      "My dear Mrs. Walworth,
         Only those who have passed through deep affliction can fully understand others who are similarly tried, thus I approach with my warmest sympathies, entering into all your feelings and those of your deeply afflicted daughter.
         Whom the good Lord loveth, he chasteneth.
         Surely we who have suffered so much in this life will receive full compensation in that blessed world, where sorrow is unknown.
         My own griefs have so greatly affected my health, precious idols, one by one, have been torn from me, and in place of their devotion, I have been left to battle with a cold and sometimes cruel world. But my frequent and severe illnesses warn me that my time here is short, and that ere long I will be reunited to my beloved ones, who are watching and waiting for me.
         A few weeks after you kindly visited me, I was en-abled to leave my bed and, accompanied by my faithful, middle–aged colored nurse, have found a healthful resort here. The baths are benefiting me much, but who but the Great Physician, can cure a broken heart.
         My prayers often ascend for your lovely daughter, and the son, who loves her just as much as my worshipping one did me, yet in Heaven true love burns the brighter.
                   Most Affectionately,
                   Your friend,
                   Mary Lincoln"

Ellen read the letter through a second time and sighed. There were those who said Mrs. Lincoln had lost her mind, a remark which angered Sarah every time she heard or read it. "Nonsense," she would say emphatically, "she just grieves for her great husband and dear children. People haven't been kind to her. After all, she is an educated woman as well as a Todd." Ellen smiled to herself. Education and a good name enabled everyone to rise beyond everyday concerns in Sarah's estimation. Perhaps it was true.

She herself felt educated, Ellen thought, and she certainly had a good name. John Hardin had been Mary Todd Lincoln's third cousin, and Sarah often conceded, in a gentle manner, that maybe the Hardins were a bit more educated than the Todds and certainly had more ancestors who had fought for their country. Maybe Mary Lincoln was going insane, Ellen thought, or maybe she was just unable to prevent bitterness from twisting her soul out of shape.

A new wave of blackness engulfed her, and without warning she began to sob, her face buried in the white linen sheet which covered her. Again the image of Frank floated before her, this time when he was a toddler, his face upturned to her in need and trust. Into her mind came the quick kiss and handshake she had given him a few days ago and the pain she had felt when he turned and joined the convict group.

As her sobs subsided, she thought of her other children. Reubena was only six, and desperately needed a mother. Nelly was fifteen now, Clara fourteen, and Tracy twelve. They were at ages where guidance was necessary. There were plans to be made for their future. There was money to be earned to feed, clothe, and educate them. She had already lost money from the boarders they could have had this summer. She would open the school in the fall. Terror filled her as she thought of the school, and she clutched the sheet tightly. Would anyone send their children to her now? She had feared rejection the first time she had opened the school, but now the trial had made a tawdry mockery of the Walworth name. How would people react to her now?

Although she had cringed within herself every time she read an account of the trial in the papers, she had been too preoccupied with the pain of the proceedings to analyze what this could do to her future. She had thought Frank would be acquitted, that they could go back to their lives and gradually everything would be forgotten. She squeezed her eyes shut. Now her son was a convicted criminal, and she was attempting to educate other people's children. She covered her eyes with her hands. Mansfield had been victorious. He had killed them after all. She turned over onto her stomach and pounded the pillow with her fists. No! She would not give him the satisfaction, even in death, of ruining them. Frank was not guilty; he had been driven to shoot Mansfield in self–defense of the entire family. If Charles O'Conor had been young and willing to meet a challenge like Benjamin Phelps, she thought bitterly, he would have had Frank acquitted as easily as night turns to day.

She threw back the sheet and sat up, stretching her legs over the side of the bed. She felt like a person recovering from an illness, unsure whether her legs would be able to support her as she moved to the window. Opening the draperies and the shutters, she looked into the street below. People without a care in the world, except to be seen in the best possible light, were strolling past the house and into the park. A few glanced toward the white picket fence and the pines, but most were preoccupied with their own enjoyment of the moment.

She took a deep breath of the heavy summer air. She would have Frank pardoned, she thought. He was a gentleman, a lawyer, he had done nothing wrong. They would not remain Mansfield's victims. The tide of turmoil within her was subsiding. Beyond the curiously timed sense of calm, there was a new goal at hand: being all her family needed her to be. Their need was her strength. She would write letters to everyone she could think of, including the Governor and the President of the United States if need be, for Frank's release. She would circulate petitions, and she wouldn't stop until Frank was pardoned. If she held her head high, refused to be brought down by this wrongful occurrence, then others would not see them as a victimized family.

"I must find the highest mountain," she determined, "and claim it as my own. Perhaps we have failed, but only I can reverse our fortunes by not allowing myself to be a failure."

Chapter 34

Determination leads to a rocky precipice, and only a fierce will propelled by an indomitable spirit enables one to scale the rocks.

Ellen was afraid that her assistant, Otto von Below, would leave the school, and without him, she didn't know if it could be a success. He was not only invaluable, but also a dedicated educator, an exacting teacher of ancient and modern languages and mathematics. She steeled herself for his rejection, but when she timorously asked him whether or not he would be staying, he looked at her quizzically. "Why, of course, Madam. I wouldn't entertain even the slightest notion of leaving. I consider it a great honor to be associated with you and your school." She could have thrown her arms about him and wept with relief. Her spirits soared, and she threw newfound energy into planning for the coming year. To the already existing primary and advanced departments she added a special studies class for adults and announced that lectures on art would be given at various intervals throughout the school year. In the fall, the Walworth Academy opened its doors to as many students as had attended the previous year.

Her days fell into a routine of letter writing in the early mornings and the supervision of the school and her family the rest of the day. Evenings she tried to devote exclusively to Sarah and the children.

Every morning while she sipped her coffee, before she had even dressed, Ellen would write yet another letter soliciting evidence to support the contention that Frank was innocent by reason of insanity. She had devised a plan to write letters and circulate petitions to everyone she could think of, including Samuel Tilden, the Governor of New York; William Cullen Bryant, a family friend; the Honorable Augustus Bocke, Justice of the Supreme Court; as well as to more accessible influences, such as Reverend Trumball Backus in Schenectady. And, she thought more than once as she gritted her teeth, if need be, I will write them over and over until they either go mad or pardon Frank.

Letters came from Frank weekly, and each one brought a fresh, cruel pain. He had lost fourteen pounds in his first month at Sing Sing and had been apprenticed in the prison shoe shop. "Stupidity often saves a man from going mad," he wrote.

Sarah was grieving for Frank too, but she had begun work again for the restoration of Mount Vernon and the Washington Monument. In 1859, during a Masonic Convention in Chicago which the Chancellor had attended, Sarah had met with a group of women to lay plans to restore President Washington's home. But the war had disrupted the work, and not until 1871 had the first faltering efforts begun again. Although the cornerstone for the monument had been laid by the eleventh President, James Knox Polk, it had dragged along in an unfinished state.

Sarah planned to write letters to every city and village in the state of New York and to appoint an important official in every county as treasurer. She spoke of traveling to Chicago, New York City, or Washington, but she didn't seem to have the will or energy to carry the plans through. She was only sixty–three but had aged noticeably. Her cheeks were sallow, and her eyes sunken. She slept later in the mornings than usual and tired easily. Often, in the midst of her work, a conversation with a friend, or even a meal, Sarah would excuse herself and lie down.

"Mama," Ellen said one day as she watched Sarah struggle with her work, "why don't I help you? I could work with you for two hours in the late afternoon before supper, and together we could accomplish even more." Sarah was delighted, not only with the help, but with the close companionship as well. Every day at four o'clock, Ellen would carry a tray with a pot of tea, two cups and saucers, and sometimes a few cookies to the parlor, and the two women would write letters and exchange comments as they attempted to reach out and influence the patriotism of others.

"The monument of George Washington remains unfinished in the Capital of the Republic he founded," Ellen wrote. "If you revere his name and memory, will you not contribute your aid and your efforts to complete the great structure which is designed to commemorate his virtues, his sacrifices, and his devotion to the cause of human liberty?" The circular asked that all contributions, from twenty–five cents to five dollars, be sent to Sarah as vice president at Saratoga.

"Nelly," Sarah said reflectively one afternoon as she sipped her tea, "it is so satisfying to give something to one's country. My efforts are no longer needed by my family, yet I can still put my energies to a worthwhile project. Through this monument and the restoration, generations to come will always remember the struggle and the pride with which this Republic was founded, and you and I will have a small measure in that remembrance."

As the winter snows were melting and the first warmth of April was beginning to be felt, Ellen received an offer from a Mrs. A. B. Jones in New York City to rent Pine Grove for the summer for the sum of $500. It was infinitely easier to rent to one family than to several at a time and, relieved, Ellen began making plans to move the family into the cottage wing of the house.

191

Then came the news that Frank had suffered a heart attack. "It cannot be!" Ellen sobbed to Sarah. "He's not yet twenty! How long must this imprisonment go on before everyone sees it as needless persecution?" Her life lay in ruins about her, and she was helpless to stave off the tide of destruction that seemed always waiting to strike. "There is nothing I can do for Frank," she thought, as she fought an overwhelming pity for the life she had thought would be noble and gracious. "All I can do is keep so busy I can't think or hurt for him." She continued to receive letters from him weekly reciting the mundane news of prison life and sometimes including a poem or two. "I'm so glad to receive the poetry," she told Sarah. "It means he's using his mind. If he is using his mind and learning a skill at the same time, perhaps all is not wasted for him." His letters and poetry she read aloud to the family at supper, asking that Dolly, too, be present to hear them. One poem Frank dedicated to her, and with mute tenderness she smoothed the page and read it repeatedly.

To My Mother

Kings have their kingdoms, and Queens have their kings,
And thou of royal caste—O what has thou?
The star of empire glitters on thy brow.
And thou wast born, me thinks to regal things.
Great boon was thine: Seraphic beauty flings
Her twilight radiance round thee even now.
But fate to thee did nobler gifts allow,
For birth but props and Beauty hath fleet wings
A dauntless spirit, heart within control
Move in accordance with thy ruling mind.

"A dauntless spirit," Ellen murmured with tears in her eyes, "heart within control." If only he knew how hard she fought for control, how hard she fought to keep from giving in to total depression. "It is imperative to move in accordance with thy ruling mind," she thought resolutely, "if that is what my children see in me."

She kept his poem with her at all times so that when she was tempted to give up, when the sunlight seemed a cruel taunt to her own darkened spirit, she would read the words and find new strength.

In late spring she received a letter that Frank had suffered an acute attack of bronchitis. Her anxiety resulted in a vow to have his poems published. She was certain that seeing his words in print would breathe new life into him. But from all the publishers she contacted came the same reply. "I'm sorry, Madam, but the prominence given to the trial prevents our publishing his work at this time."

"Don't worry, Mama," Frank penned when she wrote him of her efforts, "this is just more proof that the wages of sin is death."

Due to his poor health, Frank was moved to the state prison at Auburn in early summer. There he would be allowed to work the land in hopes that the fresh outdoor air and exercise would strengthen him. "The prison doctor gave me much encouragement in getting rid of my lung condition," he wrote, "but has not given me any encouragement in getting rid of my heart condition. My heart condition, the doctor said, was brought on by my crime and durance."

Ellen was up early the morning of July 4, awakened by an unreasonable sense of dread, feeling the years stretching before her in a murky fog. She had made a pact with herself not to dwell any further on the future than necessity enforced. She could see only a few months at a time, and when she tried to think beyond that, there would be the murky fog and then grayness would descend on what should be light and joy.

She dressed hurriedly, hoping action would dispel the dread, and went outside into the morning coolness to make her plans for the day. She had promised the children a picnic by the lake, a promise which made Ruby squeal and dance in circles with delight, for they seldom left Pine Grove together.

At half past ten, Ellen went into the kitchen to supervise the lunch Dolly was packing for them. "Isn't Mama up yet, Dolly?"

"She didn't ring for her coffee yet, Miz Ellen, and I don' wanna disturb her."

"Take a cup of coffee to her, Dolly, and tell her I told you to. Remind her of the picnic."

Ellen had decided to wear her yellow dress. Perhaps if she dressed in a bright color, forgoing her usual browns and blacks, it would lift her spirits. This was a day of celebration, and she would fight to dispel any gloom that might gather within her.

She was brushing her hair when Dolly's cries reached her. "Miz Ellen! Come quick, come quick." Ellen started into the hallway just as Dolly came hurrying toward her. "Miz Ellen," Dolly almost shrieked, her eyes wide, "I think she dead!" Even as she hurried to the bedroom, before she opened the door and saw Sarah's still form in the bed, she knew Dolly was right. A sheet was pulled up to Sarah's waist and she lay in the bed as though sleeping peacefully, fully expecting at any moment to awaken and greet another day.

193

Ellen could no longer feel grief, only an endless exhaustion. Through the funeral service, through all the visits made by well–known and well–meaning people, she moved and spoke calmly and purposefully. She wanted to cry and grieve for her mother, but she couldn't. So much of her life had been spent in mourning that only an interminable ache was left for Sarah. Only when Ellen looked at Dolly, the kind, black face contorted by grief, the eyes barely able to contain her misery, did she feel that she, too, might crumble.

The day after the funeral, Ellen went to Sarah's desk, sat down, and started writing to everyone Sarah had previously contacted. She informed them of her mother's death and announced that she would be taking Sarah's place in this patriotic effort to restore the first President's house and to build a monument to him.

Pine Grove seemed a foreign land without Sarah. Ellen didn't brood, but the house was tomb–quiet. The Jones' family kept their distance, not wishing to intrude with their happiness upon the Walworth sadness. Even Ruby and Tracy tiptoed wherever they went, and Clara and Nellie often squinted through red–rimmed, swollen eyes.

Wednesday of the following week, Ellen received a letter from Frank, and, pouring a glass of cool tea, she took the letter into the backyard to read. It had rained all day on Tuesday, but now the sun was shining on a newly washed world. Ellen breathed the redolent smell of pungent pine deeply.

"She was so fond of me," she read after she opened Frank's letter, "entertaining such a high regard for my character and so indignant at the justice meted out to me. She seemed to me in the last year to have lost much of her old and natural manner of taking the world easily and good–naturedly. I cannot but connect her death in some measure to the wrongs that have been done me, and this mixture is a draught rather bitter to quaff. It is a deprivation, too, to be barred from the funeral rites and, more especially, from you in your sorrow."

Tears ran freely down her face for Frank, who had been prevented from attending his beloved grandmother's funeral, and for Sarah, whose death had undoubtedly been hastened by her family's troubles. She, Dolly, and the children were all bound by an invisible cord of grief for Sarah, but Frank was alone. If he grieved too much, if his guilt and loneliness became too much to bear, wouldn't his health be irreparably damaged, Ellen wondered? She got up from the bench and wiped her damp cheeks with the back of her hand. Walking slowly toward the house, she made the decision that had been playing about the edges of her mind since Frank had the heart attack. In order to reassure herself of her son's health, she would move to Auburn.

Chapter 35

In Auburn, Ellen found a small apartment from where she could easily travel to the prison to see Frank. Much to her relief, she found he had color in his cheeks and a hint of sparkle in his eyes that she hadn't seen since he left Georgetown. Yet there was a jaunty insolence about him that disturbed her, and she was startled to see a man where there had been a boy.

"I see the outdoor exercise agrees with you," she told him cheerfully when they were seated at the visitor's table.

"Dr. Wilkie speaks encouragingly of my improvement and ultimate recovery," he said. "I haven't had any of my worst attacks since the first two weeks I was here. I've gained weight; I'm now within four or five pounds of 160." He looked at her intently. "And you, Mother? Are you all right?"

"Of course. I just needed to reassure myself of your health. "I'm going to stay here in Auburn for a few months to be near you. Dolly and Clara are taking care of the younger children. It's so good for Dolly to have them near. She's suffering so."

Frank hung his head. "I shall miss Grandmother. I'm so sorry for all the pain I've caused."

Ellen saw Frank's shoulders heave and fall on a deep breath, but she remained silent. When Frank finally looked at her, she saw that pain and tears filled his blue eyes. "I'm not ashamed of myself at all. I still feel that although what I did may not have been right, it was necessary."

"Frank, there is no violence in your character. You have always been gentle and honest, and everyone who knows you realizes those qualities." Not trusting herself to speak further, she covered Frank's hand with her own. "What do you hear from Corinne?" she asked after a moment.

"I had a letter last week." He frowned, two creases deepening between the heavy, dark eyebrows. "When I went to Sing Sing, I told her not to write anymore." He sighed and ran his hand through his hair. "She has to forget us, because now there is no future. But still—she wrote."

"Of course. And she will continue to write," Ellen said emphatically. "She knows you, and she understands your actions. You're quite wrong about the future, you know. You will get out of here. I'll see to that."

Her own hopes often waned into bleakness, but Frank must never give up hope of being released, she thought fiercely. Being near him here in Auburn, her determination to secure his release became even sharper. Lucious Robinson, who had been a close friend of the Chancellor's, was the new governor. Perhaps he would review Frank's case with more compassion than his predecessor had. If she could influence Governor Robinson with her will, she thought, perhaps together they could make his release a reality.

Reassured that Frank was recovering his health, and away from the pressures of school and family, Ellen relaxed. She turned to books like a thirsty human turns toward water. She started writing poetry, the blank page a catharsis for her troubled soul. When she received letters from home, she took them to Frank on her visits, just as she had shared his letters with the family at supper. She received letters from Reubena often, always on blue stationery embossed with a rose.

"Ruby is showing signs of genuine artistic talent," she said to Frank one afternoon, "just listen to this letter."

> "Dear Mama,
> It is snowing and blowing out of doors, we woke up this morning to find the ground quite covered with snow. I have decided to put the butterfly on black cloth for Tracy's shaving thing. I am going to put runners on my doll carriage, and I have made one of them. I took a drawing lesson today. I drew your knitting basket with a piece of red silk in it and a spool and thimble."

Frank laughed. "It's good to hear you read the letter, Mama. It makes it seem like we're all together somehow. Reading them alone makes me feel removed and more isolated than I am."

"Have I told you," Ellen asked gently, "that Nellie is going to go to Europe with Father Clarence?" Frank looked at her in heavy silence. "I know. I received a letter from him last week, and he told me. It doesn't do any good, Mama," he said reading her mind, "to wish I had gone when I had the chance. Father would have harmed one of us sooner or later."

"He has," she said, surprised at the bitterness which twisted in her words.

In the luxury of peace and privacy, Ellen's mind began to stretch tentative tentacles into a future she had previously been afraid to imagine. She had a life to live beyond her family duties, an individuality to express that was becoming a tangible need. In an effort to untangle her troubled anxieties, she began to write down what was necessary for her existence beyond the ever–pressing need for money. "In addition to the

196

anxiety of feeding and educating my family," she wrote, "is the desire, the hope, for an intellectual life. Freedom for books, freedom for writing, freedom from the self–sacrifice of constant denial of the literature I need and desire. My working days and years are now, now, now! I must struggle on without tools and in spite of distractions and difficulties. I may conquer or I may fail, but I will at least have fulfilled my aspirations in the attempt to live on a high mental plane."

She paused and tapped the pencil on her front teeth. "And what to say about religion?" she asked herself. Catholicism had once aroused new light within her, new ideas and facts. It had taken her out of what she believed to be the blindness, the prejudice, of a thousand false conceptions and hindering opinions. It had offered a new world that was not only spiritual but intellectual as well. But when her troubles had started, and as they mounted and became overwhelming, she had found no solace in the Church. Only common sense and practical action was the groundwork upon which problems could be met and solved.

She picked up her pencil. "Not religion but honor," she wrote, "not sentiment but sense, not spiritual guidance but human sympathy or lonely courage are the arms with which this warfare must be waged." She put her head in her hands. "I have enlisted my little army under a religious flag," she thought miserably. "It has secured to me, as much as to most human beings, and especially to women, a belief in some of the accepted forms of religion. Such a belief is an absolute necessity; therefore, I cannot strip my children of this belief to which I have subjected them."

Gradually she was beginning to look beyond her confines. Worn to the point of exhaustion by the school and by the need to earn money, and torn by the trials and losses she had endured, she paradoxically felt a growing power within her, as if she could explode outward in a dozen different directions. Yet she was alone and empty–handed. When she would attempt to untangle her dilemma on paper, she could only question herself. What should I do? For what purpose should I live? What use can I be in this world?

If purpose eluded her, actions did not, and in the early spring of 1877 she returned to Saratoga rested, full of energy, and with the idea of writing a pamphlet about the Saratoga Battlefield and Burgoyne's campaign. Since she had first come to Saratoga she had been fascinated by the battlefield where her great–grandfather, John J. Hardin, on September 19 and October 7, 1777, had led a reconnaissance before the Battle of Saratoga. In the early days of their marriage, she and Mansfield had often taken picnics to the battleground. She never failed to be overcome by the sights and sounds her imagination conjured of that great battle, where Colonel Hardin had successfully fended off an attack by Burgoyne's Indian allies.

If she could make it interesting enough, she told herself, if she could only impart some of the romance and excitement she felt about it, the pamphlet could be extremely useful in her school. Children were taught ancient and world history, but they knew so little of the rich heritage upon which their own country was built.

When she read that a Women's Hall would be featured at the Centennial Exposition in Philadelphia, featuring domestic arts from women across the country, she decided that New York State should be well represented. But she was hesitant, still defensive about her family problems and the pity and infamy with which many people regarded the Walworths. Yet to stay shut up within herself, she decided, would be an admission of defeat.

With the help of Clarice von Below and Mary Putnam, she organized committees for the joint purpose of representing New York State at the Exposition and securing funds for the restoration of Mt. Vernon. Across the state, newspapers printed her appeal:

> "We, members of the local committee of Saratoga Springs, by the request of the New York Central Committee at Albany, appeal to you to cooperate with the women of the state raising a permanent fund for the repair of Mr. Vernon now falling to decay; also to aid in sending a banner to the Women's Hall of the Centennial Exposition to represent our state and testify our appreciation of the noble efforts the Philadelphia ladies are making to collect and exhibit women's work. All the Ladies of Saratoga and vicinity are requested to meet for the purpose of taking part in the noble work, undertaken by the women of the Empire State, of raising funds for the repair of Mt. Vernon."

The effort was astonishingly successful. Women eager to be of use outside their homes responded willingly. Lace work, oil paintings on slate, engraved work, and oil paintings on canvas, products of pride that until now had only been hobbies, found their way into the Women's Pavilion. Their skills no longer looked upon as feminine indulgences, women proudly had a place to showcase their talents and be congratulated upon their abilities.

Ellen was invited to Albany for the formal presentation of the Centennial Banner. She dressed joyfully in a red and black silk satin dress brocaded with red floral sprigs, black lace edging the three–quarter sleeves. How good it was to wear a color other than black, gray, and brown, she thought happily. She felt light and youthful, watching the culmination of her efforts as the New York State Centennial Banner, wearing the motto "Excelsior," was formally presented to the state of New York.

Nervously, she planned a reception at Pine Grove for all the women who had contributed their energy and talent to the Women's Hall project and for those who had solicited and given funds for the restoration of Mt. Vernon. In the *Saratoga Sun* she placed an invitation:

> "The Ladies of Saratoga are invited to call at my residence and see the vase presented to the New York Room at Mt. Vernon by Mr. J. F. Knickerbocker which will be forwarded in a short time."

It had been a long time since a social event had been held at Pine Grove. Dolly happily baked several different kinds of cake and polished the tea and coffee services to a high silver sheen. "If no one sees fit to come, Dolly, we will be awfully wide after eating all these cakes ourselves!"

But women did come. Curious glances flitted around the rooms and over the furnishings, but conversations centered on the Mt. Vernon fund and the Centennial Exposition.

"Congratulations, Mrs. Walworth," Anna Durkee said to her. "All of us have been able to take a small part in preserving history because you saw the need for it."

"Because my mother did," Ellen corrected her.

"Ellen, why don't you join the Shakespeare Society?" Bertha Proudfit asked. "We meet once a month and read and discuss the work of Shakespeare. We'd like to have you."

"Thank you," Ellen responded gratefully, "I'd like that."

Then a few weeks later, largely through the excellent reputation her school was gaining, she was invited to join the Art and Science Field Club. She was stunned. The Club was comprised of professional men, doctors, lawyers, professors, and clergymen. No woman had ever been invited to join the group before.

She spent her evenings working on the pamphlet about Burgoyne's campaign. With Clara's help and suggestions from Ruby she drew a map relating to the battles and surrender. Clara drew the military movements from maps made at the time of the war by Burgoyne's officers, as well as the natural features of the country from recent topographical surveys.

"Clara," Ellen asked one evening as she watched her daughter engrossed in the study of a map, "what do you think of the idea of organizing some of the students from our school and taking an expedition to the battlefield? Everyone can bring a lunch, and we'll picnic. Maybe I could give them an extra good grade for their effort."

"Then you could charge them more," Clara murmured absentmindedly.

"Clara! Nonsense. They'll be helping me."

The following Saturday, thirty laughing, excited students appeared at Pine Grove along with four parents to help Ellen keep them in line. "It's a good thing all of you came," she told the adults, "or I might have another battle on the field."

As the carriages rolled away from Pine Grove with the shouts and excited laughter of the students filling the air, Ellen had a momentary doubt that she would be able to keep them under control. "Well, the parents are here to help me," she told herself, "and I shall have to make it interesting enough for the children so they will take it seriously."

Once at the battlefield site she called for quiet, then began explaining the Revolutionary War and telling how that war had been necessary for America as a country. Her imagination didn't flag as she described the battles in vivid imagery, down to the sun glinting on the gun barrels. When she had the students' attention, she began handing out papers to them and grouped the children in teams of three. "With the data that is on your paper," she explained, "you are to find the location of each incident of the conflict. Remember, you are helping to commemorate the deeds of the founders of our Republic, and to stimulate an interest which may lead to every Revolutionary battleground in the country being marked with suitable monuments. And," she added with a laugh, "you must, you absolutely must, have a good time today."

As the students scattered, whooping and hollering over the peaceful grassy knolls, Ellen turned to Agnes Smith. "They don't exactly look like historical scientists," she laughed, "but this may awaken them to the history of their country."

At a meeting of the Shakespeare Society a few days later, William Stone approached her. "I hear you are writing about our battlefield, Mrs. Walworth."

"Yes. Burgoyne's campaign. My great–grandfather fought in that conflict, and perhaps because of that I'm more interested than many people."

"The Saratoga Monument Association is deep into plans for a monument to be built on the battlefield," he said. "We've engaged the architect J. C. Markham of New York City to help us. The problem, of course, is to gain enough support."

"Oh, I'm certain you will get support," Ellen told him earnestly. "I believe that a period has arrived in the intellectual development of our country when historical subjects can scarcely be claimed as belonging to a small class of people."

Mr. Stone smiled. "Mrs. Walworth, you are a credit to our community."

The following Wednesday, Ellen received an invitation to join the Saratoga Monument Association. As with the Art and Science Field Club, she was stunned. The Monument Association was also an all–male enclave. She reread the invitation. Now, she thought, now I have gained credibility as a teacher, and this will give my pamphlet full acceptance. She laid the invitation down carefully on her desk. "And I have been accepted," she thought. "I am seen as an intelligent woman who has something to offer beyond the confines of her home."

She was warmly welcomed at her first meeting of the Monument Association by all the men present. She sat ramrod straight on a small chair in the parlor of the U.S. Hotel where the Association met, trying not to cough through the rings of pipe and cigar smoke which floated about her. "They must not be allowed to smoke at home," she thought wryly as she blinked her eyes to keep them from watering. Most of the men were elderly, with the exception of William Stone and Aaron Stewart, and judging by their ages, she decided that the members' interest in history was merely to record their times before they were gone.

When she got home, Nellie and Clara were waiting for her. "I walked slowly so as to air out," she told them. "I was made chairman of the Committee on Tablets. I shall have to devise a means of arousing interest to secure funds for memorializing and marking in detail all points on the field. The reason I was chosen, I'm quite certain, is because there are only three of us with enough energy to do the job. Until now, I know the chief activity of that committee has been ossification. And," she said as she began laughing, "when the meeting was over we descended downstairs for refreshments into a room that had a mummy! They need me," she told the girls as she started upstairs still laughing, "they certainly need me."

Chapter 36

The morning of July 4, 1877, was colored by a wash of gold and not even a cumulus cloud marred the bright blue sky.

"What a remarkable year," Ellen marveled. Since the death of Sarah last July 4, the world had opened to Ellen and she had become a leading force in the community. "I know Mama would be proud." She never ceased to miss Sarah, often thinking, "I must ask Mama about—" only to be stopped short by her loss. Sarah would not have missed today for all the world, Ellen thought. She would have wanted to be in the first carriage going to the battlefield for the laying of the cornerstone which was to mark the Battle of Saratoga.

Ellen turned to look at the procession following her carriage. Carriages of civic leaders and masonic members stretched behind them, while farther back marched military units, followed by a band. "It's a splendid procession!" she cried out eagerly. "It must be two miles long!"

"I'll wager nothing like this has ever been witnessed in New York State," Aaron Stewart said as he leaned his head to the side to see the length of the procession. When they reached the battlefield, he jumped lightly to the ground and stretched out his arm to help Ellen from the carriage. "There must be at least forty thousand people here."

Standing between Aaron Stewart and William Stone as the Grand Master delivered his address, Ellen took a deep breath. "No one could possibly understand," she thought, "how filled with pride I am, standing on the same battlefield where my great–grandfather fought for the independence of his country. In my way, I am honoring his brave achievement." Tears filled her eyes as the Grand Master, in due and ancient form, presented the cornerstone. Then, one by one, articles were named to be placed inside the monument: The Saratoga County Bible Society presented a Bible; Alanson Welch, president of the village of Schuylerville, deposited a silver coin of George III dated 1777 and one of the United States dated 1877. A memorial of the opening of the New York and Canada Railway was presented by E. F. Bullard, and when her name was called, Ellen stepped forward with her pamphlet about Burgoyne's campaign.

After the ceremony, while the band played, Aaron walked with her to the long tables laden with food prepared by every organization in Saratoga. He's handsome, Ellen thought, with his slightly receding hairline and full, sensuous lips. But it was his eyes that somehow made him different from every other man she knew. They were large, brown eyes, but with a life in them that reached out intelligently to question and absorb all he came into contact with.

"Not only is this an important day for us and for the work we've been doing," he said as he handed her a cold lemonade, "but it's fun too, isn't it?"

Ellen looked up at him and laughed. "Fun, yes. I like that word. It's been a long time since I've used it."

As busy as she was, though, and despite her growing confidence as a presence in her community, lack of money was a constant threat. "How I would like to put my mind to higher pursuits than slaking the ever-present fear of poverty!" she raged more than once. Meals for the year had totaled $864, and her taxes had been raised from $125 to $140.

Summer visitors in Saratoga were often as bored as she was desperate. In the months of July and August the sidewalks were a continuously moving parade of pleats, ruffles, and laces, and hats that reminded one of bobbing flower gardens. They were Saratoga's wealth, these visitors, and Ellen decided to capitalize on them once again by offering classes in artistic needlework during the month of August.

Then, her back against the wall, she made the decision to sell the old stone barn that sat on the farthest corner of the property. Here the Chancellor had kept his Arabian steed, his horses, and his carriage. "Not sentiment, but sense," she had written in Auburn, and fighting the overwhelming blow to her pride from having to sell part of the property out of necessity, she netted $1600.

She sat at her desk, her mind conjuring images of the battle, and attempted to put it into story form. She enjoyed writing, enjoyed absorbing herself in intellectual work, even though it required frustrating lengths of time when words simply wouldn't come. She stood up from her desk, stretched, and walked to the window to try and catch a cool breeze. Just then Clara came breathlessly bursting into the room. "Mama! You have a letter from the Governor!"

Ellen grabbed for the letter and tore it open hurriedly.

"What does it say?" Clara asked demandingly as she edged behind Ellen to read over her shoulder.

Ellen read:

> "The jury, by their verdict, have found that the murder was neither premeditated nor deliberate. In that I fully concur.

The act must then have been the result of some sudden mental impression or condition, and it seems to me that it may well be regarded as a natural result of the continuing impression upon the prisoner's enfeebled intellect that his father was already in desire and intent his murderer and needed but this opportunity to become such in deed. The result of the interview was nothing but a fair manifestation of that unnatural condition of mind and body to which the father's long course of brutality, violence, and threats, and his own aggravated infirmity had brought the prisoner.

In that view, the act was as thoroughly the result of Mansfield's own passionate conduct as if he had himself discharged the fatal shot. The meeting of the two cannot be better expressed than in the words of the venerable William Cullen Bryant, who, in his letter asking for a pardon laconically says, 'If a jury were now to pass upon the evidence in the case, I think they would acquit the accused. The meeting between the father and son would be regarded as an encounter between two insane persons in which one of them was slain.' Therefore, I release Frank H. Walworth from the confines of the state prison."

"Mama," Clara cried with tears in her eyes as she threw her arms about Ellen's neck. "Oh, Mama, I have prayed so hard for Frank's release!"

Ellen hugged Clara to her, both of them shaking with relief and surprise as emotion welled up in Ellen's throat so that no sound was possible. When they could finally speak, Ellen went to the basin and poured cold water from the pitcher, and with shaking hands splashed water on her face and smoothed her hair. "Clara, don't tell anyone. Let's make this as great a surprise for everybody as we have just had. I'll leave tomorrow to get Frank and bring him home." Then she began to cry, tears of relief running down her cheeks, and at the same time she was smiling at her daughter. The prison doors had been opened for them all, and now sunlight seemed to flood not only the bedroom but their souls as well.

Chapter 37

Light cast a remarkable radiance over reality and the smallest detail seemed crystallized into every moment. Ellen felt as though she had just awakened from a very long sleep.

Yet it is possible to become so used to unfulfilled longings that they become part of one's personality, and the anxiety that had become so much a habit of her adult days hovered about her. As she watched Frank moving about the house, talking, or just sitting across the table from her, she would have the sudden feeling that all this was simply a benevolent dream, that any moment he would be snatched from them again, and she would awaken into her former life where sunlight was only a few slanting rays piercing the gray shadows of her existence.

Dolly had shed genuine tears when she first saw Frank standing in the hallway. Clara and Nelly had squealed and hugged him, and the house was filled with laughter, tears of relief, and happiness. Tracy followed Frank's every footstep, and Ruby, knowing her oldest brother as only a name, shyly curtsied. Clarence came home and joined the celebration, which included Sallie Bramlette and Corinne who were once again boarding at Pine Grove for the summer. Ellen was pleased to see the shining look in Corinne's eyes and the musical laughter that seemed to grace every remark Frank made.

Ellen kept her distance, letting Frank take his time coming home again. He went out for long walks every day, sometimes letting Tracy tag along, sometimes accompanied by Corinne, but he seemed to prefer going out alone. "Saratoga is still the same," he remarked one afternoon when he came in, "and yet, it isn't. Broad Street has been renamed Broadway. The new U.S. Hotel is larger and grander, there's a fine, new pavilion at Congress Spring, but other than that nothing has changed. Yet I feel like a stranger moving in disturbingly familiar territory that I can't seem to remember."

"It's you who has changed, Frank," Ellen said softly. Then, after a pause, she added briskly, "but that's inevitable. You would have changed anyway; and between the ages of nineteen and twenty–three, everyone changes!" She wished desperately that she could turn back the clock, give those lost years to him once again. But she was helpless to give him even the present, and could only hope he would enjoy the years left to him.

"I want to give a reception for you. Invite all our friends who would like to welcome you home."

Frank smiled indulgently. "It's not necessary, Mama, but if you would like to, it will be fine."

"I want our home to be a place of happiness again, a haven filled with friends and laughter."

Frank shrugged. "All right. Let me know if I can help."

She was enjoying herself and felt intensely alive. Dressed in a black moiré antique dress she graciously extended her hand to greet every newcomer. She was no longer afraid of Saratoga. She had been accepted, and her affiliation with the Art and Science Field Club had given her pride in her own intellectual powers and a confidence that she could fulfill herself as an individual. She had never enjoyed formal parties, but now she felt this was her victory party as much as Frank's. She had refused to be defeated, and she had won. Her pleasure at being surrounded by so many fine people, having her home filled with music and laughter once again, was mirrored in her sparkling eyes, in her erect but gracious posture.

On the sideboard was a tempting array of iced cakes and filled meringues. As Dolly passed trays of small watercress, cucumber, and ham sandwiches, Ellen moved from person to person, warmly clasping a hand, asking an interested question, or commenting on a gown. She welcomed Mr. C. F. Dowd, the principal of Temple Grove Seminary, and his wife. The two daughters of Horace Greeley arrived, one in a dress covered with massive, colorful embroidery, the other captivatingly plain in a simple, cream–colored silk, her dimples flashing with every smile. Corinne was resplendent in a silk lavender dress constructed to look like an underskirt with an open overskirt bunched up behind. She seemed to float toward Frank every chance she had, her admiration for him shining in her eyes as if he were a hero.

Frank's return had given Ellen renewed hope. "He's still young," she thought as she watched him. "He's been through much, but he still has time to become the brilliant lawyer the Chancellor envisioned. He will redeem his honor," she mused, "and the past four years will be forgotten."

Relieved by her success in securing Frank's release, Ellen felt free to devote her energies to other endeavors. Her pamphlet on the Battle of Saratoga and Burgoyne's campaign was published by the American Publishing Company, and in addition to being useful school material, it was proving to be popular among visitors and residents alike. Along with maps of the battles she had included a map of the village with a guide to drives in the vicinity of Saratoga. Placed in hotels, boarding houses, and newsstands through Saratoga, and selling for twenty–five cents a copy, it was snatched up eagerly.

She was also working on a novel, which she had titled *A Visit to the Battlefield*. While she was writing, her dream of a life of quiet intellectual activity was partially fulfilled, and she would emerge from the hours alone confident and proud for desiring and pursuing intellectual creativity. Those were the moments when she felt worthy of herself and of the promise life held.

Nellie was also writing a book. Inspired by her trip to Europe, Japan, and China, she had entitled it *An Old World as Seen through Young Eyes*. Proud of her daughter's efforts, Ellen believed that her namesake showed much promise as a writer.

Clara was planning on taking over many of Ellen's duties when school opened in the fall, and Ellen found she could rely on her to the extent that she felt Clara to be an extension of herself. Ellen remained perplexed though by Clara's seeming uninterest in boys or parties even though young men seemed to seek her out. She had even received two invitations to the hops at the U.S. Hotel this summer.

"Clara, you certainly seem to be getting very popular," Ellen remarked one evening as she sat doing some mending. "I saw William Breckenridge the other afternoon, and he asked about you." Clara looked at her directly, without a blush or giggle. "He's nice," she said noncommittally.

"You should encourage more of your friends to come to your home, especially your male friends." Ellen laid her mending in her lap and looked at her daughter's slim form, her shining brown hair, and bright blue eyes. "You're quite pretty, you know. Maybe just a tad too serious, but pretty. Before you know it, you'll be married and have a home of your own."

"Maybe not."

Ellen's eyes widened in surprise. "What do you mean?"

"I'm only interested in God's will, Mama, and to find that and do it is the only important matter in life."

Ellen frowned and picked up her mending again. "Well, I am certain that God's will for you is to find happiness in being loved and raising a fine family." When, a few days later, she noticed that Clara seemed to be immersing herself in books, but only books on Catholic literature, she felt an intense sympathy for her own mother's feelings toward herself in those long–ago days.

Frank was studying law with Joseph Hill again and writing poetry. He seemed laconical and often withdrawn, but he saw friends regularly, played billiards and whist, and began talking of taking up the new sport of bicycling.

Christmas came and went joyfully. With a pang, Ellen wished Sarah had been here for the first really happy Christmas they had enjoyed in a long time. With Frank's homecoming, despair had been banished; they were a family again, and Ellen's happiness was marred only by her endless financial struggle.

One winter morning as they were having coffee in the dining room, Ellen approached Frank on the subject of finances. "It would be a great help," she said to him somewhat tentatively, "if you could earn some money while waiting to be admitted to the bar."

He looked at her blankly. "I have very little time in which to hold a job, Mother, and I don't exactly know what I would do."

"I'm sorry I had to bring it up," she apologized, "but money is so scarce. Perhaps it is best if you study as hard as you can right now, after all. Working would only slow progress with your studies. When you are admitted to the bar, you will be able to support yourself and a family of your own with no trouble at all." When he didn't reply, Ellen narrowed her eyes and looked at him carefully. "Are you going to ask Corinne to marry you?" she asked pointedly. "She loves you very much, her affection for you is written all over her face."

"I don't know," he answered simply. "I'll have to finish my studies first and then decide."

"Corinne would make a fine wife for a rising young lawyer," she hinted.

"I didn't know you were a matchmaker," Frank teased. "Right now, all I can think about is the full day I have ahead of me." He rose and kissed her quickly on the forehead. "I'd better leave in self–defense," he said, pulling on his overcoat. She smiled as she heard the door open and close, and then she sighed. She would be relieved when he was finally an established lawyer, and when he was happily married.

She poured herself another cup of coffee and frowned as her thoughts turned once again to her lack of funds. Clara and Nellie were both old enough to help out financially. Clara had proven to be an excellent teacher of art and needlework, her quiet but firm demeanor enabling her to reach people easily. While Nellie was also artistic, she had become quite fluent in French on her tour of Europe, so it was possible she could tutor. But both girls were needed in the school, she rationalized, and she couldn't admit, even to herself, that having her daughters work outside the home would signal to the community the tight financial straits they were in.

Clarence was sending her money every month, Ellen thought guiltily, at least half his income. Well, there was only one of him, and the Church certainly wouldn't let him starve. On the other hand, there were seven in her household, counting Dolly, and the Church didn't care one whit whether they starved or not. She had only $60 on deposit at the bank; living on borrowed funds seemed the only answer to her predicament. Perhaps if she wrote to Clarence, he would contact the bank and enable her to borrow $300.

A week later she received an answer.

"Dear Sister,

I communicated your request to Mr. Olcott this morning. He says that ninety days from now (when your proffered note would be payable) you will have only $60 on deposit, as at present; which will not be a security for $300; and that the rules of the bank will not allow them to discount in that manner. It would, in any case, be a mistake in your circumstances to borrow. Better try, at once, to reduce your expenses to the limit of your means."

With barely suppressed rage she threw the letter to the floor. "Food! Fuel!" She spat the words out one by one. "Clothes! Education! All these to be maintained for a household, to be kneaded and worked out of a little piece of dough that can be swallowed in a year!" she cried aloud to the empty room. "Who can guess the horrible strain that must be expended to simply keep things going in bare decency and comfort?"

She lay down on her bed and stared up at the ceiling. What did other women do in such situations, she wondered? There were many women in worse circumstances than hers—or perhaps not, she thought wryly. There were not only widows, but single women forced to depend upon families, married women with husbands whom they couldn't depend upon for support. How ridiculous that women were expected to exist on their feminine charms when it was their talents and strengths that were needed!

She rose from her bed and walked to the window. Scratching frost from the pane, she peered out onto the street where two sleighs passed in opposite directions, the horses' breath puffing out of their nostrils in the cold air like the dragons in old stories. The snow muffled town noises, and even a shout of laughter in the distance emphasized the silence.

She thought of the meeting of the Decorative Arts Society she had attended in New York when she was appealing for domestic arts for the Women's Pavilion. She had been impressed by the society's aim, which was to offer guidance and assistance to women who were struggling to support themselves, and those dependent upon them. She aimlessly blew her breath on the glass and moved a finger over it. She had no talent in domestic arts, nothing above what was needed. Even though she herself had nothing to offer to alter her own unfortunate financial position, perhaps she could start an auxiliary of the Decorative Arts Society here in Saratoga and help others.

On March 28, Ellen mingled with a group of 120 women assembled in a room of the town hall. She had spent the past few weeks writing and rewriting a speech to persuade the women of Saratoga of the necessity for a local branch of the Decorative Arts Society. Even though she no longer feared rejection, as she waited to stand in front of the lectern, her throat felt dry and her hands clammy. When she was introduced, the sound of her name caused a peculiar, twisting sensation in the pit of her stomach, and she walked toward the front of the room with a smile that felt pasted onto her face.

"As far as ornamentation is concerned," she began in a voice that shook, "it is the aim of this society to direct your interest, your talents, and your efforts only toward such ornamentation as is worthy of thought and labor." She took a deep breath. "I would assure you that I have no personal influence or interest in this association! It has, however, one objective with which I feel the most intense sympathy, one that inspires one with enthusiasm." She gripped the lectern with both hands and looked out over the audience. "We all know that many dressmakers, boarding–house keepers, teachers, writers, and artists are laboring not only for their own livelihood but for the sustenance of husbands, fathers, children. There are women whose intellectual life is active, whose talents are pure, genuine, and elevated, and whose spirits are invincible. They are an army of living martyrs, of unknown heroines, of silent toilers whose monuments will be found in the character of children whose lives they have molded or influenced, and in the prosperity of fellow sufferers whom they have stimulated to greater efforts that are covered with laurels they might not wear." Her voice was stronger now and her timidity forgotten in her earnest plea to elevate women as wage earners and save them from victimization.

"I beg that you would not think I would reflect on all the men whose wives and daughters are working in this way. I congratulate the women of today upon their release from the servitude that was implied by that helplessness and insanity in which they were once encouraged and admired. There is dignity in labor for women as well as for men, and it is by the elevation of women from mere domestic drudgery, and imitative, tawdry fancy work to a standard of intellectual strength and artistic excellence that we will be enabled to assist all who are dependent upon us and to encourage and inspire all who surround us. We have three main objectives: First, to assist those who have worked unsuccessfully to choose some practical and popular direction for their labor. Second, to form connections with manufacturers and importers, and to obtain orders from private individuals and from dealers in decorated pottery, china, tiles, cabinet work, carvings, draperies, embroideries, and articles of household art. Third, to furnish a market, outside of a limited circle of friends, for the large amount of artistic work, done by those who do not make it a profession, but who have attained a professional skill in execution."

The society was formed within a month, and Ellen was chosen President. The group's first act was to offer lessons in sketching from nature using charcoal, as well as to give lessons in oil painting. A very good teacher was found who taught during the winter at an art school in Hartford, Connecticut, and would be only too happy to spend her summers in Saratoga.

Ellen's summer was as filled with activities as the village of Saratoga was with people. She took in boarders again and took charge of plans to hold an exhibit in the Arcade for the Decorative Arts Society. She planned and took expeditions with the Art and Science Field Club and began working closely with Aaron Stewart on a plan to place monuments on the Saratoga Battlefield marking the places of important skirmishes.

In the middle of August, the Decorative Arts Society's exhibit opened. The evening air was soft and moist; only a slight breeze stirred as Ellen, Clara, Nellie, and Ruby hurried toward the Arcade. Frank and Corinne walked a few paces behind. Now and then Clara or Nellie would look over their shoulders at the pair behind them, say something to Corinne, and then dissolve in nervous giggles. Clara and Corinne had worked diligently all summer on their needlework, the best of which was displayed in the exhibition. Nellie had submitted a pencil sketch entitled, "Window," and Ruby had a fine watercolor of a bird's nest on display.

The Arcade was crowded, and the noise of laughter and bright spirits reached their ears at the entrance. Any real conversation was an impossibility, and they had to shout greetings to friends. In addition to the talents displayed, there was a large collection of antiques loaned by some of the wealthiest families in town. Ellen had generously loaned a rich and handsome Egyptian scarf given her by Sarah and had also given an Indian shawl, which had been presented to Sarah by a Hungarian gentleman.

Congratulations flowed from one person to another as items were viewed, and throughout the room could be heard comments such as, "You mean you did that?" "I didn't know you were so talented," or "Could you teach me?" Ellen watched the shining eyes, the smiles of pride from the contributors, and saw her own daughters try to contain the joy and pride they felt as they saw their talents admired.

Later, they walked home through the streets thronged with people enjoying the night air and stopped at the U.S. Hotel to admire the new gas lamps. From the lawns of the other hotels on Broadway, Japanese lanterns bobbed brightly in the breeze. Ellen marveled to herself how easy it was to organize committees to carry out a purpose. Yet, inside her home, she thought quizzically, all was a constant chaotic struggle.

Later that night, as she was getting ready for bed, she wondered if she was attempting too much. She was trying to take her duties one at a time, but so often conflicting demands seemed to press upon her at once. "Perhaps I am attempting an impossibility," she sighed. Trying to sustain a plain, simple style of living seemed best for the health and happiness of the family, yet on the present income it was next to impossible. She lay down on her bed, pulled the sheet over her, and felt the welcoming breeze coming through the windows. "Perhaps I should sell this old house. The school is successful, but because of its success, it takes a great deal of planning and most of the profits have to go back into it to keep it operating. If I sold the house, we would all have to scatter, go wherever we could to find positions, and that would mean Tracy and Ruby being pushed out of the home before they were ready. "No," she decided, "the home must be maintained until the children voluntarily abandon it." She sighed. The labor, the time, and the responsibility all seemed more than she could bear. She pressed her palms against her eyelids and wondered if she could will herself to sleep. Music from the hotels had ceased and the streets were silent. From off in the distance, she could hear the singular sound of a barking dog.

She rolled onto her side and turned back to a recurrent thought, writing a biography of her father. Whether or not she could bring him to life, put his intelligence and vigor between the pages of a book, remained to be seen. It would be necessary to travel to Kentucky to interview friends and relatives. And, of course, she would have to return to Jacksonville. Maybe she could see Mary again. As she drifted off to sleep, she could feel the warm prairie wind, the intense light of the land encompassed by a wide blue sky, and feel the open space welcoming her.

Chapter 38

A s the train rocked and lurched its way into Kentucky, Ellen suppressed a desire to daydream and give herself to the passing landscape. She opened the *Magazine of American History* again and reread the article she had written on *The Battle of Buena Vista*. She had hoped it would enhance her credibility as an historian, as well as enable her to hone her skills on the manageable article before she set about the task of a biography. When it had been published, she was encouraged to go ahead with the story of John Hardin's life and had brought the magazine with her to lend stature to her abilities while she interviewed family and friends.

In these past few days on the train, she had taken advantage of the peace and quiet and anonymity that surrounded her and had put the finishing touches on her fictional romance, *A Visit to the Battleground*. It wasn't too bad, she thought, as she read through it again. Perhaps the characters were a bit stiff, but all in all, she had defined the work rather well, and she believed readers would feel the battle come to life through the eyes of her characters. She sighed and leaned her head back against the coach seat. There was so much she wanted to say, and hoped to accomplish. In the act of writing she found the solitude she needed, the escape her mind needed from the petty trivialities of everyday life, and the only way to use the history which had come to mean so much to her. She possessed the zealot's desire to record and preserve that which her family had made.

There was a primal feeling in being back on Kentucky soil again, in walking on the land that had nourished her father's and her mother's family, this land into which her roots grew deep.

Her uncle, aunt, and cousins in Frankfort welcomed her warmly. After her years of living in Kentucky, of Sarah traipsing back and forth between here and New York, Ellen and her Hardin and Smith relatives had grown apart and only occasional letters held them together.

In an effort to find more of her relatives or acquaintances who had know John Hardin and his family, Ellen placed a notice in the Frankfort *Daily Yeoman*.

> "Ellen Hardin Walworth is visiting Kentucky for the purpose of gathering materials for a proposed life of her father, including a sketch of the Hardin family. Her grandfather, Martin D. Hardin, was a distinguished Kentuckian who was a soldier in the War of 1812, Secretary of State under Shelby, and a U.S. Senator."

It was almost Christmas, and the homes were festive but hectic with gifts to buy and puddings and cakes to be steamed and baked. The Hardin home festooned with swags of ground pine, bunches of holly, and mistletoe hung in the doorways. It was a celebration in the best Southern tradition, with parties to attend and more relatives calling than Ellen knew she possessed. She was deliriously happy to reaffirm her place among them once again, but the one problem she hadn't considered was the painful recounting of her life. She had not completely realized to what extent misfortunes made up her life, so that without reference to her difficulties it was necessary to remain silent. Even though they were too polite to ask about her problems, her Southern family had heard about them, so there was nothing she could hide. Her problems had undeniably made up the fiber of her life. She could gloss over them, but they existed, had even given her a certain notoriety, and she couldn't deny them. She had never confronted her life through a stranger's eyes, and now the pitying looks directed her way, the catch in mid–sentence of a speaker who was about to utter a truth that might carry a germ of hurt in it was too much. Did the sum of her life really add up to a total of pity, she wondered in bewilderment.

She recounted again and again Sarah's last few years and her accomplishments with the restoration of Mount Vernon and the Washington Monument Society. It was good to talk about her mother with these people who had known and loved Sarah since childhood. She could almost feel Sarah's presence with them as they talked, and here she no longer felt her mother's loss.

She learned much about her father, his aristocratic bearing, his confidence in himself, his competitiveness. Through her relatives' words she met him as a boy, then a young man, and, finally as a successful husband and proud father.

They had heard of Mansfield's death and Frank's incarceration, but Ellen's words dwelled on Frank's release, on his recent decision to practice law with a friend in New York City. She placed great emphasis on her community work, the success of her school.

"I do so admire you, Cousin Nelly!" Ruth blurted out one evening. "You have had such a hard life, but your aim is to fill it with useful things. Here I am, all I do is go to parties and give them."

Ellen laughed. "Gaiety counts, Cousin Ruth. The most wasted life is one filled with no usefulness whatsoever."

The sometimes mild, sometimes—chilly days of January sped by, and in early February she left for Louisville and a reception with more of her extended family.

She noticed, with some amusement, how stiff her relatives were with her at first. It was not just the shyness of people searching for common ground but a readiness to offer her sympathy while trying in apology to hide the happiness of their own lives. A broken spirit people can deal with, she thought. A shy, trembling woman coming back to her roots for sustenance, that they can understand. But to be unable to shower her with pity, however kindly directed, and instead to hear her speak of her triumphs, that perplexed them.

Lemuel had been a step ahead of her and surprised her with the announcement he had placed in the *Louisville Courier—Journal*:

> "The leading article in the *Magazine of American History* is an account of *The Battle of Buena Vista* by Mrs. Ellen Hardin Walworth. It is a very comprehensive, as well as exceedingly vivid and vigorous description of that famous battle, written in a graphical and forcible style rarely mastered by a feminine hand. She is now visiting friends in Louisville and is collecting material for a biography of her father."

She stayed with Lemuel and Annie at Cozy Lodge, the home they had built on the grounds of Bird's Nest after it had been sold. Cozy Lodge was a perfect cottage, a gem of love holding Lem, Annie, and their two children. Only serenity and happiness reigned here, Ellen thought. Annie's life was devoted to Lem and their children. The gifts of grace and happiness she possessed caused the house to sparkle not only with order and cleanliness but with love as well. At Cozy Lodge Ellen could relax, she had nothing to hide from Lem and Annie. She spent her days writing and visiting with family and old friends.

She was invited to Bird's Nest one April afternoon by the people who now owned it, the Breedens. They sat in the sunshine in the exquisite rose garden, its bare form promising perfection in another few months. But the ghost of the uncertain creature she had been when she lived there made her uncomfortable and gave her the feeling once again of the failure she had felt herself to be in those long ago days. For the rest of her stay in Louisville she felt the uneasiness of trying to escape those past years.

In early May she left for Jacksonville. To see one's home after more than twenty years, to find the town thriving but not be a part of it, is to ghost walk through the haze of the past. She stayed at the Duncan home, that great white house she had so taken for granted as part of her young life. Few things inside the house had changed. The furniture looked the same, everything in its accustomed place, and here she truly felt she had come home. It gave her the feeling that any moment she would revert to a young girl again, that being away from here and all grownup was only a momentary peek into a future which really hadn't arrived. But it was Mrs. Duncan's presence which brought her back to the present. In place of the vital, energetic woman who had seemed so progressive and modern, Ellen found a woman grown frail and elderly, leaning upon a cane for support and talking in a slow, sometimes cracking voice. Of all the cruel things in life, Ellen thought, time is the cruelest.

She immersed herself in the past as she stood in front of the house she was born in, then walked to the large brick house her father had built for her mother when it seemed his future was a shining light beckoning him to political brilliance.

Mrs. Duncan accompanied her when she rode to the cemetery where John Hardin rested, his grave marked by the tallest obelisk there. She recalled with pain that day he was buried, some sixty thousand people around the graveyard, and Abraham Lincoln and Stephen Douglas standing near the shocked family, their heads bowed and lips grimly held in a thin line as their once vibrant friend was buried.

What shocked her was how necessary this visit was in the far reaches of her soul, the necessity to finalize what had been so unexpectedly interrupted. But what she hadn't counted on was the pain. She was no longer a part of Jacksonville. She hadn't expected to be, of course, but it was such a vital part of her she had expected her place here to still exist.

In the evenings after dinner, after a decent interval of conversation with Mrs. Duncan, she poured out her emotions onto paper, writing page after page of anecdotes told her by family and friends. Perhaps, she thought more than once, perhaps this task was beyond her. There was no comparison between an article in a history magazine and the riveting life of a vigorous man. Whether or not she could capture his inward fire filled her with doubt, yet she had to try, possibly for the same reason she had had to come back to Jacksonville.

She left Jacksonville eagerly to travel to Davenport, Iowa, and a visit with Mary. She had needed the information and contacts in Frankfort, Louisville, and Jacksonville if she were to write her father's biography, but since she had left Saratoga, the excitement she had felt was for her visit with Mary. As soon as the big door of Mary's house opened wide, Ellen was a young girl again, talking and laughing with the closest friend she had ever had. A bond existed between them, Ellen thought, a bond that was tighter than any she had ever known. Never had she been so close to anyone in the same way, not with Mansfield and his family nor with any other friends.

216

Dinner in the high–ceilinged, richly appointed Putnam dining room was epicurean, and Mary's husband, Charles, treated Ellen as if he had known her for years. "Indeed he has, Nelly," Mary bubbled, "all he has heard about are my references to you in all that I have said and done. We have always been closer than sisters."

In the days to come they were together every minute Mary could spare from her six sons and one daughter. She and Charles had had eleven children, but four had died during childhood. Mary's pride in her children centered on her eldest son, twenty–four–year–old Joseph, who was avidly interested in scientific subjects, particularly entomology. He was as devoted to his mother as she was to him. When he was invited to become a member of the Davenport Academy of Natural Sciences, he said he would accept only if his mother were allowed to become a member, since she had encouraged and supported his interests for so long.

Time may have assailed Mary, Ellen reflected, but it hadn't dimmed her enthusiasm nor taken the sparkle from her deep–set blue eyes. Her blonde hair was now washed with gray. She was short and plump and flitted about like the proverbial mother wren. With a tinge of envy, Ellen noticed the obvious adoration Mary had for her husband, who was a successful Davenport attorney. He had given Mary the means for a brilliant social life, and she had servants who freed her for time with her children, to participate in their interests and encourage them every step of the way. Mary was living Ellen's dream.

Only to Mary could Ellen admit her disappointment in life, in her children, without apology for herself. Their friendship was deep enough not to be rocked by one woman's troubles, or to be overwhelmed with envy by one woman's happiness.

They spent several afternoons shopping, and Ellen felt once again like a carefree young girl stealing away from home for the afternoon. "I never do this, Molly," she laughed with delight.

Mary smiled. "I enjoy it very seldom as well, for with so many children, as you know, it's difficult to get away from the house. But we must buy gifts for you to take to your family. They will be presents from me," Mary offered tactfully. They bought paints and brushes for Nellie and Reubena, several yards of silk material for Clara, and a tie pin for Frank. "And Tracy?" Mary inquired. "What would he like?"

"Perhaps the same thing we get Frank." Ellen paused a moment. She squinted into the sunshine as they stopped in front of a shop. "Oh, Molly, I'm so afraid something is wrong with Tracy, and if there is, I won't be able to face it!"

"What do you mean?"

217

"His nerves are bad. He has tantrums, throws things, and gets angry and yells. Then afterwards, he cries for hours. It isn't right for an eighteen–year–old boy, and I don't know what to do."

"Oh, Nelly, no."

"I think about Mansfield and wonder what hideous substance he possessed that he might have passed on to his son. Molly, I'm so sorry to tell you, it's been such a perfect day. But I have not told anyone, and the fear is so difficult to deal with alone."

It did her no good to envy Mary her home, her husband's love, or her serenity, Ellen realized as she started packing to return to Saratoga. Whatever fate had destined for her, it was not the warm home life she still desired above all else. She had only one choice if she were to live with any dignity, and that was to reach out beyond herself with her energy, her mind, and her talents.

She returned to Saratoga in time to open the house to summer boarders, but with a strong determination to work on her father's biography and not get lost in the small details of everyday life. She longed to close herself away from the constant demands, to live a Spartan routine with no obligations beyond her own intellectual life, one which would let her explore all her thoughts on paper. But one cannot shut out obligations without enclosing oneself in a vacuum, and the boarders were a necessary source of income.

For the first time, she wanted to push away her civic responsibilities and bask in intellectual solitude. She had willingly, even eagerly, become a member of the Monument Association, and to quit now would be to shirk a responsibility which she believed in. It was possible, she often thought, that through the pioneering efforts of the Saratoga Monument Association every revolutionary battleground in the country might one day be marked with a suitable monument, and the most noted battlegrounds might become public parks.

During the six months she had been away, the U.S. Government, mainly through the exertions of John Starin, had appropriated $30,000 for the Saratoga Monument. J. C. Markham had designed a splendid edifice with women of the Revolution depicted on the granite. The proposed carving was to show one woman standing and holding a rifle, one sitting at a spinning wheel, and one cooking at a fireplace while three frightened children huddled to the right. Also to be chiseled on the stone were the figures of General Schuyler transferring his command to General Gates.

"I'm honored that Mr. Markham has thought to put women on the edifice," she remarked to Aaron Stewart one evening as he walked her home from a meeting. "Women suffer much more than men, I believe, because they can take so little action. So much of a woman's bravery is manifested only in waiting and trying to create a sense of normalcy and home in spite of the ravages of war."

Aaron stopped and laid his hand on Ellen's arm. In the reflection of the street lamps, Ellen could see an intensity in his eyes, and with surprise, sense a need in him. "It's because of you, Ellen, because of your presence on the committee that the women's part in the Revolution was thought to be depicted." His eyes sought and held hers with a curious hard look and her heart leaped. Neither spoke, but an intense longing beat in her with such force that she felt overwhelmed. "Well," she said after a moment, "what can I say?" She brushed an imaginary strand of hair back from her face in an effort to erase her self-consciousness. "I'm quite honored."

They walked on, Ellen conscious only of the strong male figure beside her, the presence of a strength and intelligence wanting her.

At the steps of Pine Grove she paused uncertainly. "Would you like to come in for a cup of tea?"

Aaron smiled, and in a voice tinged with regret he answered, "No, thank you. I must go on home."

She entered the house feeling like another person, a person for whom one glance, one touch had transformed the world.

Chapter 39

No matter where she went or what she did, all she could think of was Aaron Stewart's eyes fastened upon hers. She flew through her days, laughing easily, and though she tried not to, she found herself mentioning his name frequently just to have some part of him acknowledged. Happiness felt good.

Sitting in front of her dressing mirror one evening, she marveled at the miracle which had brought him into her life. She had given up hope of ever loving again, and even in the midst of a busy day, loneliness had often assailed her. She had never been able to rid herself of her girlish dream of sharing evenings before the fire with an adoring husband in a well-appointed home, laughingly recounting the events of their days. "The reason I have never been able to rid myself of that image," she thought happily, "is that it is still to be!"

She looked at her reflection critically and felt profound astonishment that at the age of forty–nine she could fall in love. Her face was plump, she noted with chagrin as she turned her head to the side. Too plump, and with sudden consternation she tried to encircle her thick waist with her hands. "Forty–nine is not young and there is no use pretending it is," she murmured aloud at her reflection. Her skin was still smooth and unlined, and her large eyes shown brightly with a lively intelligence of which she was proud. Placing a finger at the outside corner of each eye, she drew the skin taut, but the corners still turned down. "Perhaps I was marked from birth for trouble the way those corners turn down." Very little gray streaked her hair, and now she carefully drew the comb through it for a center part and piled it on top of her head. Moistening her fingers with water, she crimped her hair into curls at the front of her face on either side of the part.

In spare moments when she was alone, Ellen would close her eyes and see Aaron's face before her. She wondered how it would feel to have his arms about her, holding her tightly, and what it would feel like to lead a life of perfect peace with him, to have a union in both work and repose. It might be a life based on the commonplace, yet in its very simplicity, existing far above the commonplace. "That must be what he needs, too," she often thought. "That must be what he desires in me." He had made no more advances toward her but remained warm yet carefully courteous when he saw her at meetings. Though perplexed by his distance, she reminded herself that he had volunteered to work on every committee she was on.

She pushed her black, brown, and serviceable gray dresses to the back of her wardrobe and chose a dress of blue French muslin. She dressed carefully as though she had just discovered the possibilities she contained. It would be nice to be young and have her entire future before her, with everything fresh and exciting, she reflected as she struggled to fasten the dress. Still, she wouldn't want to trade what she felt now for those uncertain days of her youth. She had risen above her doubts, her dreams, and her suffering, and now she could use all her experiences and glorify them in the thoughts and actions of her maturity. "That is the achievement of years," she told herself, "being able to gain mastery of oneself and one's fate, learning to use the experience and feelings of the different stages of life so they are like tools in the hands of human will, enabling one to think on with wisdom, dignity, and power."

"There are still cares, responsibilities, and decisions to be confronted and adjusted," she mused, "but still there has been satisfactory success in many things." Her writing was an advance toward the life of intellectual activity, but self–sacrifice was still necessary for her family. Yet, by cultivating wisdom and calmness, she felt certain she could guide her children on their chosen paths.

Frank was practicing law in New York City, and Tracy had recently entered Georgetown Medical College. She was desperately hoping that by using his mind for serious study Tracy's nervous condition could be alleviated

Nellie was busy writing her next book, which she had titled, *The Lily of the Mohawks*. It was the life of Kateri Tekawitha, the Indian maiden who had lived from 1656–1680 and had been converted to Catholicism. Up until now the story had been known only to historians.

The quiet, studious trait her children seemed to possess filled Ellen with pride. They were all fond of literature and art, Nellie and Frank emphasizing literature and Clara and Reubena both talented artists.

Clara was currently staying with Clarence in Albany and working as his amanuensis. Clara's studious and religious nature disquieted Ellen, and she hoped Clarence was encouraging her daughter to an active and useful life, one that would be both productive and social. Ellen strived to present herself as a model for Clara, hoping that her activities would influence her daughter to see that it was possible to lose oneself in intellectual activity, work in one's community, and still have a family.

221

As much as she was concerned with her children, it was a nice respite having only Nellie and Ruby at home. Ellen and Ruby were growing closer every day. She felt that her youngest child was a stabilizing influence, and her thoughts often dwelled on what she must do and be "for Ruby." Ellen had always felt guilt at having to neglect her so often, but with all the turmoil in her life, it had been impossible to give the child the attention she deserved. At thirteen, Ruby was growing into a beauty, with tiny, delicate features and blonde hair that swirled about her face in wispy curls. Everything about Ruby was wispy, Ellen noted, her movements, her voice, her very presence. Mansfield had been right when he referred to his daughter as "a fairy princess." Yet beneath her winsome exterior lay a serious demeanor, an implacable will, and a tangible talent. Her interest in art had been a trait that defined Ruby from childhood, and instead of being distracted by other pursuits, her interest had only grown stronger, and her talent more controlled.

A hard rain had fallen persistently for days, and it gave Ellen the cozy feeling of being encased in a cocoon. She looked forward to a day of few demands, happily sheltered within the walls of her room, working on the biography of her father. She was deep in concentration when Dolly interrupted her thoughts with a knock at the door. "Miz Ellen, you got compny."

"Who is it?" Ellen asked expectantly as she rose from her chair and hurried to the dressing mirror to check her appearance.

"Miz Watson," Dolly murmured softly as she moved slowly down the hall.

Ellen felt a plummeting disappointment. "Tell her I'll be there in a moment." She took a deep breath. "You silly fool," she reprimanded herself, "did you expect him to call on you in the middle of the afternoon?"

"It's nice to see you, Lydia," Ellen greeted her friend. "I didn't expect any calls with this rain pouring down."

They seated themselves in the parlor, and Dolly passed cups of hot tea. "Can you imagine wanting hot tea in July?" Ellen laughingly asked. "But it's chilly out there; I don't want you catching a cold making a social call."

"This isn't purely a social call," Lydia said as she stirred a spoonful of sugar into her tea. "I'm here to ask a favor of you." She set her cup and saucer on the table beside her. "As you know, the legislature recently passed a law allowing women to sit on school boards. Since you run a successful school, many people in town think you could do the schools in Saratoga a great favor by agreeing to run for election."

"Who else has been asked?"

222

"No one yet. But there are three openings, and it has been suggested that Jane Andrews and Mary Lee Hurd run with you."

Ellen took a sip of her tea. "I have never understood," she reflected aloud, "why women have been prevented from sitting on school boards. We bear children, raise them, teach them values, and see to their education as far as we are able, and we are allowed to earn a living by teaching in the schools. Yet–" she pursed her lips and shook her head slightly in a gesture of bewilderment. "Will there be a planning committee for a campaign?"

"Definitely. I have to warn you though, just because the law now allows women on school boards doesn't mean everyone will be happy about it. There will be many who are opposed to the idea."

Ellen took another sip of tea. "I started in '76 with a determination to do just what I feel capable of doing without regard to customs, as long as it is right and dignified. I decided I could honor outside commitments as long as they allowed me to preserve my family life and keep my personal influence in my family intact."

"You have been outspoken," Lydia reminded her, "in wanting women on the Board of Education."

Ellen gave her a rueful smile. "I guess I can't very well say no then, can I?"

The biography was not forgotten, but by necessity pushed into the background as Ellen attended teas and receptions, always eager to give her views on the objectives of the school board. The three women were invited to a forum discussion at the town hall to which the general public was invited. Before they took their places on the platform, and as the hall began filling with people, Jane Andrews whispered, "I dread this. We are not wanted on this board by many of the people in town. They are saying that we aren't capable of discharging onerous and disagreeable duties and that we will feel very much out of place on the board."

"And if you're afraid to speak out now," Ellen whispered sharply, "you are only agreeing with them." Seeing the hesitancy in Jane and Mary Lee, Ellen stood and opened the forum herself by explaining why women were needed on school boards, citing as the main reason that no one knew the needs of children better than a mother did. Now and then she paused, hoping that Jane or Mary Lee would join in. They were perched uncomfortably on the edges of their chairs, Jane's face flushed, Mary Lee looking cold and stern. There was nothing to do, Ellen thought, but plunge in. "We find, upon examining the responsibilities that will be delegated to us by the citizens of this village, that the Board of Education has three nurslings to attend—the children, the teachers, and the taxpayers. For the children we have the assistance of the teachers, but for the teachers and the taxpayers, I will admit that we may be in the beginning somewhat like the old hen with the first brood of ducks. They look rather strange to us, and we may be puzzled at their novel ways, so you must not be surprised if we flutter around a good deal for a while; and if we should be tempted to pull you out of a pond or mud puddle or rut, you will at best credit us with good intentions."

What was first seen as merely a challenge and a novelty soon gave way to real concern as more and more people in town began questioning the advisability of having women on the board.

"They want nothing more than to take control of the board," an editorial in the newspaper began, "and they can do nothing more than sit there if they are elected."

Ellen was incensed when she read in the *Saratoga Eagle*:

> "Mrs. Walworth is a lady of beauty and culture, and with varied charms of mind and manner is well adapted to shine in social circles. We have no good word for her as an official and politician, because we honestly think she deserves none."

Into the fury came a letter from the Honorable Neil Gilmour, State Superintendent of Public Instruction:

> "Three members are to be elected this fall, and why not three women to deal with the twenty–six women teachers. It is not an untried experiment, for ladies are serving with great success upon the school boards of Boston and several other places."

"Do they think we have no brains at all?" Mary Lee cried indignantly one afternoon as she and Ellen sat in the parlor of Pine Grove, commiserating on the attacks against them.

"It's to be expected, I suppose," Ellen answered quietly. "People are always afraid of something new, and this is definitely a new idea."

"It does hurt, though, for people to think that because one is a woman one can have no ideas." Mary took a deep breath and rubbed her forehead for a moment. "My husband is asking me to withdraw my name because of the attacks. He is afraid he will be made a laughingstock."

224

"If you pull out now, Mary," Ellen said sternly, "he will be a laughing stock, for you will defeat yourself."

At every meeting she attended she dressed carefully and hopefully, expecting to see Aaron in the audience watching her with pride, silently cheering her on. But after each meeting she came home disappointed with a desultory sense of relinquishment dogging her every step.

She hadn't even seen him at the last meeting of the Monument Association, and for the next few days after the meeting, disappointment was a sluggish load that she carried with her through heavy days. Much to her chagrin, she burst into tears easily. "Stop it!" she reprimanded herself. "I mustn't let myself be carried away like a silly schoolgirl." But in her loneliness she had already been carried away. In her aching desire she longed to feel his embrace. Now that she had experienced desire again and dreamed of someone with whom to share her life, life itself seemed empty without love. Without the euphoria of love, she was afraid her steps would echo in the dull void, and she would plod alone with financial and family worry, with community service and little reward.

Chapter 40

Victorious! the papers shouted, when on October 11, 1880, Ellen, Jane Andrews, and Mary Lee Hurd became the first women in New York State to win election to a Board of Education. "The influence of women," Ellen told Mary Lee and Jane, "shall be an element of strength, of advancement, and of good in the schools."

Every day through the cold rains of October and November Ellen struggled happily to run the school, work with the Monument Association, and initiate the duties of her position on the school board, all the while trying to steal time to work on her father's biography. During the period when she was necessarily spending her energy on the election, the unfinished biography gnawed at her, and now she determined to put aside at least two hours each day to finish it. Clara had come home from Albany to teach art at the Walworth Academy and had sufficiently taken over the household duties to allow Ellen more free time.

A misty rain which threatened to turn to snow showers was falling from the dark, low sky as Ellen sat in her room a few days after Thanksgiving. She was in a deep reverie, studying the manuscript before her, trying to put meaningful words on blank paper to bring to life that vibrant spirit she had known long ago as her father. She sat back in the chair and stretched her arms over her head. It was no use, she thought with a sigh. She had taken on too much and simply didn't have time for the intense concentration the biography demanded. A knock on the door added to her frustration, and in exasperation she called out loudly, "Come in!"

Clara opened the door quietly and peeked around it. "Mama, are you too busy to talk? If this isn't a good time—"

"No, no," Ellen interrupted her. "I might as well talk. Writing isn't too productive at this moment."

Clara seemed to tiptoe into the room, a characteristic Ellen found inexplicably irritating. "Clara, you move as though you're afraid of disturbing ghosts."

Clara smiled and pulled a brocaded slipper chair close to the desk. "I'm a little old to be making noise for the sake of noise, don't you agree?" She sat on the edge of her chair and nervously began to twist the corner on the tip of her wool shawl.

"What is it, Clara?" Ellen asked gently.

Her daughter looked at her a moment without speaking, and then in an uncertain low voice that was almost a whisper said, "Mama, when Frank was in prison I prayed every day for his release."

Ellen raised her eyebrows, "I'm certain we all did a lot of praying."

"I promised God," she said hesitantly, "that if He released my brother, I would dedicate my life to His service."

Ellen said nothing and sat very still.

"Mama," and there was surprising strength in Clara's voice, "I'm going to enter the convent."

"Is this what happened in Albany?" Ellen demanded. "What ridiculous nonsense did Clarence feed you?"

"He said nothing to me; he simply urged me to pray for guidance. He said only through prayer would I know if I had a true vocation."

"Vocation?" Ellen gave a short laugh. "Clara, listen to me. I'm not surprised that you should fall prey to him. Your uncle is a stimulating, intelligent man, but it's not through the church that you have to emulate that intelligence. I felt the same way about him. His is a strong personality."

"It is God's intelligence and spirit I wish to emulate, not my uncle's, as fine as it is."

Ellen looked at her daughter as though trying to see inside her soul. "You have inherited the puritanism of one grandmother, the Calvinism of another, the enthusiasm of an uncle, and the mad capers of a father. There is no more effectual preparation for a medieval nun in the last half of the nineteenth century." Ellen rose, walked to the window, and the very movement seemed to jolt a fury through her. She doubled her fist and struck the wall. "This whole age is vibrating between the superstitions and slaveries of the past, with its myths and mysticism, and the research, the knowledge or the avowed no–knowledge of the future."

"It is not myth or mysticism, Mama. It is faith granted us by grace from God. He gave my brother back to the world, the least I can do for Him is give my life for His service!"

Ellen turned from the window wearily and walked back to her desk. "Your uncle," she said sitting down heavily in the chair, "cannot leave anyone alone. He took Mother's inheritance and now doles it out very carefully to us; he tells us what to think and how to behave; he is always encroaching upon the rights of others!" She looked at her daughter's serene face, pleasant even now in the midst of conflict. Clara sat looking straight at Ellen, her hands clasped tightly together in her lap.

"Clara," Ellen pleaded, "I cannot watch the effect of fanaticism upon your mind. I cannot sit idly by and watch it change and corrode your nature. What is this religion that turns right to wrong? You are contemplating slavery!"

227

"I am not giving myself to people who will impose their will upon mine or bind me in chains! This is my own decision! Service to God is not slavery. It is the highest form of freedom." Clara reached out a hand and covered Ellen's with her own. "Mama, I am not going to enter the convent tomorrow. I only wanted you to know what I was thinking. I was afraid you would fear for me, when what I want most is to have you be happy for me."

"Children and the uncultivated are always sure of what they know, Clara. They cannot tolerate doubt. So it is with religionists."

"That is not true. Please think about this for a few days before we discuss it further." Tears glistened in Clara's eyes as she stood and walked to the door. "Oh, Mama, I have thought about this for years. This is not a sudden decision." Ellen watched implacably and said nothing as Clara opened the door. "Please try to see my side of it, won't you?" her daughter begged.

Ellen nodded heavily and sat staring at the wall after the door closed. "What an idle task it is," she thought miserably, "to explain one's views and opinions, to make one's self understood." The church. She had looked for life there also when she was young. Yet the church had done so little for her, except to be there when a loved one was buried. She closed her eyes. Without spirituality a fine part of one's life was missing, but that spirituality was not to be found in the Catholic church. Perhaps not in any church. She hid her face in her hands. "The misery of seeing any child throw away her gifts of character, of intellect and talent is hard, desperately hard to meet. Poor child, to deliberately put out her own eyes and not know that she is blind."

That night Ellen slept little. A part of her was stunned, yet underneath the surprise and bewilderment lay a recognition as though a part of her had always known this would happen. "I see the follies of my own youth not only repeated but multiplied a thousandfold in this act of Clara's. She must be cured, must be rescued from intellectual slavery, from a prison that holds captive mind and body, from an association that enfeebles and degrades. I shall devote myself toward dissuading her from this completely foolish act!" How she would dissuade her she didn't know, but the decision enabled her to doze. When she roused from a short sleep and heard the clock strike five, she felt certain that with energy and determination she could devise a plan.

Ellen dressed carefully for the meeting of the Monument Association, choosing a silk and wool dress printed with red and blue flowers and green leaves. It was a cheerful but decorous dress, white lace edging the long sleeves and white lace at the throat defining the neckline.

All the members had been urged to attend since J. C. Markham would be there explaining the design and final stages of the monument.

Ellen sat quietly, hoping to give the impression of serenity. Aaron had nodded his head toward her when he walked in but had walked straight to the front of the room and seated himself next to William Stone. Mr. Markham was introduced and rose to speak, explaining the drawings of the monument, but Ellen heard very little. Her eyes drifted around the room, lingering now and then on Aaron, her whole body yearning for him. She wondered what he would say to her after the meeting. She would keep her replies light and happy. Christmas was coming, perhaps she should give a reception and invite him. Mr. Markham finished speaking, and the scattered applause brought her out of her reverie.

Cake and coffee were brought in, and she was introduced to the noted architect with long white hair and white beard. He looked aristocratic and distinguished with a high forehead and sharp, pointed nose. But her concentration was expectantly on Aaron, and when she was free to look for him, he was gone. "I had wanted to ask a question of Mr. Stewart," she said somewhat lamely to Robert Richards. "Do you know where he is?"

Mr. Richards glanced briefly around the room. "I believe he left," he said, a frown creasing the space between his eyes. "I don't know what his hurry was, he should have stayed to meet our guest."

Ellen walked home slowly, with a crushing sense of disappointment and humiliation filling her. She had not had a conversation with Aaron since the night six months earlier when he had walked her home. He had seemed interested in her that night. She took a deep breath and frowned. What had happened? He had seemed aware of her since she first joined the association and had given every indication of enjoying her company. Panic gripped her. He didn't want to see her again, for whatever reason, and didn't intend to see her. The hope of him would no longer define her days or make her visible.

She struggled through the long days, resisting the voice inside her that called her foolish, that demanded she stop thinking of him. He had provided a tiny interlude in the tedium of her life, a ray of light and hope that she could be loved, and she was unwilling to let go of it.

A flurry of activity and the scent of pine, cinnamon, and sugar filled Pine Grove as Clara, Nellie, and Ruby decorated the old house for Christmas, placing swags of pine on mantels and the bannister. A pine wreath decorated the front door, and as they made candy and baked cookies, the sounds of laughter and carols resounded throughout the house.

The merriment only deepened Ellen's sense of isolation and loneliness. She watched over the school, went to the school board meetings, but spent her free time alone in her room.

"I let myself be carried away by foolishness," she told herself firmly one evening. "I am let down, not by reality, but only by my own dreams which had not one shred of foundation. I always expected to love and be loved. I thought a happy home life the very essence of womanhood, but a home life with intellectual strivings. Even if a companion is to be denied me, I can still control a life of the mind. It's the only life worth reaching for." She walked to the dressing mirror. "I am fifty," she said aloud. "I have lived a half–century with the only result turmoil and disappointment. The woman of that last half–century is dead."

She moved to her desk, took out pencil and paper, and began to write:

Last Wishes and Requests

1. My furniture, pictures, and books are to be divided as equally as possible among my children.
2. Father Walworth will pay housekeeping debts as might be due at my death.

She looked at her second request and vigorously crossed it out. "I will leave no debts," she thought sternly, "and after his conduct with Clara, I would not ask a favor of him."

3. Martin D. Hardin is to have my body sent to Jacksonville, Illinois, and buried beside that of my father. No religious service is to be performed over me.

After the third request she paused a moment, then wrote: "In suffering she found peace. In labor she found rest."

Chapter 41

Ellen read the scrap of paper she held in her hand and sighed. The spidery handwriting was an invitation away from the daily grind of running a large home with no money, a way out of the overwhelming tension of running a school and boarding house for income, while providing a family home. Here, on this piece of paper, a Mr. Ballad had offered her a considerable sum of money for the old house.

She rose from the chair in which she was sitting, walked to the window, and absentmindedly looked out at the traffic in the street. A city, perhaps Washington or even New York, would offer stimulation, opportunities, and a wholesome intellectual atmosphere for all of them. For myself, she thought longingly, I would wish to be where I had access to libraries and associates who would help rather than hinder. People with ideas and energy who had dared push beyond a limited daily routine in favor of a wider expanse of their energies. Yet, I have made a place for myself in this community, she thought, and I should be disheartened and discouraged to sacrifice it. She gave a short, self-deprecating laugh. "How far I have come from the critical child I was who turned up her nose at everyone and everything in Saratoga!" What a labor of years it had taken to accept and be accepted. A sense of place, of belonging, is so important to me, she thought wonderingly. Even when I am only in a place for two weeks I must arrange myself and my belongings to absorb the atmosphere so it will always be part of me. Strange that I have always been homesick, perhaps even for a place I've never been.

She turned from the window and looked about the parlor. The state of New York had been strengthened by the decisions made in this house, she mused. Here so much sparkling wit and intelligent conversation had emanated from the greatest minds of the nineteenth century. "Pine Grove should be turned into a shrine," she said aloud, "for the boots of history will always echo through these rooms."

Her lips tightened into a hard line. No, she would not sell. To sell this house would be tantamount to an admission of economic failure. "By economy and effort I can maintain this old place," she decided. "Here, in this community, I can make a difference even in a small way. I could not make myself or my ideas felt in a city. If I hold myself and my time in hand, I can accomplish something here."

It was snowing, and the town seemed locked into a cold grayness. Outside, people hurried by with their heads down, bound in their own lives, their hands locked into wool or leather.

Ellen sat at her desk, her feet chilled and crossed at the ankles for warmth. A frown creased her forehead as she tried to push evasive words across paper. Her father's spirit was elusive, yet the desire to write his biography pushed against her, the unborn words fermenting into frustration.

"How can I keep doing this when so many infernal family and financial problems keep gnawing at me?"

But the million and one tasks that made up her life kept swimming in her head, demanding to be done. Her days at home were a treadmill of tedium, and she felt utterly frustrated when no intellectual work was attempted. Yet facing days filled only with the formidable tasks of raising a family and running her large house with a limited income filled her with hopelessness. Her anger with Clarence for doling out her inheritance a meager lot at a time grew daily. It was like being in the middle of a very long tunnel, the brightness of day long left behind, and the tiny spark of light at the end of the tunnel not yet in evidence. It would be there one day when her children were fully grown. It would not be long now. In the fall Ruby would enter Vassar. But meantime, Ellen could only plod on, one foot at a time, dealing with the day–to–day problems of feeding people, keeping them warm, making sure feet had shoes, and trying to stop their beloved old house from falling into neglect and disrepair. Into that schedule she would have to continue to fit her writing, her reading, the school, and her civic activities.

Nellie poked her head around the open doorway, wearing a dim frown. "Mother?" she asked quietly.

"Come in, Nellie." Ellen stretched her arms above her head. "What's the matter?"

"Mother," she began, choosing her words carefully, "I feel I must tell you that Clara is planning to leave tomorrow, to enter the convent."

"No!" Several times she had approached Nellie to ask if Clara had revealed any plans, but Nellie's replies were often vague, and Ellen assumed that Nellie knew no more than she.

"The reason I wanted to tell you, Mother, was to say that if this is what Clara wants, then this is what you must let her do. Don't try to stop her, it will only make mistrust and dislike grow between you."

Ellen squeezed the pencil she held until her knuckles turned white, then threw it down on her desk. "Clara's mind is clouded and twisted by the superstitions of a man who has known no law but his own wishes. Because they seem to be holy wishes, they are held as uncompromising."

"But, Mother, if this is what Clara really wants, why shouldn't she do it? What could be more honorable?"

Ellen stared at Nellie as though seeing her for the first time. "Honorable?" she asked her daughter dully. "The only aim of a convent is the perfect execution of manual labor seasoned with spiritual sentimentalities. How terrible compared with the healthy robustness of a mind bent on making the most and best of each opportunity as it comes from day to day, thereby preparing itself for great work." Ellen paused and looked at her daughter. "Nellie, I know this is hard on you, and I thank you for telling me your sister's plans, but I must talk to her about it."

"I came to you in confidence, Mother."

"And if you had told me she was going to shoot herself, should I close my eyes and not stop her?"

Agitatedly, Ellen counted the minutes until Clara had finished teaching art for the day. At three o'clock she almost ran down the stairs and into the schoolroom. "Clara," she commanded, "I need to speak with you before you do anything else. I'll be in the kitchen."

Clara's eyes met hers. "Of course, Mother. I'll be right there."

Dolly didn't come to the kitchen anymore until just an hour before the evening meal. She was stooped and slow now, crippled by pains in her joints, and often required the help of old Kate or a member of the family. But they hadn't the heart to give away her domain, so the kitchen was now the most private room in the house.

Ellen opened cupboard doors randomly, nervously checked the pantry, and ran her fingers over the windowsill. When Clara entered the room, Ellen stood before her reprovingly. "Your sister just told me you are leaving home to enter the convent."

"Yes, Mother," Clara answered quietly. "I wanted to tell you, but I didn't know how to make you understand."

Ellen crossed her arms. "You know I have always been opposed to convents. When an American woman enters a convent, she destroys her opportunities. I suppose you know it is not an essential of faith in the church to believe in the necessity or expediency of convents any more than it is essential to believe in the celibacy of the clergy."

"It is an essential of my faith, Mother."

"It is only a matter of discipline!" Ellen cried. "In the past convents have served an admirable purpose, and they are good now for a certain class of people, but their day has gone by, and in time they will pass out of use as surely as hermits, coat friars, bodily scourging, and other physical penances have passed by."

"You have never asked me what I see in the life I propose to lead," Clara answered calmly. "I couldn't tell you what my plans were because of the objections I knew you would voice. Mother, I don't want to hurt you, but my mind is made up. I shall leave in nine days."

Nine days. Ellen felt a momentary relief.

"Clara, dear," she said more quietly, "you will have to take a vow of poverty, which is a sham—an absolute sham. They say a vow of poverty, yet you will be entitled to hold property throughout your life if you wish. That is a false vow, which I consider derogatory to a sense of honor. The vow of obedience is the worst possible slavery, absolute intellectual slavery! Clara," Ellen pleaded as she pulled a chair out from the table, trying to control her shaking hands, "one may vow adherence to principles, to rules, to doctrine, and still preserve self-respect, free will, independence, and have room for intellectual and spiritual growth, but in these orders there is, even before they can enter the novitiate, a condition by which they pledge themselves to absolute obedience. And to what? Not to principles, rules of doctrine, but only to other individuals, so-called superiors!"

"Mother, I don't understand you," Clara said wearily. "What I am doing is dedicating my life to our Lord, to God, and you call that slavery! Please try to understand me."

Even though tears glistened in Clara's eyes, her calmness infuriated Ellen. "I lost Frank to prison, and he has never been the same, and I can't bear to watch you fade in another prison."

"I have promised God, and my mind is made up."

"No!" Ellen cried as she lunged for Clara and grabbed her by the shoulders. "You will not go!" She pushed Clara toward the open pantry, then slammed the door. She grabbed the keys that hung on a nearby hook and with shaking hands turned the lock. "Stay there," she shouted, "stay there until you see the unbearable anguish I feel at seeing you made into a dull sluggard, obedient to every demand and suggestion of any individual!"

Upstairs in her room she covered her face with her hands and wept uncontrollably. "This foolish imagining is used by a man of apparent sense and honor to convince Clara she must leave her home and family," she told herself. The thought of Clarence coercing Clara into this act released a fresh stab of anguish so sharp that paroxysms of anger and fear of losing her daughter almost choked her. "He has told her over and over again that to doubt is to have no vocation, thereby fixing in her mind the absolute necessity for a persistency of purpose regardless of consequence."

Ellen's eyes were red and puffy, and she had a headache from weeping when she opened the closet door later that evening. "I'm sorry, Clara, I'm so sorry," she said as she embraced her daughter.

Clara faced her calmly, with no evidence of a tear having been shed. "All right, Mother. I have a compromise to offer."

Ellen looked at her hopefully.

"I will stay at home for a few more months, and I will for the time being give up thoughts of the convent, but I will go to Mass every morning."

"Will you consent to put yourself under the care of a doctor? You are physically weak, your nerves are strung to their utmost tension in the constant terror of an overscrupulous conscience, and delusions are liable to afflict you."

"All right," Clara whispered, so softly the reply was almost inaudible.

Life settled into an uneasy watchfulness, each aware of the other's presence, of unspoken desires and thoughts, but each hoping for understanding of the other.

Ellen's anxieties were, to some measure, absorbed by her work on the school board, and she threw her energy into making the school system as strong and honorable as her position would allow. She was a member of the building committee, the visitation committee, and the teachers and textbooks committee.

As a member of the school board, she had protested vigorously when Wilkie Collins' novels were among the new books chosen for the public library. In her view, they were nothing but romantic trash, and money spent on the classics, on the best current literature America had to offer, would be more enriching for the citizens of Saratoga, including the children.

She was verbally slapped by the *Saratoga Eagle* for her opposition and was accused of ostentatiously protesting just to be noticed. "In view of this freak," the paper asked, "would it not be the graceful thing for Superintendent Packard to substitute then, at his own expense, the words of Mansfield Tracy Walworth?" The article shocked and galled her, but she should have known, she decided, that it was bound to come sooner or later. She hoped she had shaken off the shame of Mansfield, and now as she looked at the article, a hot flush enveloped her, and she realized that here in Saratoga he would always be remembered as having been her husband. She was not on the school board for her own gratification, as people said she was, but only for the opportunity to use what brains and talent she had to enrich her community. "If one gives up on one's beliefs and moral standards in order to please others, one will never accomplish anything!"

She was asked to give the commencement address at the high school graduation. Confidently, she reminded her audience that the standards for qualifications for teachers should be higher, that the teaching in the junior and primary grades should have more flexibility and breadth. "The grammar schools should aspire to a standard which would leave every pupil to pass the regent's examination with ease before entering high school," she declared emphatically. "I have thought that the course of study in this department should be developed into a full course of four years and the school brought up to a standard commensurate with the best high schools in the state. Never be ashamed of those simple words, high school. It is the noblest name we bear."

Throughout the summer she fought a strange lassitude that seemed to have come over her when she heard President Garfield had been shot. He was in a coma, and his vice president, Chester Arthur, had suddenly become the nation's leader. It seemed to Ellen that the world was in a coma, with terror waiting to strike and undo the freedoms and liberties that men had fought for and died over. She wondered if the nation could give in as easily as she could, and the realization of how easy it was to give up threw her into a panic.

She was in the kitchen on a morning after Thanksgiving making her lists for holiday preparations. She was moving canisters of flour and sugar and checking to see if there was fresh cinnamon when Frank walked jauntily into the room. "Good morning, Mother," he sang out, causing her to look at him sharply with surprise. "I have an announcement. Corinne and I are going to be married on December 20."

She looked at him blankly for a moment, absorbing his news, then broke into a wide smile. "Good," she said hugging him. "I'm happy for both of you." Relief flooded her as she put the teakettle on and put three spoonfuls of tea into the china pot while he chatted on happily about his future plans.

For the past few years Ellen had wrestled with anxieties about Frank and his future. Her hopes of success had centered upon him, thinking that his future would vindicate the family's misfortunes. Frank would be the great lawyer they had all hoped for, the lawyer the Chancellor had so desperately wanted, yet Frank had seemingly inherited Mansfield's disinterest in the law, as well as his predilections for writing and social pursuits. He was practicing law, but only in the most desultory way. He had recently published two articles about bicycling in the *American Wheelmen*, and had in the past two years, perfected his skill in the sport of archery. He was a founder of the Saratoga Bowmen and a member of the executive committee of the National Archery Association.

"I must say I am surprised," she said happily as she poured tea for them. "I thought you had decided against Corinne."

"I just wasn't certain about marriage, about supporting a family."

"Of course you can support a family. You are not only intelligent, but you bear one of the great names in legal history." She paused and drummed her fingers on the tabletop for a moment before looking at him. "But you must accept more cases, Frank." She could see an invisible mask pass over his face, closing out thoughts and words. "I know, I know," she said quickly. "I don't want to upset you, but I must speak my mind. You have to determine that you are the best lawyer you can possibly be, that you will earn a decent income and have no worries about the future. You know I worry, Frank, because you have the tendency to approach life the way your father did, and you see what a shambles we're in because of him." It sounded like an insult, like an accusation, and she didn't mean it that way. She went to him and kissed him on the cheek. "I love you, Frankie. I couldn't be happier than to have Corinne for a daughter–in–law."

The morning after the wedding, Ellen awakened to a dim gray light, and against the windowpanes she could see swirling white flakes and hear the boards in the old house creaking from the wind. She was planning a reception for the newly married couple on December 26, and there were still preparations to be made for Christmas, but she wasn't yet ready to face the day. She snuggled under the quilts to doze longer and savor a satisfied feeling as she let her mind wander back over the events of the lovely candlelight wedding ceremony which had taken place in the Presbyterian Church in Mechanicsville.

Later, when she went downstairs for lunch, Nellie, Tracy, and Ruby were already at the table. "Well, that was a fine wedding yesterday evening, wasn't it?" Ruby looked at her with solemn eyes, and she thought Nellie wore a strained expression. "Why is everyone so quiet on this cozy day?" Ellen inquired gently, "Or is it simply my imagination? Where's Clara?"

Nellie sat very still and looked at Ellen. "I don't know, Mother."

"Surely she didn't go into town in this storm?"

Nellie lowered her eyes to the table and said nothing.

Ellen's fork dropped onto her plate with a clatter while a spark of understanding as cold as ice shot through her. "I must go after her. Why didn't she tell me she was leaving, and before Christmas, too!"

"Mother, let her go," Nellie implored. "Clara knows exactly what she is doing. Please don't make things difficult for yourself and all of us as well."

237

"Your uncle put her up to this," Ellen replied accusingly as she rose from the table and hurried up the stairs.

"You know she will be safe," Nellie called after her. "The only way she knows she has a mission is to simply do it."

"He has helped her to go," Ellen almost cried as she pulled her valise from the closet. "He has urged her to go secretly, like a vaga-bond, and without my knowledge."

She looked down at her valise with an expression of defeat. "Why did she do this now, before the reception, before Christmas?" She sat down heavily on the edge of her bed and buried her face in her hands. "I can't ignore Frank and Corinne's party. I can't go to her now. She had been taken from me as surely as if she was bound hand and foot and dropped into a hole." There was a momentary silence before Ellen rose from the bed and began pacing the floor. "I will get her out of there, mark my words. I absolutely will get her out."

Chapter 42

The wind threw thick snowflakes into her eyes so that she had to squint to see, and with her head bent she walked carefully up the slippery walk to Kenwood Convent. Ellen had not seen or heard from Clara in three months and had vowed to herself that she would not be the first to make contact. Yet she longed for her daughter every day, wanting one more chance to try and persuade her to live a normal life. Last night, trying unsuccessfully to fall asleep, Ellen decided that this silent longing was pure foolishness. She would simply go to see Clara at Kenwood.

Breathing hard, she wiped her feet on a mat as she entered the dimly lit lobby.

"May I help you?"

Startled, Ellen turned quickly to her right and saw a tall nun with a rather severe face. "Yes," Ellen gasped lightly, trying to catch her breath. "I'm Mrs. Walworth, and I have come to see my daughter."

"I will tell her she has a visitor," the nun said formally as she turned to leave.

"Oh, not yet, please," Ellen cautioned. "I'm a great deal exhausted, and I would like to collect my thoughts a moment." She sat down on a chair, mentally rehearsing what she wanted to say to Clara, but she felt decidedly uncomfortable in the presence of her impassive companion. After a few minutes, more to give the nun something to do rather than because she was ready, Ellen leaned forward in her chair. "You could send for Clara Walworth now, if you will." As the nun left, Ellen breathed a sigh of relief, looking around the lobby as she removed her hat and pushed back strands of damp hair. Only the smell of wax betrayed any activity in the room, and even her breathing sounded audible in the silence.

Clara glided in, and Ellen smiled and stood quickly to embrace her but was stopped by a remoteness in her daughter's manner. Clara was thin, much thinner than she had been in December, but there was a light in her eyes and she seemed content. "Thank you for coming, Mother," she said, regarding Ellen as she would a distant friend. She motioned toward a sofa for Ellen, then pulled a chair close to it for herself. "I know why you have come. You might as well say what you have to."

"You know that I want you to reconsider your decision."

"I have told you over and over again why I made this decision and why I must carry it out. I'm happy here, and if I were to leave, I would miss it dreadfully."

"You cannot shut yourself away from life, Clara. You have gifts to give—teaching, art. You need love in your life. Life is full of challenges, risks, adventures. You will miss all of that."

"Mother, I know you will never understand my choice, so it simply does no good to talk about it. Now tell me. What's happening at home? How is Nellie? And is Ruby doing well at Vassar? And the school? That's what I want to hear."

"That's what I talked to Frank about while he was in prison," Ellen retorted bitterly. "Don't you see," she begged, "that this way we will never share our lives, that you and I will become pleasant strangers only reporting our activities? Our day–to–day contact will be lost. Please, Clara, don't throw your family away."

They talked until dark, Ellen pleading, Clara adamantly refusing to hear. At suppertime Clara left. Ellen sat exhausted, knowing she was defeated, knowing she had lost her daughter to this quiet cloister.

Clara had been gone only a short time when the Mother Superior came in and walked toward her with outstretched hands and kind compassion in her eyes. Ellen stood and took the hands uncomfortably, then sat down on the edge of the sofa, her back straight, as the Mother Superior sat down in the chair Clara had vacated. "I realize how difficult this is for you, Mrs. Walworth. Even though the greatest honor in a Catholic family is to have a son enter the priesthood or a daughter the convent, it is very difficult to give them up to a vocation."

"A typical Jesuit," Ellen thought stubbornly, "amiable, agreeable, and clever."

The Mother Superior talked on, sympathy radiating from her eyes and voice. Ellen sat silently, knowing her protestations would be met with Catholic logic at every point.

"Mrs. Walworth," the Mother Superior said finally, "why don't I order Clara to go home, provided you allow her to come back in a year?"

Clara walked into the room then, and Ellen no longer saw her daughter but only an acquaintance living in an alienated world. Ellen's mind searched for an answer while she bristled at the indignity of having to bargain for her child. "I believe it's a matter of too much importance to decide at once," she answered evenly. "I must have time to consider it."

The convent had provided her a room for the night, and as she lay awake on the narrow cot, Ellen knew that if Clara came home with her it would only be in obedience to her Mother Superior, not to her mother, and would do neither of them any good. It would be completely injudicious to subject Clara to such a change against her will. Even though she had told the Mother Superior she would write her answer in a week or ten days, she knew she must tell Clara goodby and let her live the life she desired.

When Ellen returned to Saratoga, she found Tracy home from medical college, having earned high honors, but ill and depressed. He stayed in his room most of the day, burst into tears easily, and often seemed confused. Alarmed, Ellen searched her mind frantically for the best way to deal with him, trying to think of an activity he could devote himself to, something creative which would calm him.

"Tracy," she said to him one afternoon, "you have a gift for carpentry and have always enjoyed working with your hands. Do you think you could enlarge the dining room by yourself? You would be doing us a great favor; we're always so cramped when the boarders are here."

The suggestion seemed to work. He lost himself in the absorption of physical work, and often Ellen came upon him humming to himself, his brow creased in concentration as he contemplated first one problem and then another.

With the family agreeing that a larger dining room was a necessity, Ellen began to seriously consider an idea that had been playing around the edges of her mind for quite a while. If she could enlarge The Homestead, as she now referred to Pine Grove, she could run a larger boarding establishment in the summers and be able to accept more students as boarders in the fall. The cottage in back of the property could be enlarged for the family and some rooms in the house reserved for them as well. The overriding concern was whether the expenses of remodeling could be met, even though eventually the extra room would be profitable. How they would manage until they could turn a profit was the question. She wrote to the architect who had designed the Saratoga Monument, J. C. Markham, requesting an appointment with him, and in her spare time poured over columns of figures, assessing her home, her bills, and her expenses.

In the spring Ruby returned home from Vassar, and in June Frank and Corinne came home to live with them. Ellen put Frank in charge of the mathematics department of the Walworth Academy, as he was a far cry from the great, vigorous lawyer she had hoped he would become. She loved her son dearly, yet she couldn't help but regard him as another defeat in her life.

His marriage had brought an exuberance to him that Ellen hadn't noticed since his childhood, and Corinne, too, seemed happy. Yet to Frank the imperative in his life was play not work, as well as the satisfaction he gained from occasionally writing articles and poetry. His enthusiasm was reserved for teaching Corinne archery and for meeting with the Saratoga Bowmen. Since 1881 he had been an officer in the National Archery Association and was now a member of the executive committee.

Throughout the summer, as Ellen supervised guests' meals and comforts and planned for the coming school years, she often gritted her teeth in silent anger as Frank discussed with great seriousness the merits of each member's ability and as he outlined in exhaustive detail to Corinne the steps she needed to practice to become a champion. "It only pays to be the best," he often said.

Ellen met Mr. Markham in New York City and brought home drawings for a Queen Ann–style mansion of fifty–five rooms, turreted, with large piazzas on both the first and second floors. The proposed changes brought stunned silence from the family. "It isn't that it wouldn't be lovely, Mother," Nellie said, "but there is so much history in this house. It's seventy years old, and so many famous people have visited here, and grandfather's courtroom—" she trailed the sentence off, having spoken everybody else's silent thoughts.

"Mother, how many years will it take to pay off the debts the changes will incur?" Frank asked. "I agree that it will bring in more money in the form of extra people, but have you considered the larger expenses to run such an establishment, to say nothing of the debts we already have?"

"There aren't many large debts now," Ellen answered defensively, "there simply isn't enough income." But privately she fretted over the decision, vacillating between going ahead with the remodeling and struggling to cope with what they had.

"The problem of this old house is a hard one to solve," she said to herself, standing in front of the white picket fence one afternoon. "I dread and fear the breaking up, yet it cannot be well to go on with debts growing and everything falling to pieces. I must have the courage to take action and not simply drift—although there is often a merit in drifting."

Alone in her room she thought over the lines of a quote she had once cut form a newspaper: "The differentiation of life is not in circumstances, but in the quality of the personal power brought to bear on circumstances. Nothing awaits one save what he himself creates out of the conjunction of his own power and circumstances." Her own power was this house, and she had used it to advantage in creating the school. Her own circumstances were poor, with nothing to alter them in the immediate future. "As I see it," she thought, "I have no choice but to use this house to enlarge our futures."

Remodeling started in late summer, and the school opened in the fall to the cacophony of hammers, saws, and workmen's voices. Ellen desperately tried to keep some semblance of order, but it was a losing battle with sawdust and plaster vying for honors over every conceivable surface.

In January, Tracy's illness escalated, and he again withdrew, spending days alone crying in his room. He was often disoriented, hardly recognizing anyone in the family. Ellen consulted a doctor who pursed his lips and shook his head after examining Tracy. "He has a brain illness, Mrs. Walworth, and he may or may not grow out of it. What I prescribe is a complete change for him, perhaps some sea air."

Heartbroken, Ellen wrote to D. in Chicago explaining Tracy's illness and describing the doctor's prescription. D. answered promptly, saying he would send some money so that she and Tracy could go to St. Augustine, Florida, where he would join them in a few weeks.

They were on deck, huddled into their coats for protection against the damp, bitter cold as the ship pulled away from the docks in Wilmington, Delaware. Tracy watched the proceedings with vacant eyes, and Ellen wondered if he really saw or knew what was happening. She held his hand and talked to him gently as they walked the decks and breathed deeply the mixture of oil and salt air. Over lunch he sat with his head bowed, eating little, and not looking at the other passengers. When they went to their cabin, in an effort to keep him from withdrawing into himself Ellen opened a book and began to read aloud. "What are you doing with me, Mother?" he asked tearfully.

"Why, Tracy, you and I are going on a lovely vacation to Florida." She smiled at him in a manner meant to convey fun and a sense of conspiracy. "We're running away from all the noise at home, from the snow and cold, and we're going to see the ocean and enjoy the warm sunshine. Your uncle D. is going to join us."

Tears began to course down his cheeks. "I have led a strange life at home." He spoke without emotion, but the tears continued to run freely.

"We all have," Ellen answered dully, "but life is strange."

As they relaxed into a routine of carefully planned activity, Ellen hoped that exercise and mental stimulation would alleviate Tracy's depression. They took long walks in the sunshine, explored the old fort, and relived aloud St. Augustine's history. Tracy began to laugh and to focus on his days; Ellen thought that perhaps the doctor was right, a change of environment with sunshine and exercise was all he needed.

In the evenings, they burned a log fire in Ellen's room, and Tracy read aloud while she embroidered. Then, after they had been there a few days, two telegrams arrived, one announcing when D. would arrive, and the other telling of Dolly's death in an Albany hospital. So much seems to be disintegrating, Ellen thought hopelessly as she watched Tracy slide into another depression. All I can do is drift with it and hope for the best. She felt numb and could only act in the immediate present and, by an act of will, blot out the past and the future.

D. came, bringing with him freedom for Ellen as he took Tracy on walks and engaged him in conversations about medical school and carpentry. Ellen was able to relax, to sleep late, and to read in the sunshine.

One evening, with Tracy in his own room and she and D. sitting before the fire, Ellen remarked, "Tracy does seem better. This is the first time he has been able to be left alone. I just wonder if he will continue to improve when we return home."

"Perhaps a trip to Europe would help him, Nelly. Lem and I could both give him the money, and I'm sure Clarence would help." At the mention of Clarence's name she frowned, and D. said quickly, "I'll ask him. If Nellie could go with him, I'm certain he'd be fine. She's traveled in Europe and speaks fluent French, so they shouldn't have any trouble."

"I don't know, D.," Ellen said doubtfully. "I'd be terribly nervous and worried sending him that far away in his condition and on his own."

"I think he needs to be on his own, Nelly," her brother said gently.

As long as there was a routine—walking, shopping, riding the ferry—Tracy seemed fine. But when she said they would soon have to leave for home, he acted puzzled and became disoriented. D. was right, she decided. A longer trip to Europe, a more complete change without her protecting presence, would surely benefit him.

They returned home to a world in upheaval, the house in the middle of being remodeled, and everything in a constant state of disarray. Nellie was delighted at the prospect of a trip to Europe, and it was decided that Frank could take over her duties as well as his own.

There was no time to worry about their welfare, for with Corinne's help, Ellen began planning for the decoration and furnishing of the house. In addition to running the school, she drove herself from early morning until late evening choosing wallpaper, painting walls, and sewing.

She and Corinne were on their knees one evening in the parlor tacking a border around red carpeting while Frank read to them the events of President Cleveland's inauguration.

244

"The parade to the White House was imposing," he read. "The multitude of spectators along the streets was far greater than the throng that witnessed the procession of four years ago. The President–elect took his seat in the barouche drawn by spanking bays, with President Arthur on his right. As the crowds on the stands in Lafayette Square were cheering and waving their handkerchiefs, the barouche drove into the avenue. The bands played, the glittering muskets of the soldiers flashed again as they were brought to a 'shoulder arms,' and the procession moved east past the gaily decked Treasury Building. Screams and yells and cheers rent the air as the crowds fell back in masses. As General Slocum led his command between the swaying, surging crowd and passed out of Fifteenth Street upon Pennsylvania Avenue where the white dome of the Capitol was in sight, a deafening roar of cheers, beginning at the Treasury, went up from the multitude, was taken up and passed along, and was repeated with increasing volume all along the avenue until the wave of sound reached Capitol Hill."

"Oh, wouldn't you love to have seen it?" Corinne squealed.

"And the inaugural address?" Ellen asked through a mouthful of pins.

"Let's see," Frank answered. "General Grant's retirement, swearing in the vice president ... here it is. 'Fellow Citizens: In the presence of this vast assemblage of my countrymen, I am about to supplement and seal by the oath which I shall take the manifestation of a great and free people. Amid the din of party strife the people's choice was made: but it's attendant circumstances have demonstrated anew the strength and safety of a Government by the people. On this auspicious occasion we may well renew the pledge of our devotion to the Constitution, which, launched by the founders of the Republic and consecrated by their prayers and patriotic devotion has for almost a century borne the hopes and the aspirations of a great people through prosperity and peace and through the shock of foreign conflicts and the perils of domestic strife and vicissitudes. The large variety of diverse and competing interests subject to Federal control, persistently seeking the recognition of their claims, need give us no fear that the greatest good to the greatest number will fail to be accomplished if, in the halls of national legislation, that spirit of amity and mutual concession should prevail in which the Constitution had its birth. If this involves the surrender or postponement of private interests and the abandonment of local advantages, compensation will be found in the assurance that the common interest is subserved and the general welfare advanced.

In the discharge of my official duty I shall endeavor to be guided by a just and unstrained construction of the Constitution, a careful obser-

245

vance of the distinction granted to the Federal Government and those reserved to the States or to the people, and by a cautious appreciation of those functions which, by the Constitution and laws have been especially assigned to the executive branch of the Government."

Ellen sat back on her heels and stretched her neck. "Why don't you cut out the inaugural address, Frank, and we'll save it for the students. Many things in my life have gone wrong," she said as she pushed herself awkwardly into a standing position, "but being born in America was the first and best thing that went right."

By the time school was out and boarders began arriving there was some semblance of order in the house. When Tracy and Nellie returned from Europe in late June, Pine Grove existed no more, and in its place stood a fashionable turreted structure that wound and snaked its way upward toward the pine branches, and Ellen renamed it Walworth Mansion.

In early summer Corinne became ill, fighting bouts of nausea and hardly able to get out of bed. When it was finally established that her illness was not due to summer sickness as feared, but to an expected child, Frank was ecstatic. He began to treat Corinne with a tenderness that poignantly reminded Ellen of her own pregnancy with Frank.

Whether due to a natural progression of interest or to his new status as an expectant father, Ellen couldn't tell, but Frank became increasingly interested in the financial matters of Walworth Mansion. To her annoyance he began to criticize his mother's actions and disagree with her every decision. One day he would say, "Mother, you must not serve extravagant meals to the boarders." The next day he would reprimand, "you must serve decent desserts or the boarders will want to stay elsewhere next year." Ellen tried to close her mind to his criticisms, but still he annoyed her and made her tense. He was desultory about his duties in school and was often late for class, but when Ellen reprimanded him, he would counter with more criticisms of her own performance. "The reason you're tired all the time," he often told her, "is because you try to do too much yourself. You should leave more to others."

"I have been driven into that course of expecting help, Frank, and it doesn't work. I must continue to work at these many things believing that others will take them up where I leave off. Only experience, not advice or urging, will cause the work to be done well."

It had been a trying year, but still she could count it as victorious. The house was furnished and decorated, and the school was thriving. There were heavy debts to meet, but she was confident they would be met. Sitting at the desk in her bedroom one night in late December, Ellen optimistically looked to the year ahead. Confiding her thoughts to her journal, she wrote: "If I may live and work to clear the debts, it will be well, but my health is uncertain, and I must constantly apply the spur to my lagging energies to keep all things going. There is a destiny that shapes our ends—rough through them as we will. It is easily done if I decide to sacrifice the intellectual life and happy solitude that in the past have enabled me to gather the courage and cheerfulness that lighten the outside hours. That I have not made it by choice is evident by the method of my work—during these past two years I have not been driven to it full well—and thus have often fretted and been harassed by it. So it would seem necessary that I secure the hours for the 'I am.' Thus may I, perhaps, gain command of my time and of my life. Thus may I live by the motto I have chosen for the year 1886, 'Dwell as if about to depart.'"

From the first day of the new year, Ellen began to work on the "I am." She conscientiously set aside time to work on her father's biography, trying to shape her writing style into one with power and force to fire the imagination, exactly the qualities John Hardin had brought to his life. She sought to further educate herself, reading the philosophies of Aristotle and Plato, as well as biographies and histories.

Nellie and Ruby were both helping in the school and writing. Their friends enlivened the house, and Ellen proudly recorded in her journal the evenings they spent at home with young men and the parties and balls they attended.

On March 11, Clara Grant Walworth was born. In spite of her longings for creative solitude, Ellen embraced this new life with zeal, seeing in the tiny shape of her granddaughter a beginning for them all.

She had harbored hopes that becoming a father would cause Frank to become more responsible toward work, perhaps to even return to his law practice, but she was disappointed. He continued being late for classes and started going out Saturday nights and not returning home until long after the music from the hotels had ceased and there was no more traffic to be heard in the streets. Ellen tried to ignore the pattern and leave the matter between Frank and Corinne. But if Corinne minded, she didn't show it and, happy in her new role as a mother, she radiated only love and happiness.

In early October the autumn rains started, bringing a damp chill to the air which seemed to sink into one's very bones. Oak and maple leaves, which only a short time ago had been brilliant in the last strong sunshine of the year, now dropped quickly onto the ground, leaving only bare branches spreading like sentinels against the dull sky.

Much to Ellen's irritation Frank began sleeping later than usual in the mornings. Then she noticed he had developed a hoarse, persistent cough. "He wheezes so at night," Corinne confided to her worriedly, "and he complains of his chest hurting."

Remembering the lung condition he had contracted in the damp, cold prison of Sing Sing, Ellen hurried to the doctor who sent an emetic, but Frank refused to take it.

On Ellen's fifty–third birthday Rhoda Thompson came to town and took her for a drive. The rains had ceased and the day was bright and lovely, but the air was brittle with a distinct nostalgic chill that signaled the desolation of approaching winter. Ellen tried to keep up with Rhoda's bright chatter and high spirits, but an anxiety of gigantic proportions began to form inside her, an anxiety she couldn't face and wouldn't name. Corinne had baked a cake for her, and that evening Frank joined in the celebration. However, he became so tired that Ellen accompanied him upstairs early, bathed him, and helped him into bed.

The following afternoon Frank rang for her, and when she walked into the darkened room, she found him wincing and complaining of pain in his right leg. "They told me ... in prison ... " he whispered, his eyes wide with fear, "that I ... would get worse."

"Heavens," Ellen cried as she moved to the windows and opened the draperies, "no one could get well in a room this dark. Let's have some sunlight! You will get well, Frank," she said briskly as she stepped back to the bed. "You will because you have a wife who loves you and a lovely daughter. I'm going to send for the doctor, and we'll get you well once and for all!"

The doctor's eyes looked wise and kind as he patted Ellen's shoulder. "He has bronchitis," he informed them, "but I see no reason he shouldn't recover soon. He must be kept warm with mustard plasters on his chest, and every hour give him a dose of chloral and whiskey."

Frank's restlessness increased, and Ellen and Corinne took turns sitting with him, watching helplessly as he thrashed about the bed, his closed eyes sunken in bluish gray circles. They continued the mustard plasters and the medicine, smoothed his sheets, and plumped the pillows. Then suddenly, around nine o'clock one evening, three weeks after he had fallen ill, his restlessness subsided. His breathing became even, and Ellen and Corinne looked at one another hopefully. Silence fell as the struggle left him and, though his face was peaceful, his lips moved as if to form forgotten words. Then, an hour later, his breath began to labor in audible, uneven gasps, and his eyes rolled back in his head revealing white emptiness. Watching him, her eyes dry, Ellen stood transfixed, a study in dignity, while within herself, her mind shut like a steel trap, refusing to accept reality.

Nellie, Tracy, and Ruby stood in the semi–darkness, and Ellen wondered dully who had called them as she watched Tracy bite his lower lip to keep it from trembling. Nellie had her hands over her face, and Ruby, her blond hair shining like a halo in the dimly lighted room, stood silently with tears streaming down her face. Ellen felt wooden and far removed from this place, as if she could see the scene but wasn't a part of it, for her own life was receding into a dark void where she could feel nothing. Suddenly the room was strangely quiet, and Ellen realized the agonized, laborious breathing had stopped. She put her hand to her mouth and bit the side of it to keep from crying out. Then there was a sharp intake of breath, like a sob turned inward, as she bent over the still form of Frank and kissed his forehead. She turned and left the room blindly, vaguely aware of murmuring and a woman's high–pitched cry. In the hallway she heard her own footsteps slide across the soft carpet as though they belonged to someone else, and only the baby's wails made her aware of the emptiness in the big house.

Chapter 43

Ellen awakened with a start and quickly sat up. She didn't know what time it was, but she knew she had letters to write before her day started, letters being her only weapons in the fight to release Frank from prison. Before her feet touched the floor, painful reality washed over her, and she remembered that now Frank was imprisoned forever.

She sank back against the pillows and waited to sink into the stupor in which she had lain for two days. But her mind was sharp and clear, and she knew that she had to rise and face reality. She turned her face into the pillow. Having to live with the dull pain of loss, while her daily tasks carried with them reminders at every turn, was more than she could bear. "I still dream and feel and suffer. Now I can usually check the dreams, control the feelings, turn from the suffering. Yet one tie to my old self holds me fast—that is to witness dying." Loss carves a deep crevasse, carrying with it the timeless warning of mortality.

"I must begin to think and to act," she told herself, longing for energy and determination. "Something should spring from the bitter ashes of death."

She returned to her active days, hoping that work would assuage the pain, but she fell into an accepting passiveness. There was no strength within her to run the school or the house, and trying to accomplish even the most routine chores left her exhausted. Her weariness made her feel like she was dragging iron chains. "I am growing old," she told herself with alarm. "I am only in my middle fifties, but all this suffering has aged me beyond reason." When she spoke, her voice startled her with its thin, reedy sound; it was the voice of a defeated woman.

Yet there were the days and nights when she rallied against defeat. Her ancestors had fought physically and mentally to make their young country a haven for human dreams and actions. "They endured," she often thought as she clenched her jaws. "Surely I, too, have inherited some of their spirit."

In the still nights when Saratoga lay asleep under a blanket of snow, she would awaken suddenly and listen for the sound of Frank's footsteps on the stairs. Then pain would engulf her, squeezing her heart, as if prodding her nerves to feel again. Those were the times when she would get up and go into the nursery to gaze at Clara's sleeping face and smell the sweet baby smell of life, innocent to all pain and sorrow.

She set a rigorous course of study aside for herself, determined to read the *Memories of H. LeWhite, Life of Tecumseh* and the *Life of Sir Walter Scott*, as well as Ingersoll's *History of War of 1812*.

Fighting for a purpose, she tried to write again, but writing forced her to think and conjured up painful memories. "The noblest heroism," she wrote one day, "is the persistent purpose to lead an intellectual life, to accomplish good, and to win happiness in spite of one terrible calamity."

Slowly, she felt herself coming to life again, numbness and pain giving way to a force stirring within her. "To face trial," she thought, "to endure it yet live above it, to give it due attention yet allow no fretting over it—how difficult the task, yet how—necessary."

Still there were days when she could not get out of bed, and persistent ailments began to bother her. She often caught colds, and one time thought she had contracted influenza. Her headaches, always persistent, began to persecute her, leaving her weak and shaky.

"Mother," Nellie said firmly one evening, "let me run the school this coming year. I do not believe you should undertake the task, you need to gather your strength."

The two women began to work several hours each morning, discussing what should be done and how. If Nellie ran the school, that would leave a vacancy in the art and French departments. They also needed someone to take Frank's place in the mathematics department. But aside from the difficult task of finding new teachers, Ellen would be confronted with Frank's absence every day, and she still couldn't face the obvious emptiness.

One morning Ellen suddenly dropped the pencil with which she was writing a column of figures and looked at Nellie helplessly. "I want to close the school," she said softly. "I simply can't face it right now."

"Can you do that, Mother? It isn't only the income, but it's been the focal point for all of us for so long."

"I could give private English lessons," Ellen answered, "and you can give art lessons." She sighed and passed a hand over her eyes. "I believe it is sometimes essential that we die to the practical life about us—or that we have a season of suspended animation, when the world and its affairs are as a tale whose truth is told, or a dream to be forgotten."

In late November, Rhoda Thompson brought to Ellen's attention the fact that the State Library in Albany was taking applications for the position of librarian due to the death of Dr. Henry Holmes. "It would be a perfect position for you, Ellen," she enthused, "and I know you could have enough people sign a petition on your behalf."

The thought of a state position, one requiring a great deal of mental thought, galvanized her into action. She placed an advertisement in the local paper announcing that she was an applicant before the State Board of Regents for the position of librarian at the State Library in Albany. Nellie helped her as they petitioned merchants and educators, as well as all the prominent citizens. They organized an evening reception for close to one hundred people, and Ellen, smiling and gracious, explained to each and every one what she would bring to the position and why she desired it.

"I know I haven't the credentials of some of the candidates," she told Rhoda one afternoon, "but I do have the advantage of having run a successful school and knowing books, not to mention influential people." But when George Howell, an historical researcher and writer in the State Library who had assisted with editing historical documents, was chosen for the position, Ellen realized how limited her credentials were. Disheartened, she again was left with an empty school and little energy.

Yet her desires had risen to the surface, and only now, living in the quiet, cavernous house in the middle of winter, did she realize how few but bitter memories surrounded her. For years she had bounced between the duties of what she had to do and the satisfaction of what she wished to do. She had struggled to separate herself from the drudgery and stand above it, and often she had failed. At times she could feel the present weaving limitations around the future she so ardently wanted. A few months before Frank's death she had calculated that in two years she would hopefully be free to change her occupation, her interests, even her leisure.

Now, while purpose eluded her, change beckoned hopefully. The mental stimulation, the charged atmosphere she had always longed for, resided for her in the nation's capitol. With no reluctance to leave Saratoga, and with a faint excitement stirring within her, she decided to move to Washington, D.C.

252

Chapter 44

The intense heat of a Washington summer was giving way to a hint of coolness in the air. Ellen stood at the open window of her small apartment and gratefully lifted her face to the fresh breeze. Like the listless leaves being stirred on the trees, the air awakened hope within her.

Even though her book, *Battles of Saratoga*, had recently been published and well received, she could not summon the old vitality she longed for. At times she was excited, even euphoric about her new surroundings, but then she would slide back into the mental, physical, and spiritual hypnosis under which she had languished for nearly a year.

In the morning she awakened to an emptiness within herself, which gave way by late afternoon to acute longing, bringing with it pain as real as a sharp, physical stab. She missed Saratoga, she missed a family, she missed the purpose they created for her. Guilt over leaving a grieving daughter–in–law gnawed at her, and she could not shake the ominous weight she felt at leaving Tracy on his own.

As she watched the carriages rattling by on their way to some unknown destination and listened to the rhythmic sounds of the horses' hoofbeats, she gave a wry laugh. "Solitude was always so dear and so eagerly sought," she said aloud to the air, "and now I am surfeited with solitude." Her own voice sounded strange in the emptiness that enveloped her. "I, who have longed for time for reading and writing and study, now find it impossible to harmonize my mind and my actions."

She had always gone within herself for answers to the complexity of her life. As she surveyed her living room, looking at the chair–side table where she had so carefully and lovingly arranged her treasured books, she began to muse:

"Perhaps a new and different spirit will animate this old being. While the same abilities and energies lie buried within, a different impetus will drive them to action."

She wandered aimlessly into her bedroom and looked at her face in the dressing mirror. She had gained weight, and her features were puffy, but for a woman in her middle fifties, her skin remained remarkably smooth. Happiness had eluded her most of her life, yet her eyes still held an expectant vulnerability, as hopeful as a young woman. Suddenly she straightened her shoulders and fixed a steely gaze on the uncertain reflection in the mirror. "I cannot go back, nor do I really want to," she silently told herself. "Regardless of where I am, there must be movement. In any event, let it be upward and onward!"

She had come to Washington to banish the defeats of her past, and now with a conscious effort to make a new beginning for herself, she began to take typing lessons and look for employment.

By the beginning of 1890 she had successfully turned her back upon guilt, homesickness, and lethargy and had secured a position with the Department of the Interior as a clerk and statistician. Slowly her energy was returning, and once again the old literary ambitions were stirring within her.

She renewed her interest in the National Historical Association and began to attend their meetings. When she read an announcement in the newspaper that the grave of George Washington's mother, Mary, at Fredericksburg, Virginia, was to be sold at auction to the highest bidder, she was incensed. Not only did the action seem macabre, it seemed like a desecration of the nation's history. Ellen immediately wrote to the paper asking if the auction couldn't be delayed until an organization could be formed to take care of the matter. By return mail, she was informed that a great many women were indignant at the thought of the auction, and an organization was being hurriedly formed to save the grave. Immediately she wrote to the other women mentioned by the paper and told each of them about the funds she had helped secure for Mt. Vernon. She became a member of the Mary Washington Memorial Association, whose object was a public appeal to purchase the grave and erect a monument worthy of the mother of the first United States President.

As spring's warmth banished the damp chill of winter, Ellen's energies accelerated joyously when Ruby secured a job as a model attendant at the Patent Office. Ellen basked in the happiness that suddenly radiated in the tiny apartment when her daughter moved in with her. Excited by the city, by her job, by the artwork and photography she continued to pursue in the evenings, Ruby was a swirl of sunshine, constantly creating a bevy of stimulation. Ellen, who had always longed for someone who could awaken her mental energies, was surprised that the perfect companion had turned out to be her youngest daughter.

Ruby had joined the suffragist movement at Vassar, and while many of her classmates marched and argued for the right to vote while still looking for the perfect husband, Ruby decided that she would never marry, that she would never be dependent upon anyone but herself.

"Nonsense, Ruby," Ellen admonished one evening as they cooked supper, "that's only half a life. It's important to love, to have children. The home is a necessary part of life."

"Was it so necessary for you, Mama? All your life you have fought conflicts, you have strained to be part of a larger picture while you scraped financially and worked like hired help and suffered your children's fates. What makes that so necessary?"

254

"It didn't turn out right for me," Ellen admitted as she sat down to the table. "But when it's right, Ruby, when there is a lovely home and children and good friends to share your happiness with, it's almost a sanctity."

"I intend to sanction my life as I choose and not have to suffer the choices of a husband."

Ellen looked at her beautiful daughter, the one daughter she had been so certain would make a brilliant marriage. Now she felt a pang of sympathy for Ruby, for her stubborn intent to lead a solitary life. "This isn't what I envisioned for you," Ellen said softly. "Yet, who knows, perhaps you are right."

The suffragist movement was sweeping the country, bestowing a golden dawn upon women whose intellectual demands went beyond serving a husband and children. The movement had been started in 1848 by Elizabeth Cady Stanton, a housewife and mother whose mind pushed against the limitations imposed upon her by a small town barren of any intellectual stimulation. With four of her friends, she had conceived the idea of a convention to discuss the social, civic, and religious rights of women. The first convention had been held on July 14, 1848, in the Wesleyan Chapel at Seneca Falls, New York. During the raging anger of the Civil War, the rights of women suddenly seemed unimportant compared to the bloody battle that was being waged to unite a divided nation. But now, in the late nineteenth century, the movement had gained force and was uniting women brave enough to demand a larger place in the world.

Washington was full of a number of women working for various reasons in government departments, and slowly Ellen began to form tentative friendships among her acquaintances. Of all the women she had met, there were few she admired and enjoyed more than Adelaide Johnson. Adelaide possessed a superb intellect, an inexhaustible energy, and an infectious enthusiasm for both her work in the Interior Department and her various causes. She proudly considered herself a suffragist and was most enthusiastic about the Wimodaughsis, the name of a women's organization formed from the first syllables of wife, mother, daughter, and sister.

"Our objective is to have a clubhouse for women," Adelaide explained to Ellen, "a forum where ideas concerning a woman's role in the world can be discussed and acted upon. Ellen, you must come to a meeting," she insisted with some authority. "The ideas are not only stimulating, but the women are the most interesting people you will meet in Washington. It is only through organizations of this type that women's lives will emerge from subservience."

Ellen studied her friend for a moment. "Woman's power emanates from the home. I don't mean the suffragette movement isn't helpful," she amended. "Heaven knows where we would be without the Property Act. Because of that act, as a married woman I was allowed to hold on to my real estate. Yet my feeling is that women need to be encouraged toward self–reliance and self–fulfillment so they will find greater joy in being wives and mothers."

"And you, a widow, forced to earn a living," Adelaide almost snorted. "Think of the women unable to earn a living, forced to raise their children in abject poverty."

"Necessity teaches self–reliance quickly," Ellen answered. "I could not trade my pride for less than my family deserved. Supporting my family took a great sacrifice of time and thought I would rather have given to them. Do you know how I really wanted to live?" Ellen asked. "I wanted a quiet life, one that would have enabled me to guide my children's lives with a measure of security and serenity, with time for study and writing. For a life like that there doesn't need to be an organization, only luck."

"A life like that," Adelaide retorted, "is only a dream that encourages women to be bound in chains with no key handy for the lock when they awaken."

"You win," Ellen laughed. "I'll go to a meeting with you and see for myself."

Ellen found that Adelaide was right. It was stimulating to be among women with a larger picture than keeping house, women with their eyes fixed on the far horizon of the future. As Adelaide introduced Ellen to the women, she followed every introduction with a list of Ellen's credentials. "My friend, Ellen Walworth, the first woman to sit on a public board of education in New York State," or "My friend, Ellen Walworth, an historian and author."

The leader of Wimodaughsis, suffragist Anna Howard Shaw, welcomed Ellen warmly. Among the club's stockholders were prominent names in the suffragist movement, including Elizabeth Cady Stanton, Susan B. Anthony, and Clara Barton.

Ellen felt an instant kinship with Mary Desha when she learned that Mary's ancestry also sprang from Kentucky soil. She was a native of Lexington, a descendent from a Kentucky Revolutionary Colonel, and she had become a clerk at the Pension Bureau five years earlier following her brother–in–law's election to Congress.

Yet despite the women she had met, despite the enjoyment she had felt for the evening, Ellen still had reservations. "It all seems to me a bit aimless," she confided to Ruby after the meeting. "Just to organize for women's rights ... the important thing is what women will do with those 'rights.' It might be for you, Ruby, but I'm afraid I'm just too old–fashioned."

Chapter 45

Coming out of the office building one hot July afternoon after work, Ellen found Adelaide waiting for her, brandishing a copy of the *Washington Post*.

"Have you seen this?" she cried excitedly.

"Seen what?" Ellen asked, not bothering to hide the exhaustion she felt after spending the day in an office devoid of even the smallest breeze.

Adelaide seemed undaunted by the heat. "It seems that a new organization called the Sons of the American Revolution convened in Louisville in April but refused to allow women to attend." She chuckled gleefully. "Wait until you read Mary Lockwood's article taking them to task."

"Let's find some shade and, if we are lucky, a breeze," Ellen pleaded, "and I'll look at it. I think my clothes are permanently stuck to my skin."

While they walked, Adelaide told Ellen about Mary Lockwood. She had, since 1876, been the proprietress of a Washington hotel. During that time she had founded the Travel Club of Washington and headed a local temperance society. She had written magazine articles on the tariff, a textbook on ceramics, and a volume on *The Historic Homes of Washington*. "This article is excellent," Adelaide enthused. "It tells the story of Hannah Arnett, the wife of a Revolutionary patriot who, along with some of his friends, was discussing the feasibility of deserting the Revolutionary cause and accepting amnesty from the British. At the time, the Revolutionary tide was at a very low ebb."

They came to a bench under the shade of a magnolia tree, and Ellen gratefully sank down on it. She passed a hand over her perspiring forehead, then fanned herself for a moment before opening the paper.

"I won't say a word until you've finished reading," Adelaide promised as Ellen's eyes scanned the page.

"The group told Hannah the case was hopeless," she read. "The Revolutionary army was starving, half–clothed, and undisciplined, driven back everywhere. 'We are ruined and can stand no longer against England and her unlimited resources.'

Hannah Arnett listened and spoke in a strangely sweet voice. 'Brothers,' she said, 'you have forgotten one thing which England has not, and we have—one thing which outweighs all England's treasures, and that is the right. We are poor and weak and few, but God is fighting for us; we entered into this struggle with pure hearts and prayerful lips; we had counted the cost and were willing to pay the price, were it in our heart's blood. And no—now because for a time the day is going against us, you would give up all and sneak back like cravens to kiss the feet that have trampled upon us. And you call yourselves men—the sons of those who gave up fame and fortune and fatherhood to make for themselves and for dear liberty a resting place in the wilderness! Oh, shame upon you cowards!'

Hannah Arnett talked on: 'Take your protection if you will; proclaim yourselves traitors and cowards, false to your God. For me, I stay with my country, and my hand shall never touch the hand nor my heart cleave to the heart of him who shames her.' She turned to her husband and gave him a withering look that sent a shock through every fibre of his body. Continuing she said: 'Isaac, we have lived together for twenty years, and through all of them I have been to you a true and loving wife; but I am the child of God and my country, and if you do this shameful thing, I will never own you again as my husband.'

A latent courage put on a new activity; manliness renewed its strength in strong resolution. Before these men left the house of Hannah Arnett that night every one had resolved to spurn the proffered amnesty and had taken a solemn oath to stand by their country. Where will the Sons of the American Revolution place Hannah Arnett?"

Ellen lowered the paper and with a glint in her eye looked at Adelaide. "She certainly did put them in their place. I'm not certain it will do any good, though. They will probably brand Mrs. Lockwood a fanatic and pull even more tightly together."

"Of course it will help," Adelaide retorted. "We will be forever slighted if women continue to meekly say nothing when this sort of thing happens. Mary Lockwood is to be commended. She saw an injustice and answered it."

When Mary Desha's note arrived a few days later, Ellen was delighted. The note had been hastily scrawled and was short and right to the point, asking simply if Ellen would be interested in forming an organization of Daughters of the American Revolution.

Adelaide had told Ellen that Mary was incensed when she read Mary Lockwood's article and had written to her at once asking what could be done.

Ellen had seen Mary Desha a few times since first meeting her at the Wimodaughsis and had grown to enjoy her company more and more. Mary had the gift of igniting one's intellect one moment and then diffusing it the next with a witty remark. It was a delightful balance and one that was seldom encountered in the serious demeanor of those women who considered themselves intellectuals.

Ellen sat down at once and answered Mary's invitation. She would be happy to join, she wrote. Would they be interested in meeting at her apartment?

The evening of August 9 was torn apart by a thunderstorm. Reflections of lightning danced through the apartment as Ellen fluffed pillows and straightened books and newspapers. In the kitchen, a freshly baked coconut cake waited on the counter along with Ellen's china and silver coffee service. "It feels good to be receiving guests again," she thought. She went to the window and peered through the rain–soaked glass and jumped when a tree limb came crashing down across the street.

A carriage slowed at the curb, and Ellen recognized the tall, slender figure of Mary Desha stepping onto the walk. Ellen waited a moment for the elevator to ascend and then opened her door as Mary walked down the long hallway. "You're the first one here. Let me take your umbrella."

"It's a mean evening," Mary said. "I hope the others make it. Weren't you the smart one to offer your home? You don't have to go out in the weather."

It was only a few minutes later before a knock came on the door, and Ellen hurried to answer it. The heavyset but distinguished–looking woman before her introduced herself. "Mrs. Walworth? I'm Eugenia Washington."

"Please come in," Ellen said, genuinely happy and impressed to meet the great–granddaughter of Colonel Samuel Washington, George Washington's brother. "The only other person here right now is Mary Desha."

"You must want to drown me, Mary," Eugenia said with a heavy drawl as she walked into the living room, "or why else would you have invited me out on an evening like this?"

"Please make yourself comfortable," Ellen said, "while we wait to see who else comes."

"Flora Adams Darling won't be here as she is in Culpeper, Virginia," Mary said, "but she is vastly interested in the organization. She suggested we wait to organize until mid–September, but I thought it important to start as soon as possible."

The impetus for starting a woman's patriotic organization had come from William O. McDowell of New Jersey, the great–grandson of Hannah Arnett and a vice–president–at–large of the Sons of the American Revolution. At first several struggling branches of the Sons had admitted women, but its desire for union with the more conservative Sons of the Revolution led the first national congress in 1890 to exclude them. Yet, as early as June 1889, the irrepressible McDowell had begun petitioning for a Daughters of the American Revolution. After the decision at the Sons' convention (which also happened to deprive him of most of his influence in that organization) he unsuccessfully redoubled his efforts. When he had read Mary Lockwood's article in the *Post*, he had written a letter to the paper thanking Mrs. Lockwood for recalling the name of his ancestor, expressed his interest in the establishment of a patriotic society for women like her, and offered his cooperation. After suggesting the society be named the Daughters of the American Revolution, he had promised to help draft the organization's constitution and bylaws. McDowell requested that interested women of Revolutionary ancestry communicate with him, including three Washington residents: Mary Lockwood, Mary Desha, and Eugenia Washington.

"My enthusiasm for some unified form of patriotic endeavor was first awakened in 1875," Ellen told the two women, "when I read a statewide call in a California newspaper for all men of Revolutionary descent to march in a July Fourth parade the following year. I thought to myself then, 'Why just men?'"

"Women suffer just as much as men in a fight for liberty," Eugenia mused. "They might not get hit with cannon fire, but they pay a great price emotionally as well as physically, running their homes and raising children without husbands, brothers, or fathers to help. I have never understood why men disapprove of women expressing patriotic feelings."

"We might as well get started," Mary said abruptly. "It looks like the bad weather is going to keep everybody else away."

"We must have had the strongest ancestors," Eugenia laughed, "for us to be the only ones to brave the elements."

"Mary Lockwood would have been here tonight except that her work with the Historical Congress for the World's Fair is keeping her too busy right now." Mary smoothed her dress over her knees and folded her hands on her lap. "Our purpose, of course," she said, "is to have a club-house for women, a place where we can meet and talk over patriotic ideas and see if there is a realm in government we might influence."

"Mary," Ellen interrupted, "the Wimodaughsis is also building a clubhouse for women. I think we need more than just a building. First, we need objectives."

Mary looked at her blankly. In the few times they had been together, she had formed an admiration for Ellen's accomplishments and a quiet respect for her background.

"The Sons have intense patriotism as their objective and a desire to influence the patriotism of others," Eugenia interjected. "What's wrong with that?"

"If we are to be the feminine branch of their organization, then we must accept those objectives," Ellen stated. "But to establish our own identity, why not devote ourselves to a department entirely our own and try to form an historical library? Maybe even a picture gallery of the wives of the Presidents."

"Before we decide upon anything, perhaps we'd better examine this parcel which Mr. McDowell sent to Mrs. Lockwood," Mary said as she opened the package. She began to take out the pages slowly. Her lips were tightly pressed as though she knew a secret she could not let escape, while her eyes, round and wide, danced with a twinkle of suppressed merriment. Inside the parcel were full organizational plans for the Sons of the American Revolution, their constitution, and a bound notebook for the amended and approved Daughters of the American Revolution. "Look at this!" In her excitement Mary almost shouted. She held up an application blank with the word Sons neatly scratched out and Daughters substituted above and Mr. McDowell's name inscribed on it. "He has even enclosed a check for his initiation fees and his dues for one year."

"So a man is our first member!" Eugenia exclaimed. They laughed at the absurdity of the situation as they bent their heads over the table to examine the papers.

"With everything already here," Ellen said, "we only need to choose a time for our next meeting and become fully organized."

"I think we should go ahead this evening and form a Board of Management. If we wait until we have enough interested women, it will take endless meetings to organize." Mary's voice was brisk and firm. "Eugenia, I think it only fitting since you are related to our first president, that you be listed number one on our roster."

"And you be chairman," Eugenia told Mary. "You have organized everything. Don't you agree, Ellen?"

Ellen nodded her assent. "I'll volunteer for the duties of secretary," she offered. She felt excited, being in on the ground floor of a new organization and contented with her first acceptance into a group of people who had not previously known her.

"Then that leaves me for registrar," Eugenia announced with satisfaction.

"We'll need a motto," Ellen said as she rose to go to the kitchen for coffee. "How about 'Amor Patriae?' "

"Perfect," Mary stated emphatically. "It's simple, yet dignified." She sank back against the chair cushion. "We have accomplished more by ourselves than we would have with fifty women present."

Ellen came back into the living room carrying a tray with coffee and slices of cake on crystal plates. "And when will we meet next?" she inquired again as she poured the coffee.

"I need to speak to Mrs. Lockwood and see when she can be present," Mary said. "Flora Darling won't return until early October. Perhaps we should wait until then."

261

"In the meantime, we should be listing names of those we think might be appropriate to hold other posts in the organization," Eugenia said.

"If we want the Daughters to succeed," Ellen said slowly as she put her coffee cup down, "we should name women whose husband's are well–placed. We don't want to be looked upon as just another suffragette organization."

Mary looked at her for a moment with tightly pursed lips. "You're probably right," she said reluctantly. "It's unfortunate that women are only known by their husband's contributions."

"Why not approach Mrs. Benjamin Harrison to be our President–General?" Ellen asked.

"A brilliant idea, Ellen," Eugenia said. "She's the only one who could be our President–General!"

Ellen dressed hurriedly for the meeting at Mrs. Darling's apartment in the Strathmore Arms. Because it was Saturday she had slept later than usual, then had spent the rest of the morning writing letters. She had written a long letter to Tracy in Saratoga telling him of her activities and asking him to take good care of his uncle D.

D. had written to Ellen saying that he thought he would go to Saratoga to be with Tracy for a while. It was a letter that sounded as empty as if he had mailed her a blank page. Since the untimely death of his wife, D. had floated like a lost soul. At least, she reflected as she picked up her handbag, Tracy wouldn't be lonely with D. there. They had forged a close bond when she had taken Tracy to Florida, and now she could relax knowing that Tracy considered D. his best friend.

Mrs. Darling's apartment was crowded with some two dozen women as well as an advisory board from the Sons of the American Revolution that Mr. McDowell had brought.

"Ellen," Mary Desha called to her as she threaded her way through the crowd, "I want you to meet Mrs. Darling before the proceedings begin."

Flora Adams Darling was a diminutive woman who was originally from New Hampshire and claimed to be related to the Presidents Adams. She had married Colonel Edward Darling, a man twenty–two years older than she, and moved to his home in Louisiana. She once had confided to Mary that she had developed a friendship with Jefferson Davis so intimate that she assisted materially in the collection of data for his memoirs, and that his last personal letter was addressed to her. During the Civil War Colonel Darling had been killed and the Federal authorities had jailed Flora in New Orleans, where she had contracted scarlet fever. She was still fighting a claims case that had been brought before Congress over the theft of her securities and jewelry during her arrest.

Even though an attack of malaria in 1876 had destroyed her hearing and impaired her eyesight, she had become a government clerk. She was also the editor *The Gotham Monthly*, which she had cofounded with two other women in New York the previous winter.

Her widow's weeds only accented her vivacity, Ellen thought. "I'm so glad to meet you," Flora trilled in a high Southern drawl. "Isn't it wonderful that Mr. McDowell brought an advisory board here?" She gave the delightful impression of a bird that can't quite get settled on her perch. "You must all find a seat now, and we'll start this meeting."

Mr. McDowell took his place next to Mrs. Darling at her dining table. It had been his idea to hold the meeting on the anniversary of the discovery of America. "After all," he had said, "it is a date particularly appropriate for the organization of a society of women, since it was due to a woman's generosity and wisdom that Columbus was provided for the means to fit out his fleet for his perilous voyage."

Flora thumped the gavel she held on a large book and then passed it to Mr. McDowell. Ellen listened carefully as the constitution was read and the names of the officers were politely approved by the audience. When Mrs. Benjamin Harrison's name was read as the choice for President–General, the applause was wildly enthusiastic. Mary Desha remained as chairman of the executive board. Other posts were filled by the wives of three generals, one admiral, one colonel, and the director of the Smithsonian Institute. Clara Barton, the nurse who during the Civil War had gone directly to the battlefields bringing supplies and nursing the wounded, was named surgeon–general, Ellen stayed as secretary–general, and Mrs. Levi Morton was named treasurer. Mary Lockwood, whose letter had started it all, was named historian–general. Flora Adams Darling accepted the post of vice–president–general–at–large, in charge of organizing chapters around the country.

"Don't you agree," Flora asked Ellen as they mingled after the meeting, "that we must keep our sisterhood of Daughters free from entangling alliances with bands of women aiming at the 'fads' of today? That is, I believe we must entrench ourselves within the charmed barriers of Revolutionary descent and social consequence."

"You're most certainly right," Ellen agreed emphatically, thinking of the suffragette leanings of Mary Desha and Mary Lockwood. "It is imperative that we be known as a patriotic organization and not an army marching for 'rights.'"

"We must call on Mrs. Harrison to make a formal announcement of her unanimous election. Let's see, this is Saturday. Don't you think Monday morning would be appropriate?"

Ellen eagerly anticipated her meeting with the First Lady. She thought there was no place on earth more imposing or thrilling than the magnificent white structure on Pennsylvania Avenue. It was the seat of political and social power, and from here sprang the freedoms guaranteeing the right of happiness to every citizen of the Republic.

President and Mrs. Benjamin Harrison had developed a reputation for being cold people. Always socially correct, Mrs. Harrison had been taught the dignity of her person by her father, president of the Oxford Female Seminary in Ohio. She had led an active public life with her lawyer husband long before he entered politics. During President Harrison's Civil War service she had visited the war camps, ready to take over any duties of nursing and feeding soldiers for which she was needed.

Mrs. Harrison and her three daughters stamped their imprint of gentility on the nation, with the reports of their activities of embroidery and beading, china painting, and raising exotic plants.

It was rumored that she was unhappy living in a public building like the White House, and that she intended to build a new Executive Mansion, more suitable for a family.

Mrs. Harrison received them in the Blue Room, and her personage conveyed the dignity of the house itself. Although short and amply endowed, she carried herself with a stature suggesting graceful height. Her light–brown hair was piled on top of her head, a fringe of curls at the front. She greeted Flora and Ellen with the barest hint of a smile and glanced at the slate of officers, which Flora had handed to her for her approval.

"My only objection to this," she said rather apologetically after she had read the slate, "is to the chairman of the executive board. I feel that anyone holding this key position is the logical person to represent me officially at many places and on most occasions. Therefore, I think it should be held by a married woman, one with social prominence and a residence of some pretension in Washington."

Flora blanched for a moment, then recovered quickly. "Would Mrs. William Cabell be appropriate? She and her husband own Norwood, the exclusive girls' school, and in addition to being an educator, she is quite socially prominent."

"Yes, I know her," Mrs. Harrison responded. "Someone like that would be an excellent choice if she would accept the post."

"I committed a grave error of judgement in naming Miss Desha to such a place of prominence," Flora lamented as they walked down the steps of the White House. "I'll write to her as soon as I return home and tell her she must be sacrificed for the good of the cause."

Chapter 46

"I've been decapitated!" Mary paced back and forth in Ellen's small living room, her face contorted with fury. "I don't believe for one minute that Flora Adams Darling is a descendent of a President. I'm certain none of her ancestors fought for the Revolutionary cause, although knowing her, they must have been capable of starting a war!"

Ellen sighed. "Mary, we have to remain above fighting with each other over positions; we are all working to further faith in our founding fathers. Our nation is threatened by subversive foreigners. And we must do our part to save the country from radical labor unrest."

Mary refused to listen. She stopped pacing and stood in front of Ellen, her eyes wide. "I don't believe she is even very bright. She keeps repeating that stupid phrase: 'I believe in men for offices—women for pleasure.'"

"Isn't patriotism what we are all about?" Ellen tried to keep her voice calm. "If we women unite as Americans, it is possible we might help stem the torrent of socialism and anarchy that threatens us from foreign countries. If we are united, our society will have the power to stimulate the best men of our country to hold fast to the early principles of government."

No matter how much Ellen cajoled and pleaded for reason, Mary continued to denounce Flora loudly and strongly, holding her personally responsible for the Harrison ultimatum. Flora retaliated.

"At the first meeting," Flora reminded the Daughters, "our illustrious leaders did more than just examine the papers sent to them by Mr. McDowell. They also did not hesitate to appoint a number of officers, including themselves."

Ellen continued to speak out on the necessity of unity in thought and work in the patriotic objects of the Society.

Mary, somewhat mollified by Ellen's point of view, asked the members to offer their free expression of opinion in regard to the management of the Society.

Flora insisted she had been receiving anonymous letters which were a stigma against certain members of the Board and called for the matter to be investigated. When the Board declined to look into the accusations, she began to take matters in her own hands and act as though a Board of Management did not exist. She refused to report to it or acknowledge its authority, and she personally advised the Regents in the various chapters to do nothing further until the meeting of the Congress in February. She began to write abusive and insulting letters to the Board, threatened legal proceedings against the members, and finally forbade the use of her name in the Society.

Mrs. Cabell deplored the altercations and ignored them as best she could, insisting that the first enterprise taken by the Daughters should be a search for a home. "The women of America, largely represented by the Society," she said, "need a house where their books can be lodged to grow into the greatest collection of colonial and Revolutionary history in the world, a spacious hall where debates and addresses can take place, with fire–proof apartments to house relics and treasures. A commodious place is needed where officers and members can meet for business transactions."

A seal was designed for the Society and approved by the members. It was to consist of a figure in the dress of 1776 seated at a spinning wheel and rocking a cradle. The motto would read, "The hand that rocks the cradle rules the world."

Mrs. Harrison issued an invitation for a meeting to be held in the White House. The entire lower floor of the Executive Mansion was thrown open for the occasion. As the women's eyes swept over every surface and their minds memorized every nook and cranny, they had to concede that Mrs. Harrison, unable to acquire the funds for a new Executive Mansion, had nonetheless campaigned successfully for a thorough remodeling.

Electricity had been installed to take the place of gas lamps, and servants could be summoned by electric bells. Private bathrooms had been added. It was reported that a methodical extermination of rats had been undertaken, and the old rotting floorboards, as many as five in some places, had been removed and replaced by new flooring.

The meeting was called to order in the Blue Room, which had been lightened with blue wallpaper covered with baskets of flowers. An elegant crystal chandelier hung in the center of the ceiling and crystal wall sconces sparkled around the sides of the circular room. In place of the dark figured carpeting worn to thinness over the years, a new parquet floor gleamed. The heavy, ornate black walnut furniture had been replaced by lighter French Regency pieces. "It's like Versailles!" Ellen heard one woman whisper loudly.

After the meeting, tea, chocolate, and coffee were served, along with small sandwiches and cake, from a table covered in blue linen holding a centerpiece of orchids.

The conservatory in the west wing was opened, and the women strolled amid the tall palms and ferns, banana, fig, and nut trees, and admired the masses of orchids which Mrs. Harrison cultivated. There was a feeling of elegance and sophistication mingling with the ever-present aura of power.

Ellen believed in the aims of the Daughters, and to that end, she was willing to work for the Society, but the endless squabbling, the running to meetings and recording minutes was exhausting her in its seeming triviality. Ironically, she noted there was now no more time for study or writing than there had been when she was raising her children.

When Mrs. Cabell asked for ideas to further communications between national headquarters and the various chapters, Ellen repeated the idea that Flora Darling had once proposed. "We should consider a magazine," she said, "not only to further communication between national headquarters and the chapters in other states, but also to promote and report patriotic endeavors to the country at large." There was a murmur of approval in the room. Because it was her idea and she was a published writer and a member of the American Historical Association, Ellen was appointed editor of the magazine.

Excited, yet nervous over the immense undertaking for which she had volunteered, Ellen found ideas tumbling through her mind, one after the other. Some she discarded as absurd, others she wrote down as feasible. "The magazine will have to contain the reports of the Continental Congress and from time to time the reports of the Board of Management," Ellen explained to Ruby. "But I want it to be more than just reports, I want it to be informative and entertaining, a magazine in every sense of the word."

"You will need photographs and illustrations," Ruby told her, "and I can help with the layout."

"There must be space given to the Sons of the American Revolution." A shadow of anxiety passed over Ellen's face. "There are bound to be mistakes."

"I should think the Daughters will be lenient and charitable," Ruby answered indignantly. "If not, you can console yourself with the knowledge that you are giving your best efforts to the cause, and they must be content with what they get."

"We're going to need help, Ruby. Advice." Ellen bit her lip in concentration. "Working at the Interior Department gives me an excuse to write to the Assistant Attorney General and see what he thinks of the idea." She rose abruptly, got a pencil and paper, and sat down with Ruby at the dining table to draft the letter.

267

Within a few days they received an answer:

"We have no doubt the magazine will be a success under your management. Perfection does not exist in this world, and if it did, would all be pleased?

I think I would print the papers of the ladies, rather than the gentlemen's speeches. The ladies ought to be given preference in this magazine.

As to a sketch of my life and picture, while I greatly appreciate the compliment, I think it would be wise to leave it until later. It would also be wise to include the chapters and to send statements of what they are doing and to print pictures occasionally of famous spots renowned on account of Revolutionary events. I would advise not much expense for pictures; it might be wise some time during the year to print a picture of the Presidents, Generals, the Daughters of the American Revolution, and the Sons of the American Revolution."

Ellen was elated. After a full day at work, even if she had meetings in the late afternoon and evening, she and Ruby sat up until late in the night, discussing and sketching out their ideas of what the magazine should be and what it should encompass. The apartment was pervaded by a sense of adventure, of unleashed creativity, of experimentation and discovery. The two of them were talented and full of drive, ambition, and imagination. The room hummed with the warmth of comradeship, the thrill of working together, praising, criticizing, suggesting. Their relationship grew beyond that of mother and daughter; they respected and admired each other as individuals.

In late May, Ellen began to feel a sluggish exhaustion. For no apparent reason, she often became short of breath. She consulted a doctor, who told her that her heart was weak, that she needed not only quiet but also outdoor exercise and a good diet. She was to restrict meat, butter, sugar, and milk.

With the first issue of the magazine ready for the press, Ellen took a leave of absence from her job and made plans to return to Saratoga for the summer. The Walworth Mansion was being leased for the season by Mrs. Wilson Bell of New York City, but Ellen could live at The Logs, the old Walworth cabin by the lake, with Tracy.

Ellen shut out the world her first week at the lake. Late one morning, gazing at the sparkling water, at the clear blue sky overhead with soft white clouds floating over its surface, she thought it incredible that death could threaten. "It makes me a little anxious," she mused as she strolled in the clear air, "but brings no fear. The pressing purposes of my life are accomplished, the rearing of my family is about over. If personal hopes, desires, ambitions, have been pushed aside, what matter; they have given rest in labor, ease in trouble, hope in the throes of despair." Still, no matter what words her thoughts formed, the regrets lay there with her, a sharp ache reminding her that the ignorant, untrained spirit she harbored might have reached after heights of knowledge and power under a freer life. There was so much she felt herself to be, and so many barriers that had blocked that self. She wanted those early years now, wanted them so badly that she would have clawed back through time if she could to retrieve them. Time! "It may be used as precious gems are worn," she thought, "for high days and holidays. The leading of a life of active service work should be over and the spirit set free or it will die. The spirit should devote its activities only to the better part of life, to that which is good and true and beautiful, to work that is enduring or that will enlarge and elevate human sympathy."

Her return to Saratoga gave her the satisfaction that all was well with her family. Clara was still polite, though distant. Ellen still struggled to resign herself to Clara's vocation and to the distance between them.

Nellie had published her book about Kateri Tekawitha, *The Lily of the Mohawks*, and had received good reviews. She had recently moved to Albany to work as an amanuensis for Clarence. He had generously purchased a house close to his own, not only for Nellie, but for Corinne and little Clara as well. Tracy was well and happy, supporting himself by doing odd jobs of carpentry in town and amusing himself by the improvements he was able to make on the cabin by the lake.

In the quiet beauty, the warm sunshine, and the absence of pressing duties, Ellen began to relax. Her daily walks brought serenity and seemed to banish her shortness of breath. Fresh color came into her face, and her eyes sparkled. She began to use her mornings for work on the magazine, drafting ideas and writing articles. The rest and quiet enabled her thoughts to flow freely, and as she worked, she felt she was reaching out across the continent, influencing the minds of others. She had always felt the necessity of having others see the importance of the nation's history as she saw it, and now the magazine was the venue for that endeavor.

In late June, she received the first completed copy of the magazine. On an off–white background, *The American Monthly* was spelled out in black letters, with the insignia of the Daughters of the American Revo-

269

lution below it in blue and white. Ellen held it in her hands with a mixture of disbelief and satisfaction that she had just completed the first important work of her life. Thumbing through it, she thought proudly that it could take its place as an educational tool among the best publications of the day.

She had opened the issue with a picture of Mrs. Benjamin Harrison and a brief biographical sketch. The prospectus explained why it was necessary to publish a magazine devoted to the cause of a true and liberal Americanism. It would "perpetuate the memory and spirit of the men and women who achieved American independence by the encouragement of historical research in relation to the Revolution and the publication of its results." It would keep alive the injunction of President Washington in his farewell address to the American people "to promote as an object of primary importance institutions for the general diffusion of knowledge, thus developing an enlightened public opinion and affording to young and old such advantages as shall develop in them the largest capacity for performing the duties of American citizens."

There were reports on the annual congress of the Sons of the American Revolution and the proceedings of the first Continental Congress of the Daughters of the American Revolution. In addition to the reports from national headquarters and reports from various chapters around the country, Ellen included pictures and biographical sketches of Mary Virginia Ellet Cabell and of Eugenia Washington. There were articles from chapter members: *Early History of Pittsburgh* by Julia Morgan Harding; *Bombardment of Bristol, Rhode Island* by Emma Westcott Bullock; *Peace and Liberty, the Legacy of Our Forefathers* by Mrs. Mitchell S. Nevins of Rome, Georgia. Ellen had also included a picture and biography of Dorothy Payne Madison, known to history as Dolly. She included her own *Battles of Saratoga*, the *History of the Saratoga Monument Association*, *Visitor's Guide to Saratoga*, and her fictional account of *A Visit to the Battleground*. She included the favorable reviews of her work, which had appeared in *The Magazine of American History* and the *New York Home Journal*.

In the fall, she returned to Washington refreshed and renewed, only to find that Ruby had decided to move to New York City to study art and to give private painting lessons. Ellen thought she had finally been able to accept her children's independence, but Ruby's absence filled her with the old panic of loss. Still, she was proud of her daughter and her independence and would not stand in the way of any decisions Ruby would make. During the past two years they had forged a bond too strong to ever be broken. They were an inseparable part of one another.

In October, Mrs. Harrison died. If the nation was stunned, the Daughters were at a loss, for to them, Mrs. Harrison was much more than a figurehead. She had taken an active interest in the objectives of the Daughters of the American Revolution and had attended as many meetings as she could and hosted receptions when it was possible. Her presence would be sorely missed. The Daughters decided that to memorialize her devotion to her country, a life–sized portrait of her should be painted. Ellen was appointed to secure funds for the painting and to find an artist. After looking at hundreds of portraits and talking to women who had had their portraits or those of their families painted, she finally decided upon the artist Daniel Huntington. She wrote an appeal to the Regents in the various chapters around the country explaining why there should be a portrait of Mrs. Harrison and expounding her belief that portraits of all the First Ladies should stand in the White House:

> "They were illustrious for domestic and social virtues that are typical of American life and should represent that side of our history, no less important than its legal, political, and warlike features."

She felt an immense satisfaction with her life and all she was doing. To be true to herself, to her destiny, was to be an influence upon others. Her loneliness, which she had grown used to, was assuaged by the words she put upon paper. The love which had been denied her for so long, which she had tried to cling to in her children, had found its expression in the energy of an accepted intellectual labor. "Love may be lavished on an abstraction," she reflected as she ran her hand admiringly over the smooth cover of the magazine, "and it may be lavished on an idea. If a labor is of value, some underlying element of love inspires it."

Chapter 47

Ellen greeted her sixtieth birthday with incredulity and a touch of fear. Now, when her creative energy was pushing her to recognition in many directions, she was facing old age.

She was writing articles for the magazine and editing it, she was caught in the whirl of activities for the Daughters of the American Revolution, and she was being invited to participate in numerous activities in Washington. She had recently been invited to lunch in the White House. Clara Barton, chairman of the Ladies' Citizens' Committee, had, just last month, requested her presence at the National Reception authorized by Congress, which was held in the Rotunda of the Capitol. She had been invited to attend The World's Columbian Commission ceremonies in the dedication of the buildings of The World's Columbian Exposition at Jackson Park in Chicago.

She had once read, "It has a definite and fixed conception of its own power." The phrase was imprinted upon her mind, even though she had forgotten what it was in relation to. "It is impossible to attain that of which we are uncertain. There must be within us a consciousness of power and a plan for its use if any contained effort is required to obtain the object in view," Ellen mused.

The object in view was, and had been all along, her own intellectual fulfillment. Even in the days when she had been surrounded by small children with no income and a capricious husband, she had been conscious of a power within her. In the days when Frank was in prison, the force for some successful action on her part had pushed within her like a desperate need.

"My soul and I shall count on one year longer," she mused as she contemplated her birthday. "Some good thought may linger, some aspirations may push on to worthy deeds, but there will be no fretfulness. It only spoils the sweetness of the passing hours for oneself and for others."

The second day of January was cold and rain hit the windows with a soft staccato touch. Ellen was sewing a beige wool dress for herself when the letter came.

Would she be interested, she read, in giving an address at the ninth annual meeting of the American Historical Association in conjunction with the World Historical Congress to be held July 11 to 13 in Chicago?

A surge of unbridled excitement bounded through her as she reread the letter. Chicago was turning its best face toward the world in preparation for the World's Fair, called the World's Columbian Exposition, named in honor of Christopher Columbus. Every notable association in the country was eager to be a part of it. The country's leading educators, librarians, and writers would attend this congress of The American Historical Association. A thrill of pride shot through her. She accepted.

During the next days, panic and excitement tugged at her as she groped for an idea for her speech. It was like planning the first issue of the magazine all over again, when all her thoughts and ideas seemed ridiculous and absurd.

"The two great questions of the day are politics and economics," she said as she lunched with Mary Lockwood one afternoon. "The relation between wealth and poverty; I wonder if that should be the thrust of my address?"

"It's too broad," Mary said disdainfully. Since Mary was a member of the Board of Lady Managers for the Exposition, Ellen had invited her to lunch to be a sounding board for her ideas. "Think of something you know firsthand, that you are close to," Mary advised. "What's wrong with the subject of the Daughters? That's probably what they expect you to talk about."

"As important as the work of the Daughters is, I don't think an address on our need for a building is impressive enough to hold the attention of college presidents, even if that need is to house historical papers." Suddenly Ellen straightened her shoulders and looked at Mary with wide eyes. "When I worked at the State Department, there were piled up before me, for reference, dozens of precious volumes of manuscripts, many of them worn and torn. Often as I handled them, I was moved to tears by the thought that by a single accident the nation might be stripped of these treasures of the past." She smiled. "Mary, if the Daughters need a place to house Colonial and Revolutionary documents, why shouldn't the nation have such a place?"

The World's Columbian Exposition was built around a lagoon, every building a different style of architecture. There was the electricity building, where at night a central column was illuminated by thousands of miniature incandescent bulbs of every imaginable color, changing in tint and pattern with kaleidoscopic rapidity. There was a woman's building, where all the decorations had been planned and executed by women. Each state had its own building; a territorial building provided a joint home for the territories of New Mexico, Arizona, and Oklahoma.

There was a dignified festivity in the room at the Art Institute. The evening social reception was a chance for the members to get to know one another. Ellen marveled that she was there at all. Dressed in a black

273

watered silk dress, she stood with her Washington friends, Mr. and Mrs. Horatio King, the Honorable Ainsworth R. Spofford of the Library of Congress, and Dr. Frederic Bancroft, librarian at the State Department. Amid the din of voices, clinking of crystal and china, and the sounds of occasional laughter, they conversed with one another in between introductions to the other guests. Dr. Bancroft introduced Ellen to Professor Howard Caldwell from the University of Nebraska and Theodore Roosevelt from the Civil Service Commission in Washington. She met Jessie Fremont Perry, the widow of the famous explorer John Fremont. Martha Lamb, editor of the *Magazine of American History*, sought her out and congratulated her on the quality of *The American Monthly*.

The following morning Ellen awakened with a knot in her stomach and her nerves quivering. She read through her address aloud and found the certainty of its quality calming. She had coffee and toast, then began to dress. She had chosen a summer dress of beige cotton to withstand the day's warmth. It had a pointed basque waist and was smooth across the front but pushed to fullness in the back. It was a feminine dress, yet one given dignity by the square neckline.

The heat was already beginning to sting the city as Ellen walked up the steps of the Art Institute, squinting against the brilliant morning sunshine. The room where the meeting was to be held smelled faintly of tobacco and was warm, with only a hint of air coming through the open windows. She stood for a moment as people began filing in, all wearing an air of expectancy and importance. Her breathing was shallow and her hands clammy, but she nodded, smiled, and offered a "good morning" to those she had met the previous evening.

Dr. William F. Poole, of the Newberry Library in Chicago and Chairman of the Chicago Committee, called the congress to order. He formally nominated Dr. James B. Angell, President of the University of Michigan, as temporary President and named Dr. Herbert B. Adams, a professor at Johns Hopkins University in Baltimore, as temporary Secretary.

Ellen heard only Professor Angell's voice, not his words, as he launched into his address, "The Inadequate Recognition of Diplomatists by Historians." In her mind, she went over her speech, taking deep breaths as unnoticeably as she could to calm herself.

When she heard her name called, she smiled, rose, and walked to the podium conscious only of her own motions as she tried to blot out the sea of faces around her. She reached the lectern and stood for a moment, directing her gaze over the heads of her audience and willing herself to calmness. Her legs shook, but her voice was strong as she said, "The title of my address is 'The Value of National Archives to a Nation's Life and Progress.'"

"Archives hold the evidence of facts," she began. "What the Bible is to the theologian and what the statute law is to the lawyer, the state archive is to the historian." Hearing her own voice relaxed her, and her legs steadied. She took a breath and looked out over her audience once again.

"We, in this country, are fortunate in inheriting the English characteristic that sets a value on all official and family records. Perhaps no nation has been more careful than England in the preservation of her archives, and perhaps no nation has been more careless in this direction than the United States; yet, I reaffirm my statement that we do inherit the English pride of country and ancestry which is possibly the impelling motive in an unusual care for Government and family statistics. We have been careless because life with us in the past was too experimental and too intense to admit of very definite record and painstaking protection of such rapid records as were made. Like children, too, we had not learned the relative value of the things not purchasable, as compared with money and the things that money will buy; a natural mistake for a people suddenly emerging from the stress of poverty and war, as in the Revolution, into the possession of great and unexpected fortunes as followed in the succeeding years. Questions vital to the life of the nation involved in the War of 1812, and in the late war, have agitated even the most quiet students of the land. Questions of policy and finance involving the Louisiana Purchase, with control of the mouth of the Mississippi River, and the war with Mexico, bringing its grand acquisition of territory, have stirred the whole people to a degree that allowed little time to consider the history they were making from month to month and year to year.

The form of our Government, too, has been detrimental to an early collection of historical records; the separate states have had a desire to retain all records relating to each one within its own borders, even while they were more or less careless of the safety of the most important documents. The result is that partial and incomplete histories of the establishment of the country have prevailed, and some colonies, as New York, have had scant justice in the histories of the nation.

The earliest literary effusions of the Anglo–Saxons, even while metrical in form, were historical in matter, and among their first efforts in prose was the *Saxon Chronicle*. This, like our own early history, was made piecemeal in the various counties and convents. The frequency with which the *Saxon Chronicle* is quoted by historians proves its value. The ecclesiastical claim to make a record for every Christian of his baptism, marriage, and death; to try him for crimes and misdemeanors, and to protect him from both private and judicial vengeance was a means of preserving the history of individuals and communities, for the noted events of the Government were also celebrated and recorded in the churches. As the courts of law gradually developed, they took the people, and the government of which they formed a part, under their supervision; thus the records passed slowly from the church and convents into a final independence of them. By the conservation of family records, they have in many cases become official archives.

In the preservation of her archives and an appreciation of their value, England has a rival in Spain. I cannot refrain from mentioning a striking illustration of the fullness and accuracy of those records, and the facility with which they can become available. The old Spanish fort at St. Augustine, Florida, is, I believe, the only work of its peculiar kind on this continent. A retired army officer, visiting St. Augustine, heard that the picturesque Fort Marion there was in imminent danger of degradation. He appealed successfully to the engineer on inspection duty and induced him to recommend the renovation of the old fort instead of its destruction. The proposition was accepted by our Government, and the officer who was to supervise the work was authorized to write to the Spanish Government and ask for any information they could furnish in regard to the original plans of the fort, now so dilapidated as to be difficult to restore. To the astonished gratification of the officer he received, in a very short time, a full case of the original plans and drawings of the fort and the surrounding country, with a complete account of the expense of building, the number of men employed for the work, the provision for them, etc., and all this after an interval of about three hundred years.

The Italians have, in the Vatican, still an unexplored wealth of historical treasure that will continue to enfold for ages its hidden narratives. You remember how Cardinal Maii picked up an old manuscript in the Vatican written in a clear, bold hand; reading it, he was impressed only with the indifferent style and folly of the writer, but as he read he observed some strange characters of a different kind from this bold writing; he traced this hidden lettering into words that made a quotation from Cicero; his curiosity still further excited, he pursued his investigation, which resulted in the discovery of the long–lost literary treasure, the *Cicero de Republican*; by the application of chemicals the later writing was obliterated and the ancient one restored.

The Government of the United States, with all the excuses which have been presented, still appears to have been culpably negligent in the collection and preservation of the national archives.

That the Saxon instinct to hold on to all that is of value in the past, for utility if not for veneration, is strong within us is proved by the quick awakening of this country to the memories of this historic year, and to the appeals of various associations having in view the restoration of historical records and the veneration of ancestors. The people are always in advance of their legislators; these last are held back by motives of policy, but the people strike out for what they want, and in time they bring their legislators to their way of thinking.

Would not the vote of the people on any day decide that the few thousand dollars necessary to print the Revolutionary papers now lying, in their single original copies, in the State Department, should be expended promptly and generously for that purpose?

Such valuable papers are not only on the shelves of the public Departments; they are scattered all over the country. Would not a vote of the people, if taken today, be in favor of the appointment of offices of the Government whose duty it should be to collect and preserve these documents?

Would it not be well that we, who are gathered here in the interest of historical research, should make our opinion and desire heard concerning the Revolutionary records, by means of a strong resolution addressed to the Congress soon to convene; this resolution shall embody a petition for the collection and preservation of the Revolutionary and other national archives?"

She stopped speaking and there was a moment of silence followed by thunderous applause. A few people got to their feet while applauding, and Ellen felt her face grow warm in a flush of pride and gratitude.

Dr. Poole rose and strode to the podium.

"The historical papers in the State Department are not accessible to the historical student except as a special favor, and they are not arranged, classified, and calendared. The State Department has no space for historical archives and no archivist who understands their management or has time to give to the needs of historical investigators. Indeed, these are not the functions of the State Department. At Ottawa, however, Canada has a department of archives; it is an excellent one, and under the charge of a most competent archivist. American historians, when they need to consult the original documents relating to our own history, often go to Ottawa to see papers which should be in Washington."

Charles Kendall Adams rose. "I move that we appoint a committee to draw up a resolution expressing the views of the association of the necessity for the National Bureau of Archives." The motion was carried and a committee appointed. In addition to Ellen, President Angell was

277

appointed, as were the Honorable William Wirt Henry of Richmond, Virginia; Dr. J. L. M. Curry, Secretary of the Peabody and Slater Education Fund in Washington; the Honorable George F. Hoar, Republican Senator from Massachusetts; and Dr. James Schouler, Professor at Boston University.

In one passionate plea, Ellen had slaked what she often regarded as her untrained, ignorant spirit, and joined her voice, along with that of her father's and her stepfather's, in a cry for recognition of a national patriotism. Love for her country had been borne and nurtured in her, and she had turned that love into a concrete plea for a necessary edifice.

She attended the meetings of the next two days, reveling in her victory. On Tuesday evening Dr. Schouler read *Methods of Historical Investigation*, and Professor Ephraim Emerton of Harvard University contributed a paper on *Historical Doctorate in America*. Ellen listened politely, but sat secure in the knowledge that it was her idea that had ignited the minds of those present at this congress.

Basking in her success, she spent the following week in Chicago visiting with D. and then left for a week in Davenport, Iowa, and a visit with Mary.

Chapter 48

Pulsing with vitality from the Chicago congress, feeling herself to have acquired an invulnerable intellect, Ellen felt ageless. But when she saw Mary, she was shocked. Her childhood friend had grown old.

When Mary laughed, her voice still sounded like the clinking of crystal but her eyes no longer twinkled. She walked slowly, as if searching for energy, and her face wore a look of resignation. In contrast to Ellen's sense of vitality, Mary's days were marked with routine.

Mary, too, had endured the anguish of losing four of her eleven children, including Joseph, who had died at the age of twenty–six. Her husband, Charles, had died in 1887 and with him had gone her strength.

"So often, as always dear Nelly, I longed for you. When Joseph died, Charlie was there for me, of course, but when Charlie died, it was all over for me. Only the thought of our warm friendship and all you have endured kept me living. My children's deaths are the difficult ones, even though I miss Charlie terribly. Only another woman can feel the slash in her loins that results from the death of a child."

Every day they went to the Davenport Academy of Natural Sciences, the place that had been so dear to Joseph, with Mary explaining in tireless detail her dreams for the continuation and growth of the Academy. "This place keeps Joseph alive for me, Nelly."

"It keeps you alive, too, Molly. You must find a direction for your energies. You can't know yet all you are capable of doing."

Mary looked at Ellen and smiled. "My daughter Elizabeth and I have been traveling, and we have decided to visit every country we possibly can. Between that and the Academy, I have no more energy."

The two women sat up late into the night talking as they had when they were girls. With Mary there was a comfortable point of reference. It was a shared sense of family, of continuity. Together they went back in time, wept over each other's sorrows, laughed at their follies, and rejoiced over each other's victories. As always, their talk turned philosophical.

"Sorrows are to be expected, Molly. Life is the real palpitating existence that carries one forward through the difficulties, the trivialities of everyday experience."

Mary sighed. "I am going on, Nelly, but not forward. It's too late for me to go forward."

"Nonsense, Molly! It is exactly at this point, when all is lost, that one must turn hopefully to the heights! One's soul must move steadily toward the distant lights and leave behind the fretful stream and threatening clouds of the valley. The higher life finds expression in a thousand forms. In connections with others, in the joy of living, in the awakening of dormant power."

Mary sat speechless for a moment, then burst into laughter, the clear thinking tones of her voice sounding briefly like the young girl of the far past brimming with enthusiasm. "No wonder your speech was so well accepted in Chicago. You inherited your father's gift for rhetoric and persuasiveness!"

Ellen returned to Washington pondering, as always, the contrast between Mary's life and her own. She had often envied Mary the love that had surrounded her in a comfortable and secure life. Yet Ellen recognized that the absence of that security was the only reason she had sought and subsequently found the stimulating intellectual life. But why, she wondered with a sigh, why wasn't it possible to have both?

Back in Washington, she was once again plunged into a whirl of activities and meetings with the Daughters. On the evening of February 22, Mrs. Stevenson presided over the unveiling of the portrait of Mrs. Caroline Harrison, which took place at the Church of Our Father. The life–sized portrait was wrapped in an immense American flag. As Mrs. John Risley Putnam of Saratoga drew the cord, "The Star Spangled Banner" floated out on the air, and the portrait of Mrs. Harrison stood in silent reverence.

Ellen had been asked to speak at the unveiling, and as she stood beside the portrait, she turned her head to gaze at Mrs. Harrison's figure for a moment before turning back to her audience:

"Mrs. Harrison, as our first President–General, projected the vision of the Daughters of the American Revolution as women destined to become factors in national life because of their quiet influence at the hearth side.

As woman is supreme in the home, so in the development of national life, she is destined to become a factor, if not a guide, in the affairs of a nation. Modern life now demands the role of women to stretch beyond the limitations of family and social life.

It is on the basis of this larger life that has opened to women that the Society of the Daughters of the American Revolution has been founded. It would arouse women to the realization of the fact that if a nation would preserve its identity, it must cherish its individual characteristics."

Ellen felt herself being stretched beyond her own comfortable limitations, so much so that the creative satisfaction that *The American Monthly* had provided was becoming a burden. Ellen was not only in charge of the business management and the literary content, but was the sole editor. She had no clerk, no proofreader, and no pay. Mary Desha assisted her when she could, as did Reubena when she came to Washington, but it was essentially Ellen's responsibility. Ellen talked to John Stevens, editor of *The American History Magazine*, about a possible merger, yet she was loath to give up control of *The American Monthly* or to see her efforts swallowed by another publication. Yet, as she and John spoke, she felt it the only possible outcome. She liked and trusted him and felt the merger would only strengthen the aims of the magazine. But when she brought up the subject of the merger at a meeting, the Daughters were outraged. It was the work of the Daughters of the American Revolution, they cried indignantly, and reflected their patriotism and their deeds. They feared their communications would be at a standstill without the magazine. Finally, Mary Lockwood agreed to help Ellen for a few months with the understanding that Mary would then take over the magazine.

She ran at full tilt, working on the magazine, attending meetings of the Daughters and of the American Historical Association, as well as committee meetings for the formation of a national archive. She was becoming increasingly depended upon by influential people, and was gaining a reputation for efficiency and organization. "I have a feeling," she commented wryly to Mary Lockwood one afternoon, "that efficiency and organization is no more than the application of great energy to late nights."

Her eyesight was becoming worse and worse, Ellen thought as she held the *New York Herald* under the light. Only at home, like now, did she squint under the light to see better. Much to her own surprise, vanity prompted her to keep the illusion of good eyesight in public. Now she picked her way slowly through an account of a Women's Law Class being given at the University of the City of New York.

The very word "law" had always projected within her a vision of life at its highest, and she had never been able to understand Mansfield's or Frank's indifference to it. She was no longer young enough for a law career, even if she could secure the funds necessary for the education, but the practical aspects of law for women was an opportunity to enter in even a very small way, those studies she had so admired and for which she had always felt she had a natural aptitude. She read about Dr. Emily Kempin, who had been awarded the degree of Doctor of Laws by the School of Jurisprudence at the University of Zurich in 1887 and who had come from Switzerland to New York to practice and to lecture on the advancement of legal knowledge among women.

If she could take the course, she reasoned, she might be able to lecture on some aspects of practical law and supplement her always meager income. She could continue her work with the Daughters through the New York Chapter. She waited until the lease was up on her apartment and until she knew the magazine was in safe hands, then left for New York City and moved in with Ruby.

With Ruby, there was once again a constant flow of the creativity that Ellen basked in. The walls of her daughter's apartment were covered with still lifes she had painted, likenesses so perfect that Ellen thought it possible to smell fragrance from the flowers and fruit. Ruby had studied painting with the eminent artist and teacher Arthur Dove and was giving lessons in her West Fifty–Seventh Street apartment for two dollars a lesson.

Ruby had a tiny, curvaceous figure, and with her finely chiseled features and blond hair, she was intensely admired by men. Yet she was too busy to notice men. As a Vassar graduate, confident of her intelligence, she had given a speech before The Working Girls' Society in New York where she proclaimed herself a staunch supporter of woman's suffrage. She contended that men denied women the vote because they feared future demands for equal pay and elective office. All of Ellen's disappointments in her children were redeemed in the person of Ruby.

The Women's Legal Education Society had grown out of the Arbitration Society, an organization founded by Mrs. Leonard Weber, wife of a prominent New York City physician. At first Mrs. Weber had been interested only in teaching a few poor women the rudiments of hygiene and invalid cooking, but soon found that most of their mental suffering resulted from wrongs that needed legal advice. With Dr. Emily Kempin she had formed a legal dispensary, aiding the poor in the protection of their rights by providing them with legal advice and assistance at court. So many men and women came that there was not a sufficient number of charitable women who had enough legal knowledge to give assistance.

That dilemma gave rise to the Woman's Legal Education Society, which resulted in the Women's Law Class. The first class was opened at the University of the City of New York on October 30, 1890, with three students in attendance. Now, six years later, Ellen enrolled in a class of forty–seven women.

Her studies gave her a feeling of reverence. It was law that had formed the nation and kept it strong, and it was the study of law that protected the citizens of this free republic from unscrupulous corruption. The opening group of lectures began with an introductory discussion of the United States Government and state governments and on the rights and duties of members of the state. Specific principles of law were dealt with in the succeeding lecture groups, beginning with laws regarding real estate titles, deeds, leases, and mortgages. These lectures were followed by an examination of the laws of making contracts, sales, and partnerships and loaning money, bills, and notes. The concluding group of lectures examined laws affecting special classes of persons, including husband and wife, parents and children, guardians and wards, and executors and administrators. Wills and rights of inheritance were also considered. In addition, there was a series of lectures on parliamentary law designed to help in the formation of clubs.

Ellen had always liked New York, and though the air did not crackle with power as it did in Washington, she was nourished and stimulated by the energy the city generated. Individual lives seemed delineated by the productiveness that sprang from raw vitality.

The New York Chapter of the Daughters of the American Revolution seemed awestruck at having one of the founders in their midst. Ellen spoke frequently at their meetings, recounting the founding of the Society, but judiciously leaving out the quarrels that had often ensued. She told them of the exhausting and exhilarating efforts of founding the magazine and why she had decided to capitalize on the merits of the Women's Law Class. She was in demand as a speaker at many functions, always extolling the praises and virtues of women's widening roles in the affairs of the world and always reminding her audience that it was women's role as nurturers that suited them for a broader spectrum in national life.

Through the Society of the Daughters of the American Revolution and the Women's Law Class, she widened her circle of acquaintances. Helen Miller Gould, daughter of the financier Jay Gould, became a close friend, as did the socialite Mary Louise Whitney. She was often invited for tea at the home of Emily Roebling, an earlier graduate of the law class and the wife of the builder of the Brooklyn Bridge.

The lights of the city shone like halos and illuminated the white flakes falling in the black night. Ellen pulled her arms close about her in contentment and turned from the window to watch Ruby scraping carrots for stew.

"Sometimes I marvel that out of despair and desperation I found the world and secured a place in it."

"Mama, I believe you were always looking."

"Perhaps. It's odd though, the difference between one's expectations and one's reality. I had expected you would create a place in the world through a husband. I still hope for it, yet you have a satisfying place for yourself."

Ruby looked at her silently, then turned back to the stove. Ellen admired Ruby's movements—graceful, sure, and concentrated—whether she was painting or stirring a pudding or hurrying out the door.

"I believe these law classes will open up a new direction for me, but what direction I don't know. After graduation, I'll move back to Saratoga to be with Tracy and to make the necessary repairs and improvements on the Mansion. Then I'll see how I can use this new knowledge."

"I'm running the home this summer," Ruby reminded her, "and giving sketching classes there."

"I know, and I certainly trust you. But if we are to continue to have boarders, repairs must be made in certain areas. I thought I could oversee the efforts and maybe write a book on parliamentary law. There is certainly a necessity for guidance in clubs. Then, if the book is well received, I could also give lectures. At least that's a way of money getting without being so blatant." Her sigh was one of resignation. "The infernal need for money does keep one's intellect attuned."

Chapter 49

S he was happy to be back in Saratoga. The old sense of familial purpose engulfed her. Although her children were grown, Ellen felt once again like a caring mother, keeper of the home.

Energetically, she inspected the house and made lists of all she needed to do. She chose wallpaper and hired paperhangers to refurbish the main rooms. She hired a carpenter to finish the vestibule and a window in the second dining room and to open the balustrade for the front steps. She hung lace curtains in the parlor and dining room and sewed blue silk curtains for two of the guest rooms.

As usual, she tried to banish her trepidations over spending too much money on the house by reasoning that the Walworth Mansion would be in demand by summer boarders. Thankfully, Mrs. Andrews had agreed to stay for another summer, and although Ruby was ostensibly in charge of the house, Mrs. Andrews had proven indispensable as a housekeeper. Katie was efficient as usual, not only in the kitchen but in the laundry as well, spending hot afternoons boiling tubs of water, triumphantly tackling the relentless job of ironing.

As June approached, Ellen traveled to Albany to see Clara, hoping to talk Nellie and Corinne into spending the summer in Saratoga. Clarence was seventy–seven, blind, and hard of hearing, but he hadn't lost his powerful oratorical skills, and when he delivered an occasional sermon, it was to a packed church.

After Sunday mass, Clara, who greeted her mother happily, joined her, Nellie, and Corinne. Ellen chose to ignore the polite distance Clara kept between them; after all, this was her own daughter, whom she had carried and loved. Perhaps there was some way God would heal the distance between them if she were patient. Surely, Ellen thought with a measure of exasperation, surely it was not meant that God should come between a mother and daughter!

Corinne's daughter, Clara, nine years old, was delighted to have her only grandmother with her again and, with a flicker of a smile, kept glancing shyly at Ellen throughout dinner.

When Clarence excused himself and rose from the table to go to his room for a midday nap, Ellen broached the subject of Nellie and Corinne returning to Saratoga for the summer. Corinne's eyes lit up. "I would love that, Mother. There is so much gaiety there in the summer."

"I'm afraid I can't," Nellie said softly. "Father Walworth needs me."

Ellen bristled. "I need you too, Nellie." Dislike for Clarence rose within her like brackish saltwater. Even in old age, he would not give up control of Ellen's family or their finances. Not only did he keep her financially dependent upon him, but he had also coerced her children into leaving home! "I do not understand the hold this man has on you," she said in a tight voice.

"He always does what's right, Mama," Nellie said with a note of reverence in her soft voice. "He's an ideal man, a man of God."

"What have I done to have my children turn to such a man, a man who has had such disastrous consequences upon our lives?"

They looked at her silently.

"I should not even have to come here to ask you to come home for the summer!"

"Mama, we have our own lives, as you do, and we're happy with them, but we love you very much." Nellie's eyes, soft like her voice, pleaded with her mother to understand.

"Then why can't we be together?" Ellen shot back.

Corinne, eager for a more festive life, decided to return for the latter part of the summer, but Nellie was adamant.

As Ellen was leaving Albany, Nellie embraced her. "I am happy, Mama. I have a sheltered existence but a most satisfying one because I live close to the nest of the liberty–loving eagle, close to the rainbow of hope, close to the silent stars."

On the way home Ellen puzzled over Clara's and Nellie's acceptance of their impregnable lives. The spiritual side of life must not be ignored, Ellen conceded, but did spirituality not exist in life outside the church? She herself felt spiritually satisfied in church as well as when listening to a great piece of music or reading a book such as Porter's *Plato*. The intellect of the soul could die in a cloistered existence.

As June arrived, the town laughed with a carnival gaiety and a seething mass of humanity in search of diversion roamed the streets. Banners and streamers hung from the hotel verandas, and music floated on the air from early morning until midnight. The casino and race track were alive with colorful characters hopeful of easy riches. Ellen's anger and disappointment were tempered by the celebratory mood and by Ruby's return for the summer.

With repairs on the house well underway, Ellen eagerly entered society again. The Saratoga Chapter of the Daughters of the American Revolution greeted her warmly and leaned upon her expertise heavily. She attended the opening concert at the U.S. Hotel and joined a weekly whist group. She began taking elocution lessons and started writing her book on Parliamentary Law. In early July she gave a lawn party.

The morning after the party, she was watching workmen cleaning the scattered debris left in the yard when Tracy called to her from his upstairs window. "Mama? I can't get dressed."

"Why not?"

"Somebody stole my clothes."

She hurried upstairs to find his clothes pushed to the back of his wardrobe and the contents of the bureau scattered under his bed.

Ellen faced him sternly. "Tracy, no one stole your clothes. You did this yourself! I'm going to stand here until you put everything in its place and you are properly dressed!"

Sullenly, Tracy began bringing out the clothes from under his bed and rearranging his wardrobe.

Ellen watched him anxiously, angry with him and with herself for being so unsure of her ability to handle the situation. The doctors could tell her so little, she thought sadly. She had long ago ceased to mourn the mental instability of a bright child. The perplexing question that caused her to grieve now was how to handle it. She could give him love and independence, but she didn't know how much discipline was needed, how much it might help or disastrously hurt him. When she left his room, he was sitting on his bed fully dressed, his hands folded in his lap, his empty eyes fixed on a further emptiness enclosed by the tight horizons of his mind.

Headaches began to plague her. She kept her malaise to herself, gritted her teeth, and went about her tasks, feeling that in Saratoga she was continually confronted with defeat. When the pain became severe or she felt temper welling up within her, she tried to hide for a few hours in her room, lying on her bed, but there she was overwhelmed by doubts, responsibilities, and anguish over Tracy's problems.

She poured out her perplexities to her friend Rhoda. "The moment I'm around Tracy a heaviness envelops me. If only there were someone I could turn to, someone to guide me. I hurt for him, yet he makes me so angry."

Ellen was astonished at Rhoda's ability to visit at precisely the right time. Like Mary, Rhoda often appeared when Ellen was ill or depressed, as if summoned by telepathy, to take Ellen for a drive. There were happy days, too, when they would reach out to one another for the simple joys of shared companionship.

She had used the excuse of the headaches, too many activities, and general depression to avoid the task she dreaded yet had hoped to accomplish over the summer, the sorting of the Hardin and Walworth letters and papers. "I've been procrastinating," she confessed to Ruby.

287

"One's own past is not pleasant to relive. Maybe that's why I was never able to finish my father's biography." Nevertheless, she vowed to spend two hours in the late afternoons in the cottage where the papers were stored. If the past suffocated her, she could return to the present in the evenings by means of a concert, a whist game, or a walk with Ruby.

One afternoon Tracy appeared at the cottage with a tear–streaked face. "Someone broke my bicycle." Ellen hastened to the side yard, where Tracy mutely pointed out his prized means of freedom lying on its side, its wheels in a far corner of the yard, the handlebars bent. That night Ellen wrote a hasty note to D., who was living in Florida, telling him of the incidents and pleading for advice. By return mail, D. assured her Tracy would be all right and invited him to spend two months in Florida.

Ellen's book on parliamentary law was published that year. She had circulars printed to advertise it and to announce that she was available for lectures. She started lecturing in Saratoga to interested people, both residents and tourists. By the time fall approached, she was filling her calendar with lectures in Saratoga as well as Boston and New York City. If she was puzzled by her apparent failure as a mother, she was satisfied by her accomplishments. The years of anxiety and excessive humilities had not destroyed her sense of self or her ambitions. Through the Women's Law Class, she had gained another avenue of income; one that was hard earned through her unfearing pursuit of knowledge.

Chapter 50

Ellen wretched violently into the slop–jar, clutching the bedpost with one hand, the other hand splayed across her throbbing forehead. She remained in that position for a moment even after the heaving stopped, her heart pounding with effort and her legs shaking uncontrollably. Finally she moved to the marble–topped washstand and poured water from the pitcher into the basin, scooping one handful of cold water after another against her face. She patted her cheeks, her forehead, and her chin slowly with a linen towel, then returned to her bed and lay down, waiting for the weakness to subside and fighting not to give in to the despair which invited her to stay in bed.

She was aware only of the muffled noises rising from New York's streets, and as the icy sleet hissed against the windows, she pulled the quilt up to her chin and closed her eyes against the winter light which cast a gray pallor across the room.

The black powders the doctor had given her to help her sleep produced this violent nausea every few days. The doctor had promised her that her headaches would lessen with a good night's sleep, but she preferred insomnia, she thought groggily, to this nausea which was becoming increasingly sharper. She sighed and tried to slide into a void, to blank her mind of any and all thought.

When the pounding in her head subsided, she reached toward the nightstand for her glasses and the newspaper in an effort to postpone getting out of bed. With both hands, she fitted the small wires behind each ear and pushed up on the glasses against her nose. Our Flag is in Havana at Last! thundered the same headlines she had read the day before. Ellen frowned and scanned the article again, reading that President McKinley had ordered the USS Maine and the USS Montgomery to Havana on a goodwill visit. "Everything is now in readiness for the final act of the drawn–out ordeal of Cuba," she read. "It is hoped the climax may not long be delayed."

In the few weeks of 1898, the American public had been gorging themselves on a daily diet of graphic details as they read eyewitness accounts of kidnappings and murders in Cuba. There were grisly tales disclosing the massacre of some insurrectos by Spanish troops. The victims, Ellen read, were "youths in their adolescent years—their number included some girls whose raven tresses were matted with blood."

Ever since Thomas Jefferson believed that adding Cuba to the confederacy would round out the nation's power, the island had been on the American mind. In 1823, while serving as Secretary of State under President James Monroe, John Quincy Adams had said, "It is scarcely possible to resist the conviction that the annexation of Cuba to our Federal Republic will be indispensable to the continuance and integrity of the Union itself."

President Monroe had feared that Great Britain might take advantage of both Spain and the United States by seizing Cuba and Puerto Rico. To forestall such a occurance, he issued the *Monroe Doctrine*, which pledged the United States against such changes in the western hemisphere.

Caught in a vise of excitement fueled by lurid daily reports in the press, the American public agreed with the Assistant Secretary of the Navy, Theodore Roosevelt, that a war with Spain could be postponed but not averted. Even though President McKinley had announced that his administration frowned upon American citizens helping the insurgents, the flow of men and arms to Cuba increased daily. One Spanish official had been heard to have cynically remarked, "Every time the insurrectos raise their flag the band plays 'The Star–Spangled Banner.'"

Ellen frowned as she lowered the newspaper and removed her glasses. She rubbed the space on her nose between her eyes.

On the morning of February 16, while she was putting the finishing touches on a black watered–silk ball gown she was sewing for Ruby, she heard a quick staccato knock on the door and Ruby burst in breathlessly. "Mother, have you heard the news?" she cried excitedly as she unwound a woolen scarf from around her throat. "We're at war!"

Ellen gazed unbelievingly at her daughter, a questioning look flitting over her blank face. "So," she said slowly, "it has finally happened."

"We're not officially at war," Ruby amended, "but we soon will be. The Maine was sunk last night in Havana Harbor." She thrust a copy of the *New York Journal* at Ellen, black with the words, "Remember the Maine! We Demand Vengeance!" Ellen quickly read the article, which claimed to have inside information that the Maine had been destroyed by Spanish agents.

"There might not be an official declaration of war," Ruby stated, "but there should be. Once and for all, we should quell the Spanish atrocities against innocent human beings."

Ellen devoured the newspapers day after day, filled with morbid excitement. She had been bred on the language of politics and found the subject fascinating.

By March 28, the United States' involvement in Cuba was firmly cemented with President McKinley's ambiguous report on the *Maine Commission of Inquiry*, which hinted that the Maine had been destroyed by a submarine mine.

"We must organize the women of this country to help in what is obviously going to be a war," Ellen told Ruby. The two of them, along with the rest of the country, had talked of little else in the past few weeks. "Everyone responds to events differently, but the important thing is to respond, to react."

She appealed to the Daughters of the American Revolution. "We must find the means to supplement with material aid the sacrifices of time, strength, and life made by the men of the nation."

After her Parliamentary Law lectures, she would present her concerns to the women and men who inevitably plied her with questions about law and its application to daily affairs. She would artfully turn attention to the national crisis. "I do think it important, don't you, that we keep in remembrance the cause of humanity and the preservation of liberty which makes this war necessary."

It never occurred to Ellen or to an innocent nation that the preservation of liberty was not a reason for this war. Inflamed by the daily newspapers, each day crackled with energy. The streets of New York seemed to overflow with an elevated power, and carriages and pedestrians all appeared to move with a certainty of purpose.

Ellen's plan began to take form and, encouraged by the people she had spoken to, she wrote an appeal to the *New York Tribune*, which was published on April 2. Under the heading "An Open Letter," the appeal was directed "To the Daughters of the American Revolution, and Other Patriotic Women of the United States, Concerning a National Corps of Sanitary Volunteers to Aid Our Officers, Soldiers, and Sailors in Time of War."

Enthusiastic responses followed quickly in the forms of letters, telegrams, and visits by friends and acquaintances. Emboldened, Ellen wrote to the Secretary of the Navy, John D. Long:

> "Dear Sir:
>
> Last week I issued a call to patriotic women of the United States to volunteer for sanitary service in case we have a war with Spain. The response has been so earnest and enthusiastic that I am confident much may be accomplished if we act under governmental authority. At a

291

meeting of a committee of influential women of New York yesterday, April 7, the proposition was made to equip a hospital ship already owned by the Government (such equipment to be subject to the approval of naval inspectors). Or would you accept such a vessel purchased by men through the solicitation of women and equipped by the latter?

The assurance from you that our efforts are acceptable to the Government will ensure the fulfillment of any demand made upon us."

On April 15 she received a reply saying, "the ambulance ship *Solace* has been purchased and is now being fitted out for the sole purpose of caring for the sick and wounded of both the Army and Navy. The assistance of the patriotic women of America will be highly appreciated and is greatly desired in supplying the vessel with necessities and luxuries for the sick and wounded. It is believed that, as suggested by the Surgeon–General, the best use will be made of such funds as may be collected by your committee if they are placed in the hands of that officer for the procuring of luxuries for the sick and wounded, who may be on board the ship already purchased by this department; such action is, accordingly, recommended."

Brimming with confidence, she sent an invitation to fifty select and influential women:

"You are earnestly requested to attend a meeting at the Windsor Hotel, Thursday, April 21, at eleven o'clock A.M., to hear a letter from the Secretary of the Navy, John D. Long, and to consider means for following the advice it contains in regard to sanitary aid for the Navy in the present crisis."

In the Windsor Hotel on Thursday morning, women gathered as compatriots in a sincerity born of faith and pride in a free country. There was a purpose on their faces, and their eyes shown with a bright excitement of adventure.

Ellen stepped before them, wearing a navy blue high–collared dress cut just a bit wider at the hips than was fashionable. Confidence and energy made her movements belie her sixty–five years, and a strong determination to preserve her heritage by aiding her country showed upon her face. Her voice–round, full, and assured—rang out:

292

"Ladies! I have called you together today to consider that war is declared for the women as well as for the men of this nation. It appears to me that no other opportunity than the state of war allows us to prove clearly that the national life throbs in our veins—that the nation is ours by right of our womanhood. We feel special anxieties as the housekeepers of the nation, that is, as the persons most concerned for the health and comfort of the men— we have a special concern, I say, because of the exposure to which they will be subjected in an unaccustomed climate. Therefore, we must try to assist the government in the general care and preservation of the health of the Army and Navy, in using preventive measures. This demands thought and money. We may send additional supplies, that is, delicacies and comforts which military rule does not provide, and the money to purchase whatever will contribute to the welfare of the men. In sending money through such a channel, we believe that every dollar will be applied promptly, directly, and economically to the desired end, for whatever criticism may be made of our Army and Navy, in one matter they are unimpeachable— that is, in the honesty and honor of the officers."

Ellen held her head high and smiled as applause resounded throughout the room. She cleared her throat, took a drink of water and gripped the lectern with both hands.

"Close to the love of kindred and home lies the love of country, dearer to us than ever in these last years of the century, because we have learned by the agonizing experience of a civil war that our union, our nation, is secure as one people, that as a nation we are impregnable in patriotism. There is no need to rouse ourselves in patriotism; it burns naturally in the hearts of American women, who love their country and honor their flag.

The time has arrived in the progress of our country when American women are expected to be awake to national interests. Let us take our charge of the burden— the care of the sick and wounded. Let us organize carefully, let us collect money and apply it promptly as emergencies arise, and I predict that when peace is happily declared not one woman now present will regret that today she pledged herself to spend time and labor in behalf of her country."

293

Though the women professed to deplore the confrontation, the thought of war excited them. Their lives had been locked into borders of comfort drawn by husbands and families who took the time and energy and emotions of these women, so even though they might yearn for a larger stage on which to play out their lives, they could have no purpose beyond their own walls. Now a national calamity was an event that gave purpose to their lives, an event they would be wrong to ignore, and it gave them a reason to shake off the bonds of tedium that ensnared them and trapped them inside silken cocoons.

On Wednesday, April 20, both the House and Senate voted for an ultimatum demanding that Spain "at once relinquish its authority and government in the island of Cuba and withdraw its land and naval forces from Cuba and Cuban waters." The American warning added that the President would wait until noon on Saturday, April 23, for a "full and satisfactory response." Otherwise he would use "all the power of the United States" to enforce the ultimatum.

When Spain rejected the ultimatum, Congress declared that a state of war had existed since Thursday, April 21. Appended to the war resolution was an amendment sponsored by Senator Henry Moore Teller of Colorado. The Teller Amendment forbade an American annexation of Cuba and said: "Once hostilities are concluded we will leave the government and control of that island to the people."

The day after Ellen's talk to the women of New York, President McKinley declared a blockade of all Cuban ports.

On April 23, the President sent out a call for 125,000 volunteers. Recruiting stations all over the country were swamped by eager young men, rushing to join the colors. They came from every walk of life: farmers, students, teachers, clerks, merchants, and cowboys. If they had been asked to consider what event had caused this war, these men would pause a moment, look lamely at their interrogator, and mutter something vague about the newspapers.

There were more adventures that spring than the public could hope for. Up in northern Canada, in a region called the Klondike, gold was discovered. Although its lure was great, glamour and recognition lay in the fight, and most men chose to help Uncle Sam.

The yellow press cartoonists depicted Uncle Sam with clenched fists, his sleeves rolled up, glowering into the distance. "By Juniper!" he cried, "I'll have peace if I have to fight for it!"

Among the volunteers were thousands of recently arrived immigrants and Negroes. Patriotic fervor was contagious. Even the Democratic candidate for president in 1896, William Jennings Bryan, joined the Army as a private.

On May 17, the Women's National War Relief Association was incorporated, with Mrs. Ulysses S. Grant as President. With the $600 they had received by that time, they sent half to the Army and half to the Navy.

Ellen's headaches disappeared and with them went the need for the black powders. For now, when she had sleepless nights, she turned on the lamp and worked at her desk on reports from the Women's Committee or she wrote letters to the Surgeon–Generals of the Army and Navy, or to the Secretary of War, or to the various Daughters of the American Revolution chapters upon whom she leaned heavily for support for the efforts of the Women's Committee.

The first supplies bought from money that the Women's National War Relief Association received were sent to the hospital ship *Solace* as well as to the *Relief*. As money continued to come in, practical supplies and delicacies were sent continuously to various hospitals and localities including Fortress Meyer or Chickamauga in Virginia, Yellow Fever Hospital at Santiago, and numerous transports and auxiliary cruisers. A steam launch was sent to the Yellow Fever Hospital, which, situated on an island two miles from shore, was forced to transport everything, even drinking water, by boat from the mainland. Another hospital at Santiago received stores valued at several thousand dollars. A carbonating apparatus costing about $2000 was sent to the *Relief*. In addition, electric ventilating fans, green shades for the lights in the wards, a colored awning for the upper flush deck, clothing, delicacies, and general supplies were renewed each time the *Relief* returned to New York City.

That hot July the country was well pleased. After American victories at El Caney, San Juan Hill, and Kettle Hill, the Spanish fleet was destroyed on July 4. Rumors abounded that Spain was seeking an armistice. The nation echoed the cry of Teddy Roosevelt, "It is a grand time to be alive! A bully time!"

To celebrate Independence Day, speakers stressed the glorious prospects facing the United States. Cuba was all but conquered, and in time would be turned over to the Cubans.

The country reveled in a victorious, festive mood. And all the while, yellow fever, typhoid fever, and measles ran rampant throughout the ranks of the Navy, Army, and Marines.

Ellen seated herself in a chair across the desk from Colonel Alden. She had been authorized by the Association and by the Surgeon–General to visit all the field hospitals, but first she had decided to visit General Sternberg and outline her plan to better equip the hospitals.

"I am sorry, General Sternberg isn't available." Colonel Alden said with a smile. "I hope I'm not too poor a substitute."

Ellen smiled, then got right to the point. "Sir, I have come to you to propose a plan for assisting in sanitary cooking for the sick." She did not first apologize for taking his time, since she knew her organization was necessary to the war effort. She thought of herself as an equal in this plan to help the men who had given so much to the nation. "We could erect a building or a tent," she told him, "equipped with a kitchen and hire a cook known to be well versed in invalid cooking."

She was pleased to see Colonel Alden look at her thoughtfully, rather than disdainfully, as many busy men did to a woman.

"It might," he ruminated aloud, "be adjusted in a way to be practical." He drummed his fingers on the table and then stood up. "Why don't I confer with General Sternberg on the matter? In the meantime, Mrs. Walworth, why not visit the general hospital at Fortress Meyer?"

The surgeon in charge, Major Davis, met Ellen's carriage and gallantly assisted her out. "Mrs. Walworth, I'm happy to meet you." He bowed in a courtly way. "We could use a woman's touch here. Let me take you on a tour of the hospital to help you assess our needs."

Ellen followed him through wards where men lay drained, not of wounds but with typhoid fever, meningitis, and pneumonia. Newly enlisted men, not all trained to care for the sick, moved among the beds nursing as best they could. "You can see," Major Davis said with a flick of his hand, "that bullets are not the only thing to be feared in this war. Wounds are comparatively easy to deal with compared to this. We have an immediate need for night lamps, ice bags, and medicine glasses. And, we need an expert cook if your association could possibly find someone willing to come."

She relayed the needs back to the association and was asked to visit Fortress Monroe. She arrived on July 13 as the first of the wounded soldiers were disembarking from Santiago. Fortress Monroe bulged with 500 men. A brick building, recently completed, held about one hundred patients; twenty tents containing twenty cots each had been prepared to receive the remainder.

With horror, Ellen watched men being carried in wearing the woolen clothes in which they had been wounded. "Only the strong will survive," she thought in pity, "the weak and despondent won't have a chance."

She confronted a weary Major DeWitt, the surgeon in charge. "Sir, may I telegraph General Sternberg for women nurses?"

He ran a hand wearily over his forehead. "We need good help—yes, you can ask for the women. I have written to Washington for thirty-five hospital orderlies. Ask General Sternberg for eight nurses."

Ellen looked at the men lying on the ground in quiet acceptance of less than tolerable conditions. She telegraphed the supply committee to send 100 each of underclothes, socks, handkerchiefs, pajamas, slippers, and crutches. Then she sent a telegram to Ruby who was taking an emergency course of nursing at Saratoga Hospital and asked her to come immediately.

Ruby had been helping the Association in a perfunctory way, writing letters home for the men, giving them kind words, seeing that they had enough money to return to their homes. Then one afternoon she had simply declared that she was going to nurse. "I can't go and fight, but at any rate I can nurse, and I will."

She was there before the week was out, as were four other women who were willing to volunteer until other trained nurses could join them.

Ellen located a special diet cook who not only could cook but constantly had bouillon or cocoa ready for exhausted nurses, and who would send around special snacks for the patients in the late mornings and afternoons.

As the men became convalescent, more food was needed, and Ellen pressured the director to allow her $100 a week for the next three weeks to add chickens, eggs, butter, and fruit to the general mess table.

Nellie arrived and, using her secretarial skills, helped write letters home for the men. Ellen was happy to see her, but she also felt a small thrill of victory that Nellie would leave Clarence's side to come to her mother's aid.

Ellen visited Camp Alger in Virginia, which consisted of one tent and a few medicines. Outside the tent, assistants were slowly rolling bandages, and she looked at the major in surprise. "How is this? We women are told you never use homemade bandages, but only those sterilized and specially prepared."

"We need bandages, Madam," he said disdainfully. "We do not get them, so we make them."

Ellen put her hands on her hips and surveyed the scene. "I suppose you have done the best you can," she said to the major.

He raised his eyebrows. "This is a field hospital and training camp; we did not suppose that field hospitals should be provided with sheets and pillow cases."

"Obviously no cots either," Ellen shot back.

"Just because men are ill does not mean they should not be disciplined!"

As Ellen looked at him, a flicker of disbelief passed over her face. She knew there was a controversial debate within the government over how comfortable the camps should be. Just last week one of the west-

297

ern senators had angrily demanded that more cots be sent to the camps for the ill men. "Shall we wait until these men have the threatened typhoid," she thought, "before changing the conditions?"

It seemed perfectly natural that Ellen should be sitting here in this office at this particular time and for this particular cause with the President of the United States. President McKinley had served in the Union Army during the Civil War and so had special empathy for the pitiable conditions of the camp hospitals. He was of medium height but powerfully built, and his thoughtful, intelligent eyes projected a demeanor of decisiveness.

"It is not for myself that I am here, Mr. President, but for the Women's National War Relief Organization, which is working on behalf of the returning soldiers." In a slow firm voice she told him of the Association and its members, stressing the fact that Mrs. Ulysses S. Grant was the president of the association, and gave heavy emphasis to the names of Helen Gould and Emily Roebling. "Many of us have left employment and busy private lives to work for our nation." She outlined the supplies that had been sent to the ships and to the camps. As she talked, he nodded his head now and then but did not interrupt her.

"I have heard of your association, Mrs. Walworth," he said when she had finished, "and the excellent work you are doing. You are working along the correct lines, and I hope you continue to do so. Successful work such as you are doing strengthens our country. I would encourage you to rely heavily upon General Sternberg's advice. Anything he approves, I will do for you; any paper he recommends, I will sign. I will not give a special privilege to any one association, but I encourage them all equally."

In early August, Montauk, Long Island, was designated a convalescent camp, named Camp Wickoff in honor of Colonel Charles Wickoff who had died at Santiago. It was generally thought that conditions at all the camps had improved because the Government now knew what to expect. Still, Ellen was doubtful. "After having seen the other camps, I'm just not certain as to the conditions," she told the Association. "I think I shall run down there just to see what the immediate needs are."

It was dark when she arrived, and a rain was pelting down unmercifully. A rickety carriage was at the station, and Ellen prevailed upon the young driver to take her to the public house.

"They're full of soldiers, Ma'am," he warned her.

"Just get me out there," she implored. "I'll find something."

The young driver looked at her reluctantly. "Ma'am, in this storm that road'll be all mud. We jist might get stuck."

Ellen hesitated. "No we won't," she said after a moment. "I have complete faith in your abilities."

The boy's eyes opened wide in surprise, then he acquiesced. "We'll give it a try, but I don't promise nuthin!"

The carriage swayed and bumped over the road, with only an occasional flash of lightning illuminating the blackness that surrounded them. Thunderclaps rolled around them, and the carriage jerked as the startled horses picked up speed. The rain drummed on the top of the carriage, and Ellen sat tensely, wishing she had waited until morning to come out here. Finally, a tiny pinpoint of light could be seen which grew steadily larger until the driver pulled up before a house.

"I'll wait, Ma'am," he informed her as she opened her umbrella and stepped out of the carriage. Her feet sank down into mud, and she stepped gingerly onto a wooden plank walk leading to the house. She knocked loudly on the door, wondering if anyone could hear her above the laughter and loud voices in the house and the downpour outside. At last the door opened revealing a short, plump woman. Wearied and exhausted, Ellen's mouth opened in amazement to find another woman standing on her doorstep in the night.

"I need a room for the night," Ellen shouted above the weather. "I'm from the Women's National War Relief Association, and I've come to check conditions at the camp."

"Should've come in the mornin'. There's no more room. Rough Riders takin' up all the space."

"Please," Ellen implored. "I'll settle for a sofa or even a spot on the floor. I can't very well stand in the rain all night."

The woman considered a moment, then opened the door wider. "What'd you say you was doin' here?" she asked curiously.

"Checking on conditions for the camp the government has established for the wounded and ill soldiers."

"Well, all's I got left is a sofa." Ellen followed her into a parlor where the woman indicated a small sofa. "You can try that," she said doubtfully, but Ellen, glad to be in a dry place and with important work on her mind, sank down on the sofa gratefully.

She awakened to a grim, gray day with the rain unabated. She felt disheveled and cramped. She smoothed her dress and her stockings, then went into the kitchen in search of a pan of cold water. After she had splashed her face, combed her hair, and had a cup of strong coffee, she felt reasonably refreshed to start the day.

A rickety wagon stopped in front of the house at half past eight with a milk delivery, and Ellen prevailed upon the driver to take her to the camp. The air smelled unmistakably of salt water, and in the distance she could hear the soft roar of the waves as the Atlantic Ocean broke against the beach. The wagon bounced over a narrow, sandy road rutted with carvings of wagon wheels. Ellen held an umbrella over her head, but the wind blew the rain against her, and she felt encased in warm dampness. The land was wide here, as wide as the prairie, with infinite stretches of sea and sky, broken only by ponds and wind–twisted trees. The salt air was like a stimulant, but the land that rose before them had a calming effect.

Just below a bluff, four tents were set up, and a few men wandered among them aimlessly.

"Must be the place," the driver called out.

"Yes. Well, I'll just get out here." She stiffly climbed out of the wagon and approached a man who eyed her curiously. "I'm from the Women's National War Relief Association," she announced. "We're authorized by the government to check conditions at the camps. Have you any sick men here?"

"About forty," he said laconically.

"Are you getting their breakfast?"

He shifted from one foot to the other and shrugged. "They can't take anything but milk, and we haven't any."

"When will you be getting some?"

"Well, I don't know. I think the doctor has gone down to the station. Maybe he'll bring some up."

"Show me where the sick are."

Ellen followed him to a tent where sick men lay on tarpaulins huddled together and visibly shivering with fever. Exhaustion and hunger shone in their eyes. They had received no nourishment for over twenty–four hours. A pain of anguish and anger shot through Ellen.

"It's deplorable and inexcusable that no provisions are made for men in time of war. These conditions are disgraceful."

"Here's the doctor," the man muttered as a tall, thin man approached them.

"Is there any milk for these men?" Ellen questioned.

Discouragement reflected on his face, the doctor shook his head slowly. "I have just returned from the station. I ordered milk, but it didn't arrive. I don't think there is any to be had on Montauk Point. A milkman has promised to come from Amagansett. Maybe he'll be here later."

Ellen thought of the empty milk wagon she had ridden in. If only she had realized these deplorable conditions! She pulled the umbrella further down over her head and pulled her rain slicker closer around her. She squinted through the rain as she watched two carpenters who had been nailing framework for tents pack their things as though their day's work was finished. "Are they quitting now?" she asked incredulously. "We need wooden floors beneath these men."

The doctor pointed to the men who were now walking away. "There goes the only chance we had for that. They want higher wages and refuse to work longer."

The wagon the doctor had returned to camp in was parked a short distance away, and without a word to the doctor and in almost a half–run, Ellen hurried to the driver. "You must take me back down the road to the house where I spent the night. I'll show you where. I must find milk for these men."

The ride was agonizingly slow, and she took no notice of the scenery. Ellen thought of the blank, hopeless looks upon the faces of the suffering men and mentally urged the horses on faster.

"I must know," she said urgently to the landlady when they arrived, "where you got your milk this morning."

"Amagansett."

They drove to Amagansett as quickly as they could where Ellen was able to convey to the dairy the horrors of the men on the Point. They promised her ten quarts for immediate use, and then she left for the station.

"Fast driving is a necessity," she told the startled driver. "Men's lives don't wait for convenience."

At the station she telegraphed New York to have thirty gallons of milk to be sent every morning.

She found a summer house sitting on a bluff near the camp, located the owners, and secured it as Association headquarters with a small room for herself.

She scoured the countryside for carpenters and found thirty willing to help. When she triumphantly relayed this news back to the officer in charge of the camp, he hesitated.

"I don't think it's a particularly good idea for the aid society to promise higher wages than the government will give."

"Could you please ask? I personally have met with the President, and he has promised to help us in any way he can. Men are demanding higher wages while their brothers are dying, and I do not think money more important than life."

Boxes and barrels began arriving at the railroad station, and Ellen stood in the broiling August sun coaxing men to sort out the foodstuffs first so they wouldn't spoil.

301

"Why does it take so much struggle to do what is obvious?" she wondered in frustrated dismay.

There were not enough wagons or horses to cart the amount of supplies that began arriving. To facilitate distribution, the Association sent two pairs of horses, a wagon, and a carriage.

"We need a dairy," Ellen informed Senator Alger when he arrived to inspect the camp. She pointed to cans of milk standing in the hot sun.

Montauk itself was a battlefield. The kitchen was out of doors without a floor, or a table or a shelf for dish washing. Butchering was done right next to the cooking pots. Infected clothes and bedding from the dead and ill men were pushed outside the back end of tents to wait, sometimes for days, until someone was free enough to launder them.

Ellen sat down wearily on a doorstep. "To have placed 20,000 sick men in a houseless desert looks like barbarism. This is not war. War means action, definite plans—either the march toward victory or the plans for defense. A state of war does not excuse the horror perpetrated in a peaceful community teeming with luxuries and money and among a people whose hearts and purses are open to every call of humanity."

The beauty of the surroundings only emphasized the hopelessness. The camp echoed with the tramp of mules and the constant creaking of wagons and the sounds of hammers frantically driving nails into wood. Dust swirled midst the discomfort and confusion.

Ellen felt curiously out of time and place as she watched assistants struggle to extricate articles from double tents piled high with boxes, while voices of nurses and orderlies pleaded for prompt attention.

Her gaze shifted beyond the pandemonium to the hills where cavalrymen were silhouetted atop their horses, galloping into the wind, looking like chiseled works of art in motion.

She was jerked back to the present by a letter someone handed her. It was from Ruby, informing her mother that her patients were now convalescent and she could join Ellen at Montauk if there was more urgent work for her to do.

302

Chapter 51

A t first there was only a faint glow, then slowly the sky took on a rosy hue as a finger of orange lay on the horizon of the Atlantic. Ellen watched, enthralled, as the orange grew into a tiny half–circle, then seemed to rise by some magic power into the sky, a sun full of joy in a new day. A good omen. A beautiful beginning for Ruby's arrival. She brushed sand from her skirt and licked salt that the air had deposited on her lips.

By mid–morning she was at the station, and her heart quickened as the train, enveloped in noise and steam, labored into the station.

"Ruby!" Ellen waved to her as she stepped from the train, then hurried to embrace her with a glad cry. Ruby returned the hug, then stepped back, smoothed a recalcitrant piece of blonde hair from her temple, "What's to be done?" Her blue eyes danced with excitement, and the shining blonde hair gleamed in the sunlight like a halo. Ruby was a grown woman of thirty–one, yet she wore the aura of a wood nymph, all wide–eyed innocence and fresh spring breezes.

They drove to Camp Wickoff, and Ellen showed her daughter the General Hospital, the Annex, the kitchen and dining facilities, all the while explaining to her what she had found when she first came out here in the pouring rain.

"Such a beautiful place," Ruby murmured. "Certainly, of all the camp hospitals, this must be the loveliest spot. It should help speed recovery."

Ellen pointed to the Detention Hospital on the hill, well away from the General Hospital area. "Yellow fever, diphtheria, typhoid, and measles cases are kept up there." She sighed. "Unfortunately, across the dunes from the hospital and within sight of that majestic ocean is a graveyard for those who don't recover."

The following day Ellen and Ruby were at the station to meet a new wave of wounded and ill men brought by transport from Cuba. A kitchen had been set up to make sandwiches for the men, and Ruby started buttering bread before they arrived. General Young had sent an officer to the station to protect the women, a precaution Ellen thought silly, but as Ruby started to help the waiters distribute the more than 500 sandwiches, Ellen thought with amusement that maybe male protection wasn't a bad idea. Ruby's blonde beauty was a radiance for which the men seemed grateful, and she wore her nurse's uniform like a gleaming robe. Once again, Ellen wondered how this daughter of hers had managed to remain unmarried when she so easily attracted admirers.

In the following days, Ellen marveled at Ruby's efforts. Her daughter seemed to be able to divine the place of greatest need. Not only had she increased the supplies in the wards with redoubled vigor, but she did not need to be directed—she simply found a space and filled it. Untiringly, she assisted the nurses and gave personal attention to the patients, carried requisitions to the dispensary, or quietly replaced a sick or absent nurse. It seemed to Ellen that now there was occasional laughter, and a prevailing mood that lightened the thoughts of sick and dying men.

It was three o'clock one afternoon as Ellen was struggling to prepare two wagon loads of supplies for the Detention Hospital when Ruby appeared at the tent.

"Do you want me to help you, Mother?"

"You can help me lift this box. I'm afraid I packed it too full." As Ruby took one end, Ellen bit her lip and hoisted the heavy box onto the wagon, then winced in pain. "I don't know if I should exercise these stiff joints or just let them stiffen," she exclaimed with mock despair.

"I'll tell you, I can't see, hear, or move, and I'm assisting sick people!"

Ruby stood back and, holding one hand on her hip, wiped the back of her other hand across her perspiring brow. "I was at the dispensary this morning and heard the surgeon from the Detention Hospital ask for supplies and help. He said he had no woman nurse and scarcely a male nurse who was competent." She paused for a moment, and Ellen was conscious of a bedlam of voices and the creaking of carts and banging of pots that filled the air. "Mother, in fifteen minutes I shall have my trunk packed and everything ready to go there as a nurse."

"No!" Ellen gasped. "There is too great a risk there; everyone in that hospital has a contagious disease. Besides, the work you are doing here is efficient, and everyone depends upon you."

"Mother, there are 100 people working here at the General Hospital. There, at the Detention Hospital, is the real need; that is the place for me. It is what I intend to do."

"Ruby, at times I detest your stubbornness."

"I want you to take me there, Mother, and let it be seen that I have you as a protector."

As Ellen drove Ruby up the hill to where the yellow contagion flag flew, she glanced despairingly at the straight, determined figure next to her. With a hollowness in her stomach, she felt that she was an accomplice in condemning her daughter to a dangerous and hopeless exile.

"Now you know, Mother, I shan't be able to see you, but I promise to write to you daily."

Ellen gulped hard and lifted her eyes upward. "The sky is so blue here near the water," she remarked. Why was it necessary to concentrate on nature when hiding one's true thoughts? "I am so selfish," she thought with shame.

Major Ebert was waiting for them and took Ruby's hand as she alighted from the wagon. "Don't worry, Mrs. Walworth," he said reassuringly. "Your daughter's tent will be placed next to mine, and I will watch over her carefully."

Each day a messenger brought a note from Ruby assuring Ellen that she was well and, in great detail, describing her day and her patients. Always in the notes there were requests for large quantities of foods, medical supplies, and table waters. She had been assigned, she wrote, to care for the gaunt–faced men in the contagion ward.

Ellen's qualms were allayed by her pride. No other woman nurse had volunteered at the Detention Hospital to treat the 600 men with contagious diseases.

"It is sure surprising," the camp surgeon remarked to Ellen one day, "that such a carefully nurtured woman can stand such work."

Ellen smiled. "Ruby has the simplicity of a saint and the effectiveness of a scrub woman."

Although the daily notes conveyed that she had not lost a single patient, Ellen could sense the discouragement and frustration Ruby felt over conditions at the hospital. "Mama," she wrote, "in the evenings often I sit out on the dunes and watch the ocean, wondering at the contrast of natural beauty and man's suffering. Surely, God does not ordain this. How, then, does it happen? I wrote a poem last night, and I thought you might want to read it." Ellen smoothed the paper and held it up to the light.

"The ocean moans low where the death—rattle shakes,
The wind howls a dirge o'er the desolate lakes,
We're bringing our boys whom the cannon passed by,
Whom care might have saved, we have brought home to die."

It was early September when Ellen received word that Camp Wickoff was to be closed. No more men would be brought in, and most in the General Hospital and Annex had recovered from their wounds enough to go home. The Detention Hospital and Contagion Ward were almost empty.

It had been a seemingly lost cause to open Camp Wickoff, to build shelter and find supplies, Ellen thought wryly, but now to dismantle it she had to plow through the meetings and paperwork again, this time in reverse. She traveled to New York City for a meeting with the Association, and once again to Washington, D.C., to see General Sternberg.

On her return to the camp, she found a note pinned to the inside flap of her tent: "Reubena ill." Hurriedly, she called for Major Ebert.

"It's nothing to worry too much about, Mrs. Walworth. She's been driving herself hard. With some rest, she should be fine, but I think she needs to go home and see a doctor."

When the Major brought Ruby down the hill, Ellen's dismay turned to fear. Ruby was thinner than Ellen had ever seen her, and weak, and her blue eyes shone with a foreign brightness. It was raining and a mist had settled over the dunes. The calamitous noises of the past weeks had given way to a strange quietude. "Mother," Ruby said in a low, slow voice, "I'm so sorry. Now I shall be a burden to your already too busy schedule."

"Don't be silly." Ellen laid a hand on Ruby's brow which was disturbingly warm to her touch. "We'll get you back to New York and have a doctor there take a look at you. You'll be fine."

Sunlight seeped weakly through the heavy brown draperies which had been drawn to keep the early fall light from Ruby's eyes. Ellen watched Dr. Denton examine her daughter, and as she automatically answered his questions concerning Ruby's history, a growing coldness centered within her. She fought to push the awful feeling away to no avail. The doctor's face was a mask of professional authority when he turned to her. "I'm afraid your daughter has typhoid fever, Mrs. Walworth. She needs to be in a hospital. I suggest Presbyterian. If you have another preference, I'll make the arrangements. I'd like her there, though, by six o'clock tomorrow morning." A loud and bitter cry of protest rose silently within her as she kissed Ruby on the forehead. "This shouldn't be too bad, my dear." Ellen struggled to keep her voice light. "You are well acquainted with hospitals."

Each day, in between board meetings and trips to Camp Wickoff, Ellen visited the hospital. She hurried through her days so fast that she often found herself panting. Her movements felt jerky and once she dropped her handbag with a thud that so startled her she let out a sharp exclamation of fright. Senseless anxiety surrounded her.

For three weeks Ruby lay in the hospital with a temperature of 102 degrees, but getting no worse. Then suddenly, her temperature shot up to an alarming 104 degrees. "Her pulse rate is 120," the night nurse informed Ellen matter-of-factly.

"I want to speak to the doctors." Ellen hardly recognized the harsh, shrill voice as her own.

Dr. Ibers stilled her fears. "There is no need for alarm, Mrs. Walworth. This is the body's way of discharging its poisons. My guess is that in a few days we will see marked improvement."

Ellen tried to relax, but the agonizing thoughts of Frank, of Johnny, of the babies, floated into her mind. "Nonsense!" she told herself sternly. "There has been enough tragedy in our family. It can't happen again."

The night nurse informed her that Ruby was not sleeping well. "No wonder," Ellen complained indignantly. "It's much too noisy in here." Down the corridor, a young girl cried incessantly, and her voice echoed throughout the rooms.

Ellen telegraphed Nellie and Clara and asked one of them to come. Clara arrived as quickly as possible. "I had forgotten," Ellen thought with sorrow, "how devoted Clara always was to her baby sister." Images of Clara playing mommy after Ruby's arrival filled Ellen's mind. Pictures of Clara holding Ruby's hand, comforting her, playing with her, patiently teaching her needlework when Ellen was too busy with the school and preoccupied with Frank's problems made her want to cry out with longing for her children to be little again.

"She should be in a Catholic hospital," Clara reproached Ellen.

Tension and strain began to carve themselves into tight lines around Ellen's mouth, and her eyes reflected steely fear. Her headaches returned. She couldn't sleep. She lay awake through the long nights willing Ruby to improve, and when she hurried to the hospital in the mornings, a sense of fear and dread replaced the momentary expectancy.

When Ruby's condition did not improve, Nellie came. When she sat by her sister's bed and said the rosary, Ellen clamped her jaws together tightly, so as not to lash out at Nellie for the helplessness thrust upon them.

The corridors of the hospital, so noisy a few days ago, now echoed with only soft footsteps and whispers.

"What happened to the crying young girl?" Ellen asked a nurse.

"She died."

Ellen felt ill. She demanded to see Dr. Ibers.

"No one has told me anything. Is she going to improve?" She faced the doctor resolutely, fighting the hysterics that threatened to burst to the surface.

He didn't meet Ellen's eyes. "Mrs. Walworth, I have done all I can do."

Ellen bit her lip and fought for control of her breath.

When she returned to Ruby's room, a Presbyterian clergyman stood by the bed holding Ruby's hand and intoning a prayer.

"Mother," Nellie implored with a whisper, "please get a priest."

"No!" It was almost a shout, and for a moment Ellen wondered who had been so vehement.

"Mother?" Ruby called.

"I'm here, my darling, I'm here. I'll stay right here with you. Did you see the roses Miss Raymond and Miss Morganthau sent?"

"Beau ... ti ... ful," Ruby whispered weakly when Ellen held up the vase. "They are ... sweet." Her breathing was rapid and shallow.

"You're going to get well very soon, dear."

Ellen wanted to grab Ruby, to carry her out of this threatening place into the fall sunshine and fresh, cool air.

"Mama?"

"Yes, dear?"

"Take me home."

"As soon as you are well, my dear, as soon as you are well, I'll take you home."

"Mama, kiss ... me ... goodnight."

Ellen leaned over, gently kissed Ruby on the cheek, and smoothed her bright, blonde hair.

"I will not leave this room again," she thought defiantly. "I will not leave until my daughter is ready to go with me." Automatically, not taking her eyes off the form of Ruby, Ellen fumbled for the chair and collapsed in it. She put her elbows on her knees and buried her face in her hands. She swallowed the sounds of grief and despair that rose within her and bit the palm of her hand until she tasted blood. Her throat and breast hurt with an incredible pain. Her lungs felt locked and she could not breathe. For thirty–six hours, she stayed in the room. The only sound that broke the silence was Ruby's shallow breathing.

Then, on October 17, while the hospital was locked in early morning darkness and only muffled sounds reached Ellen's ears, even the shallow breathing stopped.

308

The sun shone bright in a clear blue sky, its rays bringing life to the yellow leaves that littered the ground. The air was scented with autumn, and the day shone with a beauty that mocked the empty space of earth waiting to be filled. Ellen stood with her head held high, numbness providing an invisible shield, obscuring the harshness of reality. As the minister's voice intoned a prayer, she glanced at the pallbearers, the soldiers Ruby had nurtured to health at Montauk Point. Members of the Daughters of the American Revolution from Washington, New York City, and Saratoga crowded around the grave–site, as well as Ellen's friends and coworkers from the Women's National War Relief Association. Outside the cemetery reporters kept a respectful silence. She felt an overflowing gratefulness toward all these people, not only for showing their respect to Ruby but also for providing a distraction for her. People, even strangers, had a way of softening the sharp thrust of grief.

As the postmaster of Saratoga stepped forward to deliver his eulogy, Ellen held her head a little higher and straightened her shoulders, publicly displaying a proud refusal to bow under life's cruelest blow. Her face was hardened not only with grief but with anger toward the rest of the family, so obviously absent from Ruby's funeral.

Ellen had insisted upon a Protestant funeral, something pure and simple like Ruby herself, not a superstitious pageant suffused under the cloud of incense that her remaining children thought of as salvation. Ruby had occasionally attended Protestant services, but in their righteousness, Ellen thought bitterly, her remaining family refused to see anybody else's point of view.

Back at the house, she moved among the mourners, not expected to say anything, but murmuring polite words. Now and then a tight smile slid across her face in an effort to put those embarrassed by her grief at ease.

Seated on a sofa between Nellie and Clara, was Clarence, now an old man both deaf and blind, yet with a hint of vigor still about him.

Nellie, sitting on his right side, holding to his arm ostensibly for his support, was a study in grief and disbelief. Her face contorted, her free hand clenched tightly in her lap, she took deep breaths, visibly fighting for control of her emotions. Ellen longed to reach out to her, to hold her and murmur words of comfort but, while Nellie was kind and polite, there was a reproach in her eyes when she looked at Ellen.

Clara sat with aloof stoicism at Clarence's left side, her luminous eyes and calm face betraying no emotion. Unable to pierce Clara's aloofness, and with a clarity often exposed in times of unspeakable grief, Ellen realized that in Clara's mind they were no longer mother and daughter. Her lack of compassion puzzled Ellen. Clara had given her life to God for a life that would be born only when her earthly one was finished. Yet now, as they rallied against earthly loss, Clara had no words of comfort but remained enigmatically distant.

Tracy stood alone next to the fireplace, nodding his head but not speaking as people approached him. Once he blurted out, "I signed Frank's death certificate," and Ellen felt a maternal moment of pity for him. Did Tracy feel grief as overwhelmingly as she did, or was life so continuously overwhelming to him that this was just one more knot in an otherwise undistinguished existence?

Ellen sighed. Ruby's funeral had alienated them more in their grief than distance could have. She had tried to raise her children conscious of a spirituality, a belief, and in this she had certainly succeeded, she thought wryly. It was a fault of the Catholic Church that it left no room for freedom for one's spirit to roam in quest for truth, so that one's spirit could only bang against walls of guilt, unable to imagine fulfillment. "Then again," she thought as she looked down at the cup of punch someone had thrust into her hands, "parents are given the task of forever hoping for and forgiving their children, while children, in their stubborn willfulness, find it unnecessary ever to forgive a parent."

She longed for a flow of emotion. She was too old, too broken by loss, to go ahead with her life. There was no future, only the present, a vast blank space to be filled with endless days.

Out of habit she turned her mind to the enormous house, to the repairs that had to be made to ready it for winter and the following summer season. Armed with a notebook and pencil, Ellen roamed the rooms endlessly, noting every minor flaw, what could be done about it, and who should do it. The porch roof had to be painted and the scars on the front door refinished. Inside there was wallpaper peeling on one of the guest room walls, and she wondered idly if she should choose new paper or just reglue what was there. "Corinne," she asked her daughter–in–law one afternoon, "do you think the carpet in the front hallway looks too shabby, or do you think it can go another season?"

Corinne looked at her sympathetically. "Why don't I run the house in the summer months? It isn't necessary for you to have to stay here during the winter. I would keep you informed of any necessary repairs before I have them done."

Dear Corinne. She had run the house this past summer and done a reasonable job. Ellen looked at her, at her sweet placid face and at her hair, still auburn but without its former vibrancy. She would do a responsible job, yet Corinne always filled her with a vague uneasiness. Her soft manner and her tentative voice always left Ellen doubtful. If Corinne had once raised her voice or made an actual decision of her own without reporting all her moves, Ellen would have felt better. A person afraid of making mistakes would surely go on making them for life. Ellen took Corinne's hand and patted it. "Thank you, dear, I'll think about it. Right now it gives me something to do."

She turned to books again, but her concentration wavered. In the silence she could see Ruby's childish face wreathed in a smile, imagine her deep in concentration as she wrote plaintive letters to Ellen. "Mama, when are you coming home again?"

"I was never here. The other children, Frank's mess, the school, there was no time for Ruby." As Ellen struggled with her guilt, terrible anguish would envelop her.

Eugenia Washington ignored the fact that Ellen was in mourning and sent constant letters telling of conflicts among the Daughters, often describing in detail what was really needed, what items were being voted through that were unnecessary. And always, her letters contained a question urgent enough to require Ellen's answer.

Helen Gould wrote out of necessity since the National Women's War Relief Association was being dissolved. Compared to organizing the relief effort, dissolving the association was a complicated and endless task involving myriad letters between the members and the government. Each letter of Helen's contained an urgent request to "come, when you are feeling well enough, and help us allocate remaining funds and supplies."

It was early evening and a fire blazed on the hearth, making the house a comforting haven against the rain and drear of early November. Ellen shivered and stood closer to the hearth. "The days pass so slowly." She spoke aloud, softly, but her words seemed to echo in the emptiness that surrounded her. In despair, she wondered how she would ever get through the winter months with their cold winds and endless snows. Perhaps she should visit Mary in Iowa. The many years of sharing confidences had unwittingly permitted each woman to show the other her innermost self. Her letters to Mary were the only outlet Ellen permitted for her grief. Mary would commiserate with her, and while she appreciated Mary's kindness she realized that that was not what she needed. "What I need is work and movement among people involved in spheres outside themselves. There is pressing work being done to dismantle the camps at Montauk."

311

"You won't have to spend the winter months here." Corinne's words were like a fugitive figure chasing through her mind. "Tracy would be fine here with Corinne," she reasoned. "I wouldn't be that far away, and he can always go see Nellie and Clara in Albany."

The old stab of pity for Tracy's unused gifts and his dull routine of life shot through her. Tracy's life was his own, she mustn't be absorbed into its dullness, she warned herself. She bit her lower lip. She would go to New York; there she would have to face the pain of the past, but there she could begin a search for some activity to fill the present.

Chapter 53

Ellen opened the windows to the cold night air and breathed deeply of the new century. A cacophony of bells rang out over the city, and Albany's citizens spilled out into the streets, frantic and noisy in their joyfulness. A new year, a new century. Ellen shivered but was reluctant to close the window on this night which seemed alive with the magic of a new beginning. "The twentieth century," she murmured. She closed the window, latched it firmly, and pulled the heavy draperies across it. She had done what she could with life and would continue to do so. "But this century is not mine," she thought. "It belongs to all those just being born, to those celebrating in the streets. I hope they hang onto it and seize every moment."

She rubbed her hands together briskly, and the pain of a new world without Ruby shot through her without warning. "Bright futures died with him, never to rise." That line from the ancients sprang to her mind so often it had become a kind of litany for her.

This past year she had struggled to rise above life's blows, to grasp the force that would enable her to continue living and complete some meaningful work. She had tried to use the old formula to revive her zest—`work, exercise, and social interaction. In New York she had kept busy giving post–Parliament lectures, and she had been involved in closing the Women's National War Relief Association. Then she had traveled to Washington for meetings with the Daughters of the American Revolution. Numerous luncheons and dinners were fit in between Ellen's many trips back to Saratoga and Albany. Staying busy by interspersing household chores with mental activity had long been her prescription for keeping grief at bay. This time it had almost worked. Almost, but not quite. No matter how she hurried, how hard she worked to keep her thoughts on the present, the lack of Reubena's companionship made her days bleak and lonely. There was no one with whom to discuss what she did or what she heard or what she hoped to achieve. She would be visiting with friends, having lunch or dinner, or avidly making notes at a meeting, and suddenly, she would feel a sharp puncture of anxiety followed by an anguish so overwhelming she would have to excuse herself.

Ellen opened a desk drawer and pulled out a sheet of paper. Seating herself, she took out a pen and, clenching her jaw, began to write. "Let us fight it out—or bear it out—it is no longer a struggle, but just 'hold still'' and wait—no eagerness, no importance, no desire—only waiting with a surface patience and trying in the meantime to accomplish long–delayed tasks."

She had fought to moderate her desires, thereby hoping to find peace and contentment within herself. Her desires had always been as great as her hopes for life. If only she could quit expecting so much of herself and of others she might be content. What was it, she wondered, that made her always so restless? What compelled her to continually seek knowledge and new avenues of expression? And why, after all the hard work, had the performance she thought would be tremendous ended up small and poor?

She closed her eyes and rubbed a fist across her forehead. "I am nothing more than an old wreck, clinging to life. Once I had a large family, and now they are all gone, none successful. I can hardly see or hear, every year it gets worse, yet I go on pretending to strangers that all is well. It is only the spirit within that holds the fort."

She sighed, got up from her desk and turned out the light, then felt her way through the darkness to bed. Taking off her robe, she laid it across the foot of the bed and slid quickly under the quilts. Lying there, awaiting sleep, her thoughts went back to that long–ago evening in Uncle Abrams' Mississippi garden.

It was just a few days before her seventeenth birthday, and though the roses were still blooming, the heavy air of summer had given way to a stimulating coolness. She had snuck out alone into the garden in that time just before darkness when the sky had a sapphire light to it, and the first star was sharply outlined. As she walked out on the gravel path, she experienced a joy so intense it was almost an illumination. She thought her spirit would burst its bonds. At that moment, life was a giant birthday box with colored ribbons waiting to be pulled and gifts would come spilling out.

All her life she had vainly tried to fulfill that moment. She had tried song, speech, writing. But nothing would give utterance to that which was within and longed for expression. She would, she thought sadly, die with that joy and power unexpressed.

In mid–January Clarence suffered a stroke. "The cloister of his senses is complete," Nelly sobbed loudly over the telephone. Alarmed for her daughter, Ellen hurried to Albany. She had stopped admiring Clarence long ago and had seen him only as an adversary. Yet now he was imprisoned in silence, and she felt compassion for a brilliant mind condemned to a living death.

Ellen tried to help Nellie when, in the late afternoons and evenings, she would break into sobs by coaxing her out into the fresh air. In the mornings Ellen ignored the housekeeper and rose early to cook breakfast for Nellie, who would eat quickly in order to be at Clarence's bedside, where she would sit quietly for the rest of the day reading or writing. "Nellie," Ellen said gently to her one morning, "you must find some activity to occupy you. Sitting by your uncle's bedside all day will make you ill." A defensive look flared up in Nellie's eyes. Ellen laid her hand on her daughter's arm. "Dear, I know this is difficult for you, coming so soon after Reubena's death—"

"All you talk about is Reubena's death! You assume we are all as consumed by it as you are! No, Mother, I am upset by the fate God has bestowed upon as great a Catholic as ever lived, and I am trying to understand it! I must still help him, even if it is only by silent companionship." Nellie threw her napkin down upon the table and pushed back her chair. "Perhaps if we had all tried to live as good Catholics according to God's laws, none of these miseries would have fallen upon this family!"

With trembling hands, Ellen took a sip of coffee. She wanted to grab Nellie and shake her! The look in her eyes, the accusations in her voice—was Nellie blaming her for the misfortunes they had all suffered? Tears filled her eyes, and she quickly pushed herself away from the table. She would not let self-pity engulf her; that would only open the door to the depression she tried so hard to keep at bay. Going to her room, she began to pack. She shouldn't have been so quick to come to Albany, she reprimanded herself.

It was early morning, but the sun's rays, already piercing the frost-covered windows, promised a magic winter day of bitter cold and bright, cloudless skies. She and Tracy sat in front of the bedroom fireplace eating scrambled eggs and toast and drinking hot coffee that Bessie had sent up from the kitchen. Ellen felt cozy and surprisingly filled with a joyous happiness.

"Tracy, is there enough for you to do here in Saratoga in the winter?"

"Oh, yes. I like winter. Right now I'm building sleds for the Batchellor boys."

Kate's grandchildren. A pain of longing shot through her, but she pushed it aside.

"Do spend some of your winter evenings reading. You have a good mind, Tracy. The classics will not only teach you a great deal but will also help to keep your mind sharp." She had never been able to become totally resigned to the fact that her only surviving son was a handyman.

315

When Tracy had gone, she stretched luxuriously and then began to unpack. She moved slowly so as not to disturb the gift of peace which filled her. She meandered about the room, touching her desk, straightening a picture on the wall, fingering the folds on the draperies. With her fingernail she scraped a little frost away from the windowpane and looked out upon a quiet street. Smoke rose from the chimneys of town, straight as columns, into the cold air. She took her time dressing then decided to inspect the downstairs before she made any decisions as to what to do with the day.

The sunshine bounced long shafts of brightness off the stairway wall, and she smiled at the light. Then her foot caught on the edge of the old rug, and she had a sudden sensation of her other foot standing on air as she tried to grasp for the banister. Her back hit the stairs, and she saw colored lights and felt her leg twist under her. At the bottom of the stairway, she lay stunned, wrapped in pain, trying to grasp what had just happened.

"Just stay right there, Mrs. Walworth," an alarmed Bessie cried out. "I'll ring for the doctor."

The following days were an agony of pain. Nellie arrived, looking grieved and tired and helpless, trying to comfort a mother who had never before been bedridden. She tried to reassure Ellen. "I'll stay, Mother, until we can find a nurse for you."

"I must hurry back to Uncle," Ellen's thoughts silently echoed the words she imagined in Nellie's head. She watched her daughter, hurrying in and out of the room. For the first time she noticed the gray hairs streaking the light brown and saw the small lines that creased her daughter's tired skin. Nellie's eyes had a flat, distracted look, and her mouth was tight, as though she clenched disappointments and worries within herself. "Why, she's looking old," Ellen thought with surprise.

In a few days, Nellie appeared triumphantly with Nina Thompson in tow. Nina was a professional nurse, tall, blonde, and young. She reminded Ellen of Reubena, and Ellen gave herself up to her care thinking how comforted those young men must have felt in Ruby's presence.

In the days to come, she found that it was not loneliness that was to be feared but pain. The sharp, agonizing pain started in her leg and worked its way up to her head; there, relieved by cocaine hydrochlor and belladonna, it ended as an annoying buzz in her head. When the physical pain was subdued, memories of Ruby filled the medicated haze with a pain that no medicine could alleviate, a pain worse than any other. She did not have the energy to resist it; she could only give in to it until the physical pain took over again.

316

It was late winter before the torture passed. Ellen directed the first stirrings of her energy toward the house. With Nina's help she dressed and did her hair; it took both the nurse and Bessie to help balance her as she wobbled about the house. New matting was badly needed in the dining room, and the parlor should be repapered, Ellen noted. She checked the legs on all the chairs to make certain they were strong and pulled the draperies out from the windows to inspect for moth holes and sun damage. Finally, she slumped against the back of a sofa as Nina supported her. "I think I have had more than enough."

"We've been about for almost two hours."

Ellen laughed weakly. "Oh, Bessie, you make it sound as though a victory had just been won. The bed sounds awfully good. Will you bring the newspaper along?"

Once propped comfortably against the pillows, Ellen opened the paper and noted with surprise an account of an address Senator Hoar had recently given to the Unitarian Church.

"Unitarianism is not a creed: it is a faith, a hope, a quality of character. Its principle is love manifested in worship of God and service to man, with the practical demonstration of moral principle in individual right doing."

Ellen lay back on the pillows and closed her eyes. Religion was the dark hole in her life, a puzzle that had dogged her days. Organized religion was something to which she could not commit herself; she was unable to reconcile the laws man needed with spiritual freedom, which she was certain God ordained. Churches or associations are helpful, she decided as she drifted off to sleep, only for those people who cannot stand alone.

In September Clarence died. Ellen, alarmed by Nellie's increasing depressions, hurried to Albany with Tracy by her side.

Although Tracy was agitated and openly weeping, Ellen felt relieved by Nellie's apparent composure. "He has been freed at last," Nellie whispered as she fell into Ellen's embrace. She dabbed at her eyes with a handkerchief and embraced Tracy. "It's all right, Brother, he's with God."

Watching Nellie and Tracy console each other, Ellen realized that, for her three remaining children, Clarence was the father they had never had. "But he didn't have to be; I could have done just fine. We would have all been closer without his interference."

Picking up Ellen's valise, Nellie motioned with her head for her mother to follow her down the hall. "You shouldn't be using the stairs, Mother. You can have this small bedroom back here." Ellen, limping slowly and painfully, followed her into the bedroom. Nellie motioned toward a chair for Ellen and hoisted her mother's suitcase onto the bed. "I'll unpack for you," she said as she began unfastening the locks. "I don't want you to tire yourself out. Clara will be here in a few hours. People have been arriving at the church all morning just to file past the bier." Nellie thrust a copy of the Albany newspaper into Ellen's hands. Black headlines proclaimed, Passing of a Grand Old Man. "He was so much more to everybody than just a priest. The Albany Common Council has adopted a resolution of regret."

Ellen laid her head back against the chair. "When I first saw him I was awe–struck. He was so much more worldly than I expected. His energy, his stimulating personality, made him quite unforgettable."

"His was a force borne of God," Nellie whispered. "Would you like to go to the church with me?"

"Thank you, dear, but no. I've come to give you support and assistance, but I don't think it's necessary for me to fall into line."

"We won't stand in line, Mother. We're family."

"That's not exactly what I meant. No, I shall stay here."

Nellie looked at her mother and her eyes hardened. "There are expected to be over one hundred priests at the funeral. But people of all faiths are standing out there waiting to pay their respects to a man who was a scholar, a political activist, a temperance leader, a champion of American Indians. You were his sister–in–law. You should be there."

"Nellie, don't you think it's a little late for me to pay my respects to Clarence? You are quite aware of my feelings. I won't be hypocritical. I came to help you. I shall be here after the service tomorrow to help you receive some of these people, but I won't be at the church."

Nellie stood still and straight, but tears filled her eyes. "You are wrong not to forgive. You won't bend, Mother, not even for your family."

Chapter 54

Ellen was seventy, on the very threshold of old age. Yet age had brought its own kind of beauty. Her blue eyes had lightened, but shone with a steely will; her mouth was set resolutely. She still wore her hair swept up on top of her head, sometimes in elaborate curls or a coronet of braids. Even though she was thinner than she had ever been in her adult life, there was nothing frail about her. Her posture, her walk, the gaze with which she met the world, all exemplified dignity and determination.

Yet she still found it impossible not to fight for every next hour, every next month; she longed to be busy, to be intellectually alive; she longed for a new project to rush out and meet. She had always felt an inner push to use her life in worthwhile pursuits. Now she felt even more sharply that every hour not spent in pursuit of one's major aim was an hour wasted; she could not accept the fact that after a lifetime of seeking she had so little intellectual gain. She read, not for pleasure but for knowledge. She read to renew her strength and seek inspiration. And she constantly evaluated the past to gain perspective.

And with age came a new struggle, that of banishing fear. In the early mornings, still groggy from sleep, she would feel a heavy physical sensation deep within her as though her stomach had turned over and brought anxiety to the surface. Another day, she would think. But how many more days will there be? She felt a renewed sense of her own limitations. Human events were quite insignificant after all, she decided, and the caring for them a luxury given only to those with a future.

Her own children didn't seem to care one whit about her. Nellie's sharp retorts to her, her brusque behavior when Ellen visited Albany left her angry and depressed. She would not visit Albany as often as she had, she vowed inwardly, she would not be a clinging parent, unwanted in her children's lives.

She pursed her lips and frowned, then moved to her desk and tried to unravel her conflicting thoughts and feelings onto a piece of paper. Her left hand balled tightly into a fist on top of the paper, with her right hand she gripped the pen tightly as she wrote:

"I will have to hold myself apart from my family. I will be receptive but restrained. I will accept advances, but I will make no advances. I'll harbor no regrets, no bitterness, no ill-will. I will be completely independent of affection, time, and finances." She was interrupted by a loud knock. "Mrs. Walworth," Bessie's voice said through the door, "you have a telegram." Startled, she rose stiffly from the desk, hobbled to the door and grabbed at the yellow piece of paper. With shaking hands she read the words over and over with disbelief. This telegram, this yellow piece of paper was printed with words that spoke finality, and an abyss opened beneath her. Mary Duncan Putnam was dead.

Of course, of course, she reminded herself. We are mortal; Molly was as old as I am. Yet in her mind, they had always been giggling young girls exchanging confidences that over the years had grown somber through failures and sorrows.

Still holding the telegram, she moved to the window and stared out at the park. Death makes living sacred, she mused, and full of significance. Even with death before us, how we defer the most important acts of life—if life were perpetual, there would be no incentive to work, to think, to progress. What is progress without development? Yet how often we mistake mere change for growth. It isn't change we should seek, but light.

Just two days later, while reading the New York paper, she read of the death of Emily Roebling.

Suddenly and irrationally, she was afraid to be alone. This was not the fear of loneliness, but a very real need to touch a loved one. All determination forgotten, she returned to Albany.

"Oh, Nellie," she lamented to her daughter as they sat before the fire one evening, "what is it all about? I have always felt that one's husband, one's family, and meaningful work coupled with an awareness of spirituality make a perfect life. Although I recognized it, it has always been beyond me. Why, why have I not been able to reach what I can see?"

Troubled, contradictory thoughts tangled in her mind day and night, and only by putting the thoughts down on paper, disjointed as they were, could she disengage herself from the losses always with her. She needed to apply her mind to work, she needed a piece of writing, and for now it didn't matter if her thoughts were not to be read through correspondence or for publication. If nothing else, the blank pages of paper were an outlet for suppressed or forgotten thoughts and emotions. She felt deadened, and writing was the channel to a life power that would otherwise remain unused. It was a means of communication, if only with herself.

Then, into the void came a letter from Helen Gould asking if Ellen would be interested in forming an organization to help the widows and orphans of the Spanish–American War.

"At last, a project I can believe in! Now I won't be in your hair so much, Nellie!" She bubbled with enthusiasm once again as letters flew back and forth between Albany and New York City.

With a renewed sense of purpose, she returned to Saratoga and spent her days in a flurry of organization. Ideas tumbled through her mind, one over the other, and she decided to put the Hardin family letters and papers together again and perhaps write a biography of the family. She spent days pouring over old letters, but surprisingly they depressed her. "It's only digging up what can never be again," she explained to Tracy. "I might as well be in the cemetery opening old graves. Still, I feel bad not doing it. Those lives shouldn't be lost in the dust of carelessness."

As an antidote to the lugubrious task, she enthusiastically began seeking out friends again. In the late afternoons and evenings, she often went to a reception or party or out for a game of whist. However, her energy was largely mental. After an evening out, Ellen often suffered from an upset stomach and exhaustion that prevented her leaving her room until the following afternoon. Yet she felt alive again, and when Kate Batchellor died in July, she attended the funeral without fear or depression.

There were few happy surprises in her life, but when D. arrived a few days before her seventy–first birthday, she whooped with glee. "I should tie a ribbon around you. You're the best present I could have!"

"You know I have to come check on Saratoga now and then. I just threw you in for something extra."

Laughter filled the house again. Nellie came from Albany to stay for a few days, and Tracy dogged D.'s every step. In the evenings, they took their meals out and, once back at the house, they sat up talking until the clock reminded them a new day had begun.

"Come to Chicago, Sister," D. urged. "A trip will do you good, and Nellie can come, too, so you won't have to travel alone."

"I'd like that, D., I really would. I've been going to come so often, and then because of one stupid malady after another, I've had to cancel. I do wish," she added wistfully, "that I had come while Molly was still alive."

"Come," he demanded. "For Christmas. I want you to promise."

"All right," she laughed, "I promise. We'll celebrate Christmas in Chicago."

The wind felt like a sheet of ice against her face as she and Nellie stepped off the train and into the enveloping arms of her family. First D. and then Evelyn, then Lem, dear Lem, and then Annie. Lem was white–haired and for a moment, Ellen was surprised. He walked with a stoop, and the limp he had developed as a result of his war wounds was pronounced. Still, his eyes crinkled like they had when he was a young boy. When he looked at Ellen and drawled, "I have to touch you to make sure you're really here," it was the same Lem she had always known and loved. As they climbed into the carriage, everyone was talking at once, trying in a flurry of meaningless words to recapture the companionship they had once known.

The following weeks were an excitement of activity. Ellen spent mornings at her niece Evelyn's house, soaking up the happy tumult of a home with growing children. Happily she read to them, played dolls with them, and tried to teach them simple card games. This was how she had so often envisioned herself, surrounded by her own grandchildren, and now in this moment she felt fulfilled. Annie patiently taught her to play bridge, and in the evenings there was always a reception, a dinner, or a card game. She, Evelyn, and Annie spent afternoons at the art museum, and there were always luncheons, teas, or sometimes both. It was a time of laughter and bright spirits.

Ellen was resting in her room one day when Evelyn burst into the room. "I have something for you, Aunt Ellen." She thrust a large rectangular box at Ellen. "I hope you like it. If you don't, for whatever reason, I can take it back, but when I saw it, I thought of you." She watched as Ellen cautiously unwrapped the box and then slowly opened it and ran her hand over white chiffon. Then, her face a mask of detachment, she lifted the gown out of the box and held it in front of her.

"I thought, well, I thought maybe you were tired of black. I asked Mama, and she said it was a splendid idea."

Ellen, still holding the gown in front of her, smiled. "I like it, Evelyn. You were so thoughtful to do this." She went over to Evelyn and gave her a perfunctory kiss on the cheek. "I'll wear it to dinner tomorrow night."

After her niece left, Ellen stood holding the gown in front of her, then removed her dressing gown and slowly stepped into the filmy white material. It had been five years since she had worn anything other than black, five years of mourning. As she stood with the white gown on, she felt as if she had shed her old soul. "One does not need to make a statement of mourning," she murmured to herself. "The heavy heart within carries it always." She hung the dress on the outside of her wardrobe where she could see it and hoped that she hadn't insulted Evelyn by her lack of enthusiasm. Years of loss and her fears of rejection had deadened the spontaneous eagerness of her youth, and to be given a gift for no reason filled her with an emotion she couldn't express.

Only a persistent pain in her left side marred her visit, and while she tried to keep it to herself, at times it grew so sharp that she became nauseated and had to lie down in her room. Then there were days when she felt stupid and couldn't concentrate. And once, to her chagrin, she became quite disoriented and couldn't recall where she was.

Still, it was a warm and intense family time, and when Ellen and Nellie boarded the train for Albany two days after Christmas, it was with a certain sadness and regret. Yet, she thought as the train chugged out of the station, she was tired, and even though she planned to spend January with Nellie in Albany, at least there would be peace and solitude.

In Albany, it was a quiet family circle of mutual support, Corinne and Clara were in and out of the house. Nellie spent her days working on a biography of Clarence, and when she asked for her mother's comments, Ellen read the chapters as an editor might, looking for the flow of rhythm, words, and ideas with a detachment from the subject itself. She was happy Nellie was writing again, being creative, and working on her own without that old man forever directing her every step.

"I can never forgive him," Ellen thought over and over when she pondered Clara cloistered in her superstitions or watched Nellie's solitary activities. In his will, Clarence had sealed her grudge against him when he had left $150,000 to Nellie and $8,000 apiece to Tracy, Clara, Corinne, and little Clara, yet nothing to Ellen. Nellie was generous, giving her a monthly stipend. It was not something that had been discussed or mentioned, it was done as naturally as though it was a lifetime habit. In addition, the $2,000 Mary had willed to Ellen had only served to make her feel like a pauper. She knew Mary had meant well, that the money was a gift of love, but it had made her feel worse than she had when supporting a family. More than anything, her growing dependence made her resent Nellie's new independence.

"Mama? Clara and I are thinking of traveling to Europe, to France and Italy." They were sitting in the parlor, the flickering lights throwing shadows of their movements on the walls. "If we don't go to Paris or Florence, then maybe the west, to see the Indians."

Ellen laid aside the skirt she was sewing and looked at Nellie.

"For what are you searching?"

"Not searching. I just want to see it all. The old cobblestones of Europe or the vast expanses of the west. I'm beginning to feel confined here."

"You have always been confined here," Ellen reminded her daughter. "You have been held captive. Now that you have some money, I suppose you can go anywhere you like for as long as you like. Money does give one dreams."

The silence in the room grew explosively heavy.

"No matter where you go, Nellie, you won't find what you are seeking because you aren't using your powers of life. We demonstrate the Creator's wisdom when we use our faculties and powers of life. If we don't use our powers, then we are dead even though we are going through the motions of living."

Nellie looked at her disdainfully. "I have written two books, Mother, and both of them about life I've seen while I was traveling. I don't have to grub for meaning in my life every moment, and if you hadn't formed such a despicable habit, Father Walworth might not have found you so impossible. I am simply talking about getting away from Albany for a time."

Fear formed within Ellen, fear of being left alone, but she continued to look at Nellie, her face forming into a hard mask.

"Mother, if you need more money so you can take another trip or do anything else you want, I'll be glad to give you more."

Ellen said nothing but picked up her sewing and left the room. Her eyes filled with tears and her chin trembled. How she hated the weakness of old age! She, who had spent her life desiring independence, could not bear to be parted from her children. Tears rolled down her cheeks, tears of frustration for her inability to achieve freedom and independence. And tears of rage that those close to her could not sense her loneliness and fear.

The next morning, confronting her helplessness, she chided herself. "I cannot control everyone's circumstances, only my own. I shall will an internal repose and stability and an external rigidity that will develop a renewed power of mental activity." As she combed her hair in front of her dressing mirror, she said aloud to her reflection, "You have work to do, get to it! Nellie is handing you the independence you want. A will of my own, an independent spirit, that is.what she is giving me." She sat down on the edge of her bed. "Mental activity has always saved me and helped open the door to the world. I have the Hardin papers to work on, and I won't let self–pity rule me when I read them. I am the only one who can put them together, and they must not be lost. I shall always be interested in the Daughters of the American Revolution and the branch of the Children of the American Revolution which Mrs. Lothrup has asked me to help organize." She laughed, a short noise aimed at dismissing her fears. "Not bad for an old lady. Why on earth should I deny Nellie her interests?" Then, she thought, there were the Livingston papers. The Chancellor had passionately hoped that Mansfield would write the life of Governor Robert Livingston, that it would be his son's great work establishing him not only as a serious writer but as a scholar and lawyer as well. Mansfield, though, had approached them with only the most desultory obedience, preferring his own imagination to anything his father imagined for him, and the papers had lain in disarray.

Then Reuben, in his retirement, had attempted the task, but he had died before they were finished. Now, they lay packed away with what was left of Reuben's library, a distinguished life waiting to be brought to light. Ellen had thought of them often, and now with a sudden clarity saw them as a task waiting for her. It was not the kind of writing Mansfield preferred, but for her it was perfect. Always, the past pointed the way toward the future. Certainly, Governor Livingston's life was an inspired one, and through his papers perhaps another life would be inspired. It would only help her to try.

Chapter 55

Even though the sky was clear, the early March wind still had the bite of winter in it. Ellen sunk her chin into the fur collar of her coat and shivered.

"Are you all right, Mother?" Nellie peered at her anxiously.

"Yes, oh, yes. I'm glad it's a sunny day. Why didn't anyone ever think to hold a presidential inauguration in June?"

A hush came over the crowd as Theodore Roosevelt placed his hand on a Bible to take the oath of office. Then, turning toward the crowd with a solemn expression on his face, his bristling mustache and thick glasses plainly evident, he launched his inaugural address.

Ellen squinted, then placed a hand above her eyes to shield them from the bright glare. She inclined her head toward the sound, straining to catch his words.

"We are the heirs of the ages," he proclaimed, "and yet we have had to pay few of the penalties which in old countries are expected by the dead hand of a bygone civilization." He declared that the nation had faced perils with vigor and effort and had surmounted them. "Now," he thundered, gesturing expansively, "the conditions which have told for our marvelous well–being, which have developed to a very high degree our energy, self–reliance and individual initiative, have also brought the care and anxiety inseparable from the accumulation of great wealth in industrial centers."

After the address, they climbed into Sarah Henderson's automobile to ride to Mr. Gresham's store, where they could watch the parade in comfort. "President Roosevelt has certainly brought the world to our door." Sarah looked at her sideways as she settled herself and smoothed her skirt. "Did it sound to you like we are to pay a penalty for being a vigorous, free country? I don't know, he may be a wealthy man, but to me he's just a cowboy."

The parade moved down Pennsylvania Avenue in a celebration of freedom, new life, and hope. "Look," Nellie squealed and pointed a finger toward the window. The grand marshals of the parade, solemn in top hats and cutaway coats, frowned with concentration and attempted to keep their dignity as their mounts snorted, reared, and tried to turn sideways. "If they weren't trying to be so solemn, it wouldn't be so funny," Nellie laughed. Then a contingent of Rough Riders passed to the rousing strains of "A Hot Time in the Old Town Tonight," followed by cadets from West Point and midshipmen from Annapolis.

It had been a wonderful month, Ellen reflected. She had filled days with visits to friends and acquaintances, attended meetings of the Daughters of the American Revolution, and spent mornings at the Congressional Library.

Being in Washington again, Ellen was able to feel almost palpably the country's pulse, sensing the daily panorama of power. It awakened in Ellen a force she had been afraid was gone and gave her the necessary stimulation to turn her mind to work.

She had finished the Hardin papers and sent them out to a publisher, then started on the Livingston papers. It was difficult for her to imagine that through the long days when she cast about for a purpose, she hadn't thought of the papers. They had been there all the time, she marveled as she read through page after page of printed material. As a natural consequence of her historical interests and her love of writing, she found these projects exciting.

"What a wonderful time we've had!" Ellen's eyes danced with enthusiasm as the train rocked and creaked its way to New York.

"Did you get enough material for the Livingston papers?" Nellie clutched the seat in front of her to maintain her balance, then stood, smoothed her skirts, and sat down again.

"Enough to keep me busy for the summer."

"Mother, I know you are going to take this the wrong way, and please forgive me if you do, but why don't you consider spending your winters in Washington? You feel much more alive there, there is so much to keep you busy, and it's warmer and better for your health. I could help you find a place, why don't you consider it?"

"I've thought of it, Nellie." Ellen rubbed a hand across her eyes. "But I'm an old lady and to suddenly move and be alone—" she broke off the words and turned her head to the window.

"You're a vigorous woman," Nellie retorted. "Age doesn't matter." She smiled. "Old ladies usually sit in their parlors with knitting needles in their trembling hands. You are busy writing an important piece, working for the Daughters of the American Revolution, and attending every political function you are entitled to go to." She paused for a moment. "You have never been the model of an accepting, pampered woman. And," she added, "you have an opinion, and always an intelligent one, on just about everything you see, read, or hear."

"I thought we just had a very good time together, Nellie."

"Of course we did. I'm just saying that I do think it's too taxing for you to travel back and forth to Washington every time you want something or are invited somewhere. If you really want to stay in Saratoga, then fine." Nellie leaned her head back against the cushion and closed her eyes.

Ellen bit her lip. She had often thought of moving to Washington for the winter, but she was old. Nellie didn't understand. In Washington she would be out of her children's way, but she might be very lonely. All alone in a strange house, with a stranger for a housekeeper—why didn't Nellie offer to move with her, if it was so good for her? All her daughter had in Albany was Corinne's company, and heaven knew that wasn't much. Of course, Ellen reflected bitterly, Madonna Clara came there now and then but in her estimation, Clara had nothing to offer either.

The room was filled with a gray light when Ellen awakened on Sunday morning, and the pine branches scratched against the window in a frenzy. Outside the rain beat down upon the roof and against the windows in a torrent of staccato beats. The room was cold, and Ellen pulled the quilts up to her chin. She made no move to get up. She had promised to accompany Tracy to St. Peter's for services, but not in weather like this. And Nellie had promised to spend the day with them. Now Ellen wondered anxiously if she would come. She shuddered. "It's spring and time for warm sunshine."

She heard a light knock at the door and then Tracy's voice. "Are you coming to church with me?"

"Come in. No, dear," Ellen said to the disappointed look on Tracy's face. "Not in this weather. Do you think Nellie will come today?"

"It's only rain. I'm sure she'll be here."

After Tracy left, Ellen reluctantly climbed out of bed. She felt tired, and she would gladly have stayed there the morning, but if Nellie was coming, she had better make sure Bessie would have an early Sunday dinner.

She was in the parlor when she heard the carriage and, rushing to the windows, saw Nellie alight.

"Weather like this and you still came!" Ellen exclaimed gratefully as she greeted Nellie in the hallway.

"It's just a spring storm, Mother, the rain is letting up now." She took her hat off and shook the dampness off, then took off her gloves and rubbed her hands together. "I do think the Atlantic Ocean will be a little deeper when this rain blows out to sea."

"I didn't know when to plan for dinner, but at least the roast won't be overdone. And guess what? I tried to remember Dolly's plum cake recipe from memory while Bessie tried to follow it!"

As they sat around the table, the coals in the hearth warmed the room and the scent of roasted meat and vegetables filled the air. Ellen glanced out the window, then turned back to her family and smiled. "It's nice, us here together when it's so gray and damp outside." She relaxed into happiness. "Tracy," she said, passing the platter toward him, "have some more."

With a spoon and fork, Tracy lifted two roasted potatoes onto his plate, then took a slice of meat. "Nellie tells me you wouldn't mind moving to Washington, Mother." He said it casually, as though he was simply mentioning the weather.

Like an animal sensing danger, Ellen stiffened. She watched Tracy cut a piece of meat, chew thoughtfully for a moment, then swallow. "If you wouldn't mind, I'd be happy to go with you."

Ellen twisted her napkin nervously. "Have you two been talking behind my back? Don't you think you should have sat down and discussed this with me?" Tears sprang to her eyes, and suddenly she felt confused. "I—I have to think." Slowly, she pulled herself out of her chair. She had thought this to be only a nice family Sunday, but now she could see the purpose. Was she considered too old and insignificant to be included in family concerns?

She did not know how long she sat in her room, only that when the room began to grow dim, she stood up, startled. The house was quiet. Would Nellie have left without telling her? She moved slowly down the stairs, and when she saw the parlor lights on and heard Tracy's voice, she felt a tremendous relief. "All right," she said as she walked into the parlor, "I'll go." It was said without conscious thought, and for days afterward, Ellen was startled when she remembered the firmness in her voice.

329

Chapter 56

The years passed, each day moving slowly, yet the accumulation grew so fast that Ellen was always surprised by the new year and always wondered if it would be her last. Her joints grew increasingly painful with the years so that she had to use either a cane when walking or the wonderful new rolling chair that Tracy, Nellie, Clara, and Corinne had given her. Yet pride kept her posture straight, and she moved with as much vigor as she could muster.

She chafed constantly at growing old, wondering why she had been singled out to outlive her family and friends, to spend her days in loneliness. Yet, she was afraid of death. Fear drove her to strengthen her will and master her physical infirmities. She quit drinking coffee and tea, and quit eating meat and sugar—except when Tracy came home with an occasional treat of ice cream. Every day she went out in the fresh air, even in the coldest weather.

Nellie and Tracy had been right. Living in Glen Carlyn, Virginia, on the outskirts of Washington, was delightful in every sense. The moment she had moved into the charming cottage with its gleaming wood floors and its white woodwork, the sunlight had darted through the many—paned windows, and she had felt excited and elated. She devoured the newspapers, marveling at the feeling of being in the midst of world news. She attended meetings of the Daughters of the American Revolution when she could, and had served on the building committee. Of the original founders, only she and Mary Lockwood were alive, and their place at the meetings was largely ceremonial. In her eightieth decade, Ellen found that national affairs continued to pique her interest. Her country stood as the single exciting, viable entity in her life, and nothing else stirred as much excitement within her.

On the afternoon of April 15, 1912, Ellen proudly walked down the aisle of Memorial Constitution Hall as the twenty–first Congress of the Daughters of the American Revolution was opened. At her side was the President–General, Mrs. Matthew Scott. After the reports of the various chapters and committees had been read, the formal opening at three o'clock was a brilliant affair. With the Marine band playing in the museum, the great sliding mahogany doors between the museum and the auditorium were opened. As President Taft walked through the door, he was welcomed by two thousand Daughters waving handkerchiefs and applauding wildly. He ascended the platform, and the Betsy Ross flag came floating to the center of the domed ceiling. Holding out his hands for quiet, the President's voice boomed across the hall.

"D.A.R.: I am here to discharge the pleasant annual duty that falls to the President of the United States of welcoming the beauties of spring and the beauties of the Daughters." Again there was wild applause, and again he quieted the gathering with a gesture of his hands. "You are here to stimulate the memories of and the respect for those men who made this nation possible and who laid its broad foundation in the Constitution of the United States, and you are here, I understand, to uphold the principles of the Constitution and to insist on their preservation as long as the nation shall endure."

Ellen's mind drifted back to that night in her apartment when four women, so indignant in being excluded from public patriotism, had decided to build a working memorial to women's love of country. She felt a sting within her as she thought of Eugenia Washington, and she wished she was sharing the platform with her today. Of the three other founders, it was Eugenia with whom she had developed and enjoyed the strongest friendship.

The President's voice brought her back to the present. "We have reached a time in the history of politics in this country when we have to take down our copies of the Federalist, and of the history of growth of our institutions, and renew our vows to the principles that were there embodied in our governmental structure, to insist that they shall not be departed from, but that they shall be maintained in their vitalizing force to continue our pursuit of happiness and the guarantees of our institutions for the maintenance of liberty regulated by law."

At the end of his speech, the President left the dais quickly, and while applause still filled the hall, Miss Annin Maxwell Jones of the Saratoga Chapter self-consciously made her way to the side of the stage, next to a portrait which stood covered by a blue cloth. Ellen sat still, a half-smile on her face, while Miss Jones loudly listed all of Ellen's accomplishments in the Daughters of the American Revolution. Then an audible murmur rippled through the audience as she lifted off the cloth, and the portrait of Ellen was revealed.

She dressed carefully in a silver gray velvet gown accented at the neckline by darker gray velvet leaves. She opened a bureau drawer and began rummaging through her belongings. "If they aren't here, where else would they be?" Ellen moved to her wardrobe and began pushing aside shoes and hat boxes. "Oh, no." She couldn't go to the White House reception without gloves, and Sarah Henderson would be here any moment to pick her up. Opening her bedroom door, she called for Tracy, but there was no answer. Her heart pounded as she hurried back to her bureau and rummaged through the drawers again. A sudden thought made her straighten up slowly. "Be calm," she told herself, "try to remember who has been in the house." Just last week she had been certain one of the Livingston papers had been taken, and she still hadn't found it. "Undoubtedly, this is being done by a jealous hand," she said aloud. It would definitely be necessary now for Tracy to put a lock on her bedroom door, and she would see to it that he put new locks on the front and back doors, too.

By the time Sarah picked her up, she was almost in tears. Recounting the story, Ellen caught a quick, curious glance from Sarah. "There's plenty of time," she told Ellen reassuringly. "We'll have the driver stop at Woodward and Lothrup."

As they drove into the long driveway leading to the White House, Ellen's heart swelled with pride. The White House was the country, a venerable virgin structure to the unsullied freedom of the nation.

President and Mrs. Taft received the Daughters of the American Revolution graciously, but it was a tentatively joyous event. Everyone was thinking of Major Archibald Butt, the President's affable military aide who had been aboard the Titanic when that great ocean liner sank just three days ago. Laughter seemed a mockery to the spirit of Major Butt, who had been so obvious a figure at every public function.

That night, preparing for bed, Ellen was startled by a pain between her shoulder blades. She tried to ignore it, but it gathered into a knot and relieved itself only an hour later in waves of nausea. When Tracy came in to check on her, her face was the color of chalk, and she was drenched with perspiration.

"Mother, I'm going to call the doctor." Tracy made no effort to hide his alarm.

"I ... just did ... too much." But Tracy was out of the room before she finished the sentence.

After what seemed like hours, Dr. Talbott arrived, a mask of courtesy and detachment covering his face. He examined her quickly, prodding and probing, while Tracy anxiously stood beside him. When he finished, he drew a chair up beside the bed and sat down. "Mrs. Walworth, I don't quite know what to tell you. Your heart seems strong, but this trouble may be caused by your gallbladder. I'm going to leave some medicine here and a prescription which you can have filled in the morning." He leaned forward. "If this medicine fails to work, we will have to hospitalize you."

The medicine lulled her into sleep, for how long she didn't know, but when the pain nudged her awake again, it was still dark. Outside, horse's hooves clopped by, and she heard the wheels of a wagon rattle somewhere off in the distance. The subdued morning noises announced another day, and Ellen took a deep breath. Thoughts of the hospital did not fill her with terror. Instead, it was the image of cool, clean, white sheets and caring hands that relaxed her, and she lay there waiting for Tracy to awaken.

She had been out of the hospital only a week when she accepted Sarah Henderson's invitation to attend a Daughters of the American Revolution meeting in Vienna, Virginia. She enjoyed being among the Daughters, although there was little she could contribute now. But it was the satisfaction of seeing her efforts continued in the hands of younger, more energetic chapter members that filled her with gratitude. The members were delighted when she came, so many telling her at the tea afterwards that just her presence added luster to their meetings.

A pink glow enclosed the warm June day. Roses were in bloom, and the air was redolent with warmth and fragrance and peace. Driving home in Sarah's automobile by the long stretch of waterfront of Potomac Park, they viewed the 3,000 cherry trees which Japan had recently presented to the city of Washington. The first tree, an imperial specimen grown only in the gardens of the Emperor, had been planted by Mrs. Taft, while at the same time Baroness Chinda, wife of the Japanese ambassador, had planted a tree of the same variety.

"Can you imagine the beauty?" Ellen enthused. "Unquestionably, this will be the striking feature of outdoor Washington." They rode in silence for a moment, imagining the future. "I wonder how many more days like this I will be privileged to see?" Ellen spoke matter-of-factly, acknowledging her age and her moment in life. Sarah didn't protest, but simply nodded her head. She, too, was resigned to having already lived a full life, and was grateful for whatever time there might be left to enjoy.

"I did a great deal of thinking while I was in the hospital, and I decided that, if you didn't mind, Sarah, I would like you to be in charge of the disposal of my remains. I can't talk to Tracy about this," Ellen continued, "he got terribly upset when I told him earlier in the year that I was willing our cottage in Glen Carlyn to him. I could talk to Nellie, she might listen, but then she would go ahead and do whatever she deems right and hang my wishes!"

Sarah laughed, a short, derisive noise. "It's incredible to reach the stage in life where we can attend an event on a beautiful day, have stimulating conversation, and then talk about the disposal of our remains on the way home."

Ellen smiled. "Practicality always wins out. I don't want a Catholic burial, and I'd like to be buried in Saratoga. Not a heavy religious ceremony either. What comes next, comes next, but for the last remembrance and deed on earth, I'd like to be remembered for my accomplishments. The work I did for the schools so long ago and the work for the Daughters. Maybe what I did for the Saratoga Monument Association and the historical society." The automobile stopped in front of the house, and Sarah's driver got out and came to Ellen's door and opened it. "Have you ever seen such an abundance of roses?" she cried with delight. "Next week I think I'll give a rose tea to celebrate these flowers!"

Chapter 57

Increasingly she felt she had moved into an icy, racing stream, that life was swirling about her in a vortex, that all was monstrous and out of joint. Ellen still experienced the pain occasionally which had hospitalized her but without the intensity of that first attack. Each day seemed to exhaust her, and the trip back to Saratoga for the summer had tired her so much she could hardly leave her bedroom.

It was the second week in July when the pain recurred again, this time assaulting her in tight bands, squeezing up her left side and across her chest and back.

She saw Dr. Ledlie. "I have to agree with your Washington doctor, Mrs. Walworth. You may need an operation."

Ellen grew cold. At her age an operation was a terrible danger, even the doctor admitted that. She returned home, and Tracy helped her into bed. She lay there, studying the ceiling, staring at a light brown water mark which had stained the small part of one corner. It was the same ceiling she had stared at through so many years when she worried over finances, when she mourned her children. "That stain," she thought, "is the overflow of my troubles. This old ceiling just can't take any more." Outside the window there was music from the park and loud laughter. Saratoga summer noises. A screen door slammed in the distance, and an excited voice echoed down the street. "Life is out there, beyond me." She struggled to an upright position. "If I lay here, I will just give in, I won't get any better." She moved slowly toward the basin and pitcher standing across from her bed. She splashed her face with cold water, slowly patted it with a linen towel, then put on a cool pink dressing gown. She smiled to herself. Pink was a young girl's color, a color of hope and cheer. She took a few pins out of the bun on top of her head and pinned back some loose strands of hair. She didn't glance at the bed again for fear she would succumb to exhaustion and lay back down. Instead, she went into the hall and slowly made her way downstairs. She found Tracy outside studying the peeling paint around a window frame.

"Mother! Dr. Ledlie told you to stay in bed."

"Yes, so he did. But I'm tired of being a recluse. Saratoga in the summer wasn't made for resting. Tracy, why don't we plan an ice cream social for Sunday?"

The summer passed with Ellen making plans on her good days, then smothered with lassitude on days when she experienced pain or a

335

fatigue too great to overcome. She tried to set a date for returning to Washington, but decided to wait until after Labor Day to make definite plans for the fall and winter.

Much to her delight, D. made a surprise appearance the day before Labor Day. As he was helping her put up the flag, she found the reason for his visit.

"Nelly, why don't you go ahead with the operation and save yourself all this unnecessary pain?"

She looked at him with surprise, then dropped her hands to her sides. "So, they told you." The green and gold of the day blurred together as tears filled her eyes. "It may not be necessary. Dr. Ledlie said to wait and talk to the doctor in Washington. I haven't had constant pain, it just comes and goes. I'm afraid, D. I'm so afraid, I don't want to lie down or go to sleep anymore. I want to run down the street again, I want to laugh."

She sat down on the porch swing and hid her face in her hands. "What if I die?"

"Sister." D. sat down beside her and put his arm around her shoulder. "I can't tell you it will be all right." His voice was a near whisper. "All I can say is I don't believe you have a choice."

In the following days she asked herself the same question over and over. "In another month I'll be eighty–three years old, and I have had such few happy days. I've been given much more time than Johnny, Bessie, Sarah, Frank, or Reubena. And yet," she lamented, "I have so little to show for all my days." Fear, mixed with an indescribable sadness, walked with her through the rooms of Walworth Mansion as she touched each object, each piece of furniture. She stood in the yard with her head turned to the late summer sunshine, listening to the pines sighing in the wind.

One afternoon she stood near a late–blooming rosebush, running her finger lightly around the velvet red petals, remembering the Chancellor's pride in his roses and his energetic care of them. "This is ridiculous! Why I'm mourning myself! I will have the operation if I have to, and I will just decide to live. Whatever happens, I can't keep up this ridiculous behavior."

Once her decision had been reached, she felt surprisingly calm. Upon her return to Washington she checked directly into the hospital.

"Don't just stand there and hover about me," she told Nellie and Tracy. "Nothing is being done yet, and I certainly can't go anywhere."

A few days later Dr. Talbott announced that he would give her more time, he wouldn't do anything yet. "Let's wait a while, Mrs. Walworth. This thing just might resolve itself. I'll give you some medication to

336

help you through the rough days, but bear with me and let's see how long we can wait this thing out."

She left the hospital joyfully. "I do believe that just making a decision, whatever it is, resolves the condition," she told Nellie on the ride home.

The fall and winter passed slowly, and to Ellen's surprise, she was no longer interested in current events or politics. The world had passed her by and now belonged to others. She still received friends and attended occasional meetings of the Daughters, but she was only an objective observer.

In early June, she was preparing to return to Saratoga when she had another attack, and this time the pain was more severe than it had been. Dr. Talbott hospitalized her at once.

She was given belladonna and hydrochlor, which made her feel as though she was wrapped in a tight cocoon. She was aware only of swishing noises and the doctors and nurses moving about the bed. Once she looked over at Tracy sitting beside the bed and with surprise noticed that his face was wet with tears. Nellie leaned over her to bathe her face, and Ellen frowned, unable to remember how or why Nellie was here. "What day is it?" she asked, and then promptly forgot the reply. She didn't know and didn't care how many days she drifted in and out of consciousness, but one afternoon she awakened with surprising lucidity. Tracy's face showed obvious relief, and she felt a twinge of pity for him. There were flowers in the room, and Nellie was all bustling with efficiency, watering them and plumping Ellen's pillows. Watching her, Ellen thought of Clara. She would like to see her again, that tall, gaunt figure of a daughter. Every time they had met, Clara's black and white habit, framing her impassive face, always seemed to Ellen to represent a blankness, a void of life. "Madonna Clara," she murmured now.

"What?" startled, Nellie stopped and looked at her mother.

"I would like to see Clara."

Nellie moved to the side of the bed and picked up Ellen's hand. "Would you like me to telegraph her, Mother?"

"Yes." Ellen relaxed into the pillows. "It's so strange. Looking back, I am conscious only of a groping sense of significance and purpose in all that happened to me." She closed her eyes.

In the next hour, Ellen's quest for purpose finally ended. But her purpose would live on in her children and in the greatness of her legacy. Ellen H. Walworth would live on in posterity; her significance embodied in the white marble structure of the Daughters of the American Revolution on Seventeenth Street and in a building where the memories and history of a nation would be stored.

337

Bibliography

American Monthly Magazine 1 (July 1892).

Announcement of Ellen H. Walworth's Select School, Saratoga Springs, New York, 1874.

Annual Reports of the American Historical Association: 1893, 1898.

Astor, Mrs. B. to Mansfield Walworth, letter, 10 July 1866.

Author unknown to Ellen Walworth, letter, 16 December 1912.

Barton, Clara to Ellen H. Walworth, letter, 9 September 1892.

Bryant, M. C. to Ellen H. Walworth, letter, 16 March 1875.

The Busy Bee, newsletter, Saratoga, New York, October 1872.

Court of Ayer & Terminer Company of New York: The People of the State of New York against Frank H. Walworth, Charge of Noah Davis, July 2, 1873, New York, M. B. Brown, printer, 1873.

De Rivera, Mrs. John to Ellen H. Walworth, letter, 24 April 1899.

Dougal, Mary E., "An American Victorian Family: The Walworths of Saratoga." Master's thesis, State University of New York College, Oneonta, Cooperstown Graduate Program, 1980.

Ehringler, John W. to Chester A. Arthur, letter, November 28, 1881.

"For the Better Protection of Their Rights—A History of the First Fifty Years of the Woman's Legal Education Society and the Woman's Law Class at New York University," New York University, 1940.

Hardin, Estelle to Ellen H. Walworth, letter, 18 June 1871.

Hardin, M. D. to Ellen H. Walworth, letter, 5 December 1881.

Hardin, M. D. to Robert Lincoln, letter, 5 December 1881.

Hardin, Martin D., Brigadier General. Notice to Hardin family members regarding genealogy, Chicago, Illinois, 1 January 1880.

Lincoln, Mary Todd to Sarah Walworth, letter, 28 June 1873.

Long, John D., Secretary of the Navy, to Ellen H., Walworth, letter, 15 April 1898.

McGregor, Jean. "BPW Theme Found Early Life Here 50 Years Ago." *The Saratogian,* 20 October 1950.

"Mrs. Walworth Dies in Hospital at Washington." *The Saratogian*, vol. 46, no. 146. 23 June 1915.

The National Archives, copies pertaining to Ellen Walworth's government employment.

Papers of the American Historical Association, vol. IV (1890).

Papers of the American Historical Association, vol. V (1891).

"Retrial for the Murder of Mansfield Walworth by Frank Walworth." *The New York Times,* June 4–July 14, 1873.

Robinson, L., Executive Chamber State of New York, Albany, to Ellen H. Walworth, letters, 14 April 1817 to 14August 1877.

Sanders, Reverend Robert Stuart. "The Kentucky Genesis of the Daughters of the American Revolution Manifested in the Life of Mrs. Ellen Hardin Walworth." Speech delivered to the General Marquis Colmes Chapter of the DAR, Versailles, Kentucky, May 14, 1945.

Smith, David A. to Sarah E. Walworth, letter, 4 July 1951.

Walworth Acadamy Programme, February 22, 1872.

Walworth, Clarence A. *The Walworths of America.* Albany: The Weed Parsons Printing Co., 1897.

Walworth, Ellen (daughter). *Life & Times of Kateri Tekawitha: 1656–1680.* New York: Peter Paul & Brothers.

Walworth, Ellen (daughter). *An Old World as Seen through Young Eyes.* D and J Sadlier & Company Publishing.

Walworth, Ellen H. *Battles of Saratoga,* 1891.

Walworth, Ellen H. diary, 1880–1884.

Walworth, Ellen H. English, French, German School monthly report. 1 April 1873.

Walworth, Ellen H.. letter regarding volunteers to aid officers, soldiers, and sailors to Daughters of the American Revolution, *The New York Tribune,* 2 April 1898.

Walworth, Ellen H. "Women's Work in the Centennial," Address to the Women of Saratoga as it appeared in *The Saratoga Sun,* 20 March 1876.

Walworth, Mansfield T. *Hotspur, A Tale of the Old Dutch Manor.* New York: Carleton, 1864.

Walworth, Mansfield T. *Lulu, A Tale of the National Hotel Poisoning.* New York: Carleton, 1863.

Walworth, Mansfield T. *Married in Mask.* New York: A. L. Burt, 1888.

Walworth, Reuben Hyde. Case and Opinion upon the Will of Anson G. Phelps, the elder. New York, W. C. Bryant & Co., 1854.

"Women Graduates in Law," New York University Law School, 20 April 1896.

Yates, Richard, Washington, D.C., to Ellen H. Walworth, letter, 5 February 1853.